Anna M____

206 283-6133

Fast Wheels, *Slow Traffic*

Urban Transport Choices

In the series
Conflicts in Urban and Regional Development
Edited by John R. Logan and Todd Swanstrom

Fast Wheels
Slow Traffic

Urban Transport Choices

Charles L. Wright

TEMPLE UNIVERSITY PRESS
PHILADELPHIA

Temple University Press, Philadelphia 19122
Copyright © 1992 by Temple University. All rights reserved
Published 1992
Printed in the United States of America

Library of Congress Cataloging-in-Publication Data

Wright, Charles L.
  Fast wheels, slow traffic : urban transport choices / Charles L.
  Wright.
      p.   cm.—(Conflicts in urban and regional development)
  ISBN 0-87722-911-2 (alk. paper)
  1. Urban transportation.   2. Choice of transportation.   I. Title.
II. Series.
HE305.W75   1992   91-23993
388.4—dc20   CIP

*To those who shared
this adventure,
Glorinha, Marcelo, Denison,
Élisson, and Alan,
this book is dedicated.*

Contents

Tables and Figure

Preface

Folk sayings often set off a chain of thoughts. One of my favorites is "In practice, the theory is different." This is not an antitheoretical comment. Theories, as John Maynard Keynes reminded us in the 1930s, are always with us; theories dominate the thinking of immensely practical persons. Rather, the adage is a reaction to certain theories that are excessively complex or just plain wrong, and do not work well in practice. Another theory is needed to get the job done.

In modern times, knowledge is divided into separate subjects and professions, and the larger picture often gets lost as interrelationships, however obvious, are ignored. Nowhere is this more evident than in urban transportation. A typical situation finds a group of engineers developing a project, an economist doing cost–benefit analysis, a financial analyst trying to find a way to pay for it, some physical scientists and an architect doing an environmental-impact statement, city council members debating a subject they know little about, and the mayor trying to sell the result to the voters. Few if any of those involved understand how all this fits together or what it has to do with the city's overall transportation picture.

It would be a rare coincidence if such confusion added up to good transport planning and a satisfactory urban environment. Common sense suggests that interactions are important, that professionals, politicians, and populace need to know more about what the others are up to and about the characteristics of urban transport modes; everyone needs to see the larger picture.

It is comforting to know that, at least in this case, common sense is in line with the principles of systems engineering and a new approach to the study of consumer behavior and welfare. The latter looks less at cars and trains, for example, and more at the characteristics they present. An integrated view of the larger picture may be possible in science, as reflected in the subtitle of John Briggs and David Peat's recent book, *Looking Glass Universe: The Emerging Science of Wholeness.*

Urban transport makes more sense—and is thus easier to understand—when considered as an organic whole. This involves analyzing the characteristics of a city's transport system, its citizens, its urban design, and its population density, rather than looking at isolated projects as they spring up over the years. This systemic view helps develop a strategy for dealing with the city's transport problems; technical people then develop projects that fit the overall strategy. The analysis includes both public and private costs, the range of environmental issues, and the viability and sustainability of the system over the long run. This holistic perspective removes the current separation of project formulation from evaluation, of cost–benefit analysis from environmental-impact statements and financial analysis; urban transport is seen as an organic whole.

Citizens, systems engineers, and environmentalists will welcome this approach, since it is both correct and intelligible. The remaining true believers in cost–benefit analysis, however, are likely to be greatly offended. They have been trained to start their analysis with a project, that is, a solution. Some technicians who work with complex four-stage mathematical modeling techniques may not be happy either; they have been trained to gather an enormous amount of data and to use it to project the mistakes of the past into the future.

The characteristics approach I am proposing starts by asking what the problem is and who has the problem. Which characteristics of the existing transportation system are deficient? Whom do they affect? What are the social, political, and financial constraints? The next step is to see what solutions can alleviate the problem at a cost affordable to the city and its transport users. What are our options (transport modes and different ways of operating them) for improving the poor performance on those characteristics?

Most readers will be pleased to note that characteristics analysis does not involve a lot of mathematics (although multiplication and division are enormously helpful). There is, however, a trade-off. We have to learn something about the characteristics of transport modes and cities. Part II provides a reasonable amount of technical information on transport capacity, private and public costs, health and environmental issues, along with city layouts and population densities. I have attempted to provide this knowledge in an entertaining—or at least relatively painless—fashion. But I recognize that some academic readers are cursed with linear minds and will jump directly from the essay on method and madness in Part I to the applications and discussion in Part III. They will miss the message: once we understand the attributes of modes, cities, and users, the characteristics approach becomes, as in the song, "doing what comes naturally." The linear minds will also miss discovering the potential roles of walking and cycling in urban travel, some interesting solutions to a variety of problems, and the evidence that the best train, in certain circumstances, may be a bus. As with more pleasant urban trips, getting there is half the fun.

Acknowledgments

Authors, like most other people, like to think of themselves as self-sufficient. This is seldom true, and certainly not in my case. After over a decade of intense professional activity, a fellowship from the Brazilian Scientific and Technological Council (CNPq) made it possible for me to spend a year as a visiting scholar at the University of Michigan, where I was able to dedicate my time to writing the first draft of this book. My colleagues at the Economics Department and the Nucleus of Transport Studies at the University of Brasília shouldered the extra burden of my classes during this period. Ernesto Campos Sigiliano took care of my personal affairs in Brazil, and Antonio Carlos Firmino provided me with information and bibliography at a key moment in my research. My hosts at Michigan, Professors Charles Brown of the Economics Department and Howard Bunch of the Transportation Research Institute, arranged institutional support that made my work much easier and more productive; they also provided useful comments on early chapters of the manuscript when they were most needed. From Germany, Peter Lindner sent key data.

The University of Michigan offers not just a library, but a whole network of them, each with its own specialty areas and unique environment. I used a number of them extensively and am particularly grateful for assistance to the Sumner Library staff and to Anne Grimm, Guy Gattis and the other staff members of the University of Michigan Transportation Research Institute (UMTRI) library.

Most prefaces are punctuated with the author's gratitude to

those who have pointed out errors and shortcomings in the work before they appeared in print. I am far more grateful to those who saw something they appreciated either in the author or the manuscript and provided support and encouragement to keep going. Some of those debts go back a long way. In my sophomore year in high school, when a two-page essay was a major challenge, Gretchen Stuckey saw something she liked in my prose and encouraged me to write. In the 1970s, my wife, Glória, encouraged me to get my doctorate, when such an endeavor involved personal sacrifices and risks. My adviser, Dick Meyer, also provided encouragement during those years. For the present manuscript, John Logan of the State University of New York–Albany, an anonymous reviewer, transportation consultant Philip Gold, and Temple Editor-in-Chief Michael Ames contributed decisively with their enthusiasm and insightful comments. Mary Capouya of Temple saw the book through to production, alerted me to the need to provide conversions for metric measurements in the text, and made a number of valuable queries that resulted in a clearer manuscript. A preliminary version of Chapters 2 and 10, presented in seminar form, also drew valuable observations from Michelle White of Michigan, John Anderson of Eastern Michigan University, and Leroy Husak and Fred Hitzhusen of Ohio State University.

Howard Bunch's wide-ranging interests in transportation and deep-rooted concern for other countries and cultures made him an exceptional host at UMTRI. We cooperated on a joint paper titled "Mass Transit Innovations—2000 to 2010." This appeared in an UMTRI document, "A Report on the Feasibility of Alternative Ground Transportation Systems" (June 1990), sponsored by the Chevron Research Company, Richmond, California. Parts of that paper are still recognizable in Chapter 7 of this book, with Howard as coauthor. At the risk of omitting someone, my thanks also go to UMTRI members Dave Andrea, Mary Bennett, Charlie Compton, Kathi Compton, Dick Doyle, Mary Helen Eschman, Tom Guillespie, Bucky Horsman, Karla Karinen, Sean McAlinden, Kathy Richards, Mike Sayers, Mark Spicknall, UMTRI Assistant Director Jim Thomson, and UMTRI Director Pat Waller; they provided everything from assistance in keeping my computer working to data and encouragement. As luck would have it, the final version of the manuscript was prepared in Manila, Philippines, where Bill Parente and Rowena Ong were especially helpful.

Some parts of this book have evolved from earlier writings, although not always in an easily recognizable form. I would like to thank the editors of the following journals for their kind permission to reprint materials: *UMTRI Research Review,* the Eno Foundation and the *Transportation Quarterly, Revista Brasileira de Economia, Revista dos Transportes Públicos—ANTP.*

My parents, Arden and Genevieve Wright, and my nephew, Craig Wright, helped with our moving in and out of Ann Arbor and with many other chores throughout the 1989–90 academic year. My wife and sons excelled at coping with a new environment in Ann Arbor and, in many direct and indirect ways, helped this book toward completion. To all, my lasting gratitude.

Conversions
and Abbreviations

Conversions

*T*he International System of Units (SI) has become the legal basis for measurement in most countries of the world, including Great Britain and the United States, and it is used in this book. Because, however, many readers still think in terms of the British units, a number of conversions have been provided in the text itself. For reference, some conversion factors are also given below.

SI Unit	*British Unit*
1 centimeter (cm)	0.3937 inch (in.)
1 meter (m)	1.0936 yards (yd), 3.281 feet (ft), or 39.37 in.
1 kilometer (km)	0.6214 mile
1 square meter (m^2)	1.196 square yards (yd^2)
1 square kilometer (km^2)	0.3861 square mile ($mile^2$)
1 hectare (ha)	2.471 acres
1 kilogram (kg)	2.205 pounds (lb)
1 kilometer/liter (km/l)	2.3524 miles/gallon (mpg)

Abbreviations

AGT	automated guided transit
APTA	American Public Transit Association
CET	Traffic Engineering Agency (São Paulo)
DNER	National Highway Department, Brazil
EBTU	Brazilian Urban Transport Agency
erf/erven	"living backyard," in Netherlands, or green traffic area
GEIPOT	Brazilian Transportation Planning Agency
HOV	high-occupancy vehicle
HPUV	human-powered utility vehicle
HST	high-speed train
INAMPS	Brazil's national health care system
LRT	light rail transit
mag-levs	magnetically levitated trains
pce	passenger car equivalent
ROW	right-of-way
RRT	rapid rail transit
WHO	World Health Organization

Part I

Introduction

Chapter 1

The Urban Transport Problem

THE CIRCULATION of people and goods is essential for virtually all urban economic activity, along with the diverse social, cultural, and recreational activities that make the city synonymous with civilization. Unfortunately, in our time urban transport is also regarded as a major problem. Richard Robbins asserts that most urbanites think that their city has the worst transport problem in the world (1976:1). Each urban resident has a solution—usually different from that of his or her neighbor—but no idea of how to pay for it.

In Europe, authorities talk about "traffic calming." In the United States, commuters face expanding gridlock areas: on the LBJ Freeway in Dallas, "the only way to change lanes is to change cars" (Kalette and Sharn 1989: 1). In some large cities in developing countries, many citizens spend three hours and 15 to 30 percent of their wages just getting to work and back. Most Americans get to work much more quickly, but devote a similar share of time working to pay for their cars, running errands, and driving their children to school and social functions.

Problems, like beauty, are in the eye of the beholder. The sheer number of beholders created by centuries of movement from farm to town has made urban transport one of the most pervasive problems of modern times. In the United States, half the population lives in centers of over a million people and a third in centers of over 2.5 million; only some 2 percent still qualify as farmers (Pisarski 1987: 25). The metropolitan phenomenon is equally present in Europe, in several Asian countries, and—a fact surprising to many—in Latin America. In Brazil, about 80 percent of the population is urban, 117 centers have over 100,000 people, and one, São Paulo, has over 15 million people in its metropolitan area (Wright and Sant'Anna 1989: 1). Mexico City may now be the world's most populous city. One-third of Argentina's population lives in Greater Buenos Aires. Although Africa is much less urbanized, localized problems exist there also. The Nigerian government is moving its capital from Lagos to Abuja, repeating the Brazilian experience of transferring its capital from Rio de Janeiro to Brasília. Aside from the Nigerians' belief that this will spur economic development in the interior and diminish political conflicts among regions, an additional incentive is the impression that Lagoan traffic is unmanageable. A similar impression existed in Rio in the 1950s. These governments have acted much as a private American business firm might in fleeing a troubled inner-city area for the suburbs. Even when farm–city migration ends due to the ultimate lack of farmers, migration continues, in the form of metropolitanization and suburbanization, creating new problems while people are still thinking in terms of old solutions.

The role of beholder is of course, not restricted to users of transport facilities. Air pollution, noise, accidents, and other environmental impacts are of growing concern to everyone and, in a number of countries, objects of new layers of governmental regulation. Sadly, the existing transport system and its associated constraints reduce the overall gains from the new regulations. A reduction in unhealthy emissions, for example, may be canceled out by an increase in traffic or by new harmful emissions.

Modern urban transportation is filled with paradoxes:

The more people attempt to increase their mobility by purchasing and driving cars, the slower traffic flows and the longer it takes everyone to get to work.

Traffic on many streets in major centers like Los Angeles and London often moves at a pace comparable to that of horse-and-buggy times, despite astronomic expenditures on highways and sophisticated control and monitoring devices. There are even cases of frustrated, neurotic motorists who shoot at each other after spending hours stalled in monumental traffic jams.

Japanese businessmen can often get into Tokyo from other cities more quickly than they can move from one downtown company office to another using surface transportation.

Despite new U.S. public transport projects costing billions of dollars, American transit ridership has continued its long-standing skid toward irrelevance.

Brazil, having successfully built the world's largest biomass energy
program to achieve energy independence and to save foreign
exchange, accumulated the largest debt of any less-developed
country and eventually produced inflation rates of over 70 percent per *month*.

Despite ubiquitous computers, research staffs, and informational materials, many politicians and administrators find themselves
facing urban transport decisions with more inadequate information than ever before.

Academics and other researchers have been more successful in
producing specific information on the physical details of vehicles and
transport infrastructure than in providing us with a broader vision of
what is occurring and what our choices as a society really are. Special-
ization, the tool that deepens knowledge of particulars and promotes
technological advance, has not helped produce a comprehensive picture of urban transport. A large number of major decisions regarding
such issues as recent public transport projects and highway systems in
the United States, passenger trains in many countries, and the alcohol
fuel program in Brazil, have been based on woefully inaccurate information.

There is, of course, a lack of trained personnel; an official U.S.
publication advises that "Transportation Professionals Are an Endangered Species" (*TR News,* September–October 1989: 2). Two of the
leading urban transport groups among developing countries were
recently dismantled. The Traffic Engineering Agency (CET) in São
Paulo lost most of its senior technical staff in a confusing reorganiza-
tional scheme, and the Brazilian Urban Transport Agency (EBTU) was
closed as part of a federal decentralization and cost-reduction plan.
Only a handful of graduate schools in the United States have meaningful programs in urban transportation, and there are even fewer in
developing countries. With apologies to Winston Churchill, one might
say that never has so much been studied by so few.

Even so, it appears that the problem is more one of method
than numbers, more qualitative than quantitative. Only a modest percentage of transportation experts' intellectual production is directed
toward producing information needed for either the broader or the
more specific decisions by legislators and executives at any level of
government. Very little is comprehensible even to specialists in other
areas of transportation. In fact, most of the intellectual talent is dedicated to investigating the mechanics of a small part of the system, such
as automotive design, engines, or highway construction. Bright people
in industry are paid to find profitable ideas for their companies, and

the externalities that abound in urban transport mean that the market-place will not by itself select the most socially valuable inventions.

In academia, tenure and promotion standards virtually require the meager few with some interest in urban transport to produce incredibly specialized theses, followed by an even more specialized string of papers, preferably with enough mathematics to discourage potential readers. The climb up the hierarchy too often leads to study-ing more and more about less and less, burning out, becoming an administrator, or some combination of the above. Then come the grants and contracts—the academic's last hurdle for tenure and pro-motion, and the lifeblood of private-sector researchers. A few grants and contracts are available for learning about things like inverter-controlled ac induction motor propulsion and electrified roadways *(sic)*. The private sector finances research on Scotch yokes for two-cycle engines and the like. Much of this research appears directed toward marginal improvements in inefficient systems. Few grants sup-port research on the more basic questions of the urban transport problem.

Broader disciplines, such as urban studies, have had consider-able difficulty figuring out what to do with transportation. Econo-mists—myself and a few others excepted—have seldom expressed interest in the topic. When pressed, my colleagues typically suggest a gasoline tax of some 400 percent and the use of cost–benefit analysis as the solutions for all transport ills. The former has received a less than enthusiastic reception, and the latter has often proved to be as frustrating as gridlock on a Los Angeles freeway. Cost–benefit studies have as a rule focused on individual projects, neglecting the overall picture. They have often overestimated the benefits and underesti-mated the costs of bad projects and neglected to formulate better al-ternatives. Considerable mathematical skill has been employed to produce unrealistic predictions of the number of trips and the value of travel time that would supposedly be saved by some proposed boon-doggle. The numbers and values give the impression of being suffi-ciently elastic to justify whatever is being proposed. Among students of urban transport, there are by now few true believers in cost–benefit analysis. Even those who use it recognize its limitations in dealing with such things as environmental factors and local contexts.

Some economists and builders of large-scale mathematical models have argued that their methods would work if they were applied "properly" or if enough time and money were invested in them. Members of city councils and other persons responsible for pub-lic monies have noted the "ifs" and become reluctant to support such efforts. A perception persists that something is amiss, related to the methods and information we use and the way we think about the transport problem. The usual planning tools may be a costly means of generating the wrong information. This danger is especially evident when the models are applied in less-developed countries where the economic, urban, and cultural contexts are often quite different from the settings in which they were produced.

Even such apparently uncomplicated things as public transport classifications are riddled by counterintuitive terms and misnomers. "Light rail systems" are actually composed of very heavy rail cars; "people movers" do not move many people; "mass transit" is often for the few, and the few are not necessarily a vanishing proletariat. Public transport enthusiasts have not been particularly persuasive in their claims to have the solution for the urban mobility problem.

The automotive industry's propaganda has been more effective in exerting subliminal pressures on the public, researchers, administrators, and legislators. The private car is pictured moving alone on a winding path among mountain trees, a symbol of cleanliness, freedom, adventure, power, youth, health, sex. The media and business analysts fall into line, as cars sales are linked to jobs and overall economic performance.

The truth is less pleasant. More realistic images of the automobile include: urban congestion in developed countries and in many developing countries; huge cranes devastating mountain forests in Ohio and Minas Gerais to obtain coal and iron ore to be processed in sooty places like Gary and Volta Redonda; ecological disasters in Valdez, Mexico City, Cubatão and the Black Forest; the disappearance in many cities of the elementary right to walk safely to most destinations; a sedentary lifestyle that threatens health, enjoyment of life and longevity; traffic accidents that kill more people than do the machines of war. These images do not seem to discourage anyone from continuing down the same path; China, for instance, has been busy making plans for large-scale automotive production.

Most researchers, citizens, and politicians have at least a minimal awareness of these problems. Little reliable information is available, however, regarding the options for dealing with them or the advantages, disadvantages, and costs of alternative strategies.

My awareness of this gap has deepened over the years in my work with transport planning agencies, citizen groups, and students. As an American living in Brazil and able to observe urban transport problems in several other countries, I had a unique opportunity to see things from a different perspective. More important, I was in a position to observe how supposedly objective characteristics of transport modes led to radically different results as they were placed in different urban and economic settings.

Moreover, I needed to provide good answers to real, pressing problems. This required a method, but one simpler, less costly, and more reliable than the approaches then current in academia. It occurred to me that the best way to start was by looking at the problems themselves. Problems in turn can only be adequately described in terms of their characteristics. Transport modes, users, and cities all have their characteristics, and these are related to each other—often in fairly clear, straightforward ways. If the problem and the options for dealing with it could be analyzed with the "characteristics approach," the results could be understood and appreciated by the transport user, the specialist, politicians, and administrators. This book describes the results of over a decade of developing and applying this method to urban transport problems.

The approach builds on a small but highly significant tradition of viewing societal problems in a systemic manner, typified by works by Russell Ackoff (1974; 1978) in systems engineering and Marvin Manheim (1979) in transportation, and numerous valuable specialized contributions in both transportation and methodology. These are integrated through the use of Kelvin Lancaster's (1966a; 1966b: 1979) path-breaking theory of consumer and producer behavior. The method brings together, in a natural and intuitive fashion, the technology of production of transport goods and services, the urban setting, the needs and limitations of users, the financial constraints of the public sector, and the environmental consequences of the actions considered.

While many methodologies break down in the face of cross-national experiences that undermine their cultural and economic foundations, the characteristics approach is enriched by them. Such experiences illustrate the diversity of the options available and the contexts in which they may or may not be appropriate. To this end, I have drawn extensively on the experiences of cities at different levels of development and with diverse characteristics. I hope that the resulting vision of urban transport problems and choices will interest readers whose own cities reflect that diversity.

The next chapter presents the characteristics approach to the analysis of urban transport choices in a somewhat informal, intuitive fashion. Part II then describes the characteristics of transport modes, users, and cities. In Part III, this background is used to analyze a number of modes and choices for developing viable and sustainable transport strategies. The characteristics approach is presented in a more formal manner and applied to the analysis of a number of real-world transport problems. This is followed by an essay on viable and sustainable transport strategies. The concluding chapter summarizes the conceptual and practical differences between the characteristics approach and the traditional transport planning paradigm.

Chapter 2

On Method and Madness

---

*T*HE LACK of a clear understanding of urban transport by citizens, politicians, and scholars reflects the failure of our existing models to provide adequate insights regarding the nature of urban transportation and the options for dealing with it. The question of *perception* is a key concept in scientific method. The underlying issue is how we think about transportation, a phenomenon that conditions the options we perceive as individuals and as a society, and whether we consider those options "realistic" or not.

Some examples show how misleading concepts of realism can be in urban transportation. The first is a cartoon in the introduction of Tabor Stone's 1971 book, *Beyond the. Automobile,* which features a realist telling Henry Ford that his motorcar has no future, since it would require paved roads throughout the nation, thousands of fuel stations, and vacant lots everywhere to park the vehicles. The realist's logic is impeccable, except for the assumption that American society would be unwilling to make such astronomic investments.

In the second case, reported by Michael Replogle (1989a: 18), foreign "experts" have, among other things, produced a massive report on Chinese transportation without mentioning the word *bicycle*. The experts, who take great pride in being hard-headed realists, provide a notable demonstration of how great effort and long years of training may ultimately enable one to overlook the obvious.

A third case is represented by the "debates" on urban transportation in the United States, where each debater addresses his or her own clientele rather than the substantive questions. One side recommends public transportation (particularly passenger trains) as the solution for all ills; the other lobbies for more expressways for automobiles.

The fourth case has to do with theories that, as John Maynard Keynes reminds us, are over time more powerful than vested interests (1936: 384). One plausible theory that has unintended offshoots makes the choice of transport modes dependent on city size (Vuchic 1981: 59–115). Such a theory easily leads to the idea that a city of, say, one million inhabitants either has or needs a rapid transit rail system (Mitchell 1974: 56). I myself have participated in debates in Brasília, Brazil's modernistic capital, in which such arguments were used in a very dogmatic fashion, despite ample evidence that the city's basic characteristics are not conducive to the use of trains for passenger transportation. In the same vein, Manheim (1979) and others made devastating critiques of inappropriate mathematical models of urban transportation problems more than a decade ago. Yet, despite some progress, those and similar models continue to be used in some countries as "objective," "realistic," and "expert" approaches.

Fortunately, recent work in the history of science and other disciplines permits us to form a clearer picture of why such confusion occurs and chart a course that should enable us to avoid some of the more serious pitfalls. The initial step involves a more adequate interpretation of what constitutes objectivity and impartial observation.

From René Descartes in the sixteenth century until the beginning of the twentieth century, the scientific community held that "objective" scientific knowledge was possible, based on the detachment of the observer from the observed phenomenon. Thomas Kuhn (1962) and John Briggs and David Peat (1984) have shown this belief to be untrue. The recognition of lack of such objectivity is especially pertinent in fields like urban transport that draw heavily on the social sciences and engineering, but it also applies to the physical sciences. Werner Heisenberg found in the late 1920s that one cannot observe the value of one variable without losing information on another: the act of observation changes the very system that is being observed.

Briggs and Peat view science itself as an act of perception highly conditioned by culture, language, and academic training. This act of perception finds expression in the paradigms that enable the scientist to organize thought, to collect and to analyze data. The term *paradigm* encompasses, in addition to the scientists' theories, their often implicit and subtle assumptions, along with the symbols and models they use to solve problems. Thus "progress" in science occurs along two paths.

The first involves marginal contributions from scientists working within an accepted paradigm, analogous to filling in the details of a map whose contours and basic features are known. The second, revolutionary, way occurs when deficiencies are found in the paradigm itself. Problems appear that cannot be solved or adequately explained within the existing paradigm. This "crisis" leads to the formulation of one or more alternative paradigms that compete for acceptance within the scientific community.

In 1966, Kelvin Lancaster (1966a; 1966b; 1979), a mathematical economist at Columbia University, provoked such a crisis by challenging one of the oldest, most important, and yet least powerful paradigms in economics—consumer theory. His alternative approach, an analysis of characteristics, has such profound yet largely unexplored implications for the analysis of urban transportation problems that I have taken the unusual step of organizing this book around his basic postulates.

Lancaster's fundamental criticism of traditional consumer theory is that it ignores all the intrinsic properties of goods, such as transport modes and vehicles. By doing so, all our knowledge about people's current preferences becomes irrelevant for predicting their reactions to new modes, vehicles, and quality variations. He states that a theory unable to make any use of so much information is a remarkably empty one. Indeed, the only substantive result of the traditional theory—the sign of the substitution effect[1]—could be derived from the proposition that goods are goods, or, ultimately, that "goods are what are thought of as goods."

I have added "consideration of services" to the paradigm as a logical extension—hinted at by Lancaster (1966b: 23) in his discussion of the labor component of consumption and production choices. Transport is often considered a service rather than a good and, in any case, most goods involve a service component in their sale, distribution, and maintenance. Conversely, the provision and consumption of services is generally related to the consumption and use of goods.

Lancaster's theory enables us to utilize the information embodied in the intrinsic properties of transport modes, vehicles, and services to predict people's reactions to new ones and to changes in their performance. For our purposes, the theory may be reduced to four postulates and translated into transport terminology:

1. Transport users and other urban residents receive utility from the characteristics that a mode, vehicle, or service possesses rather than from the mode, vehicle, or service itself.

2. Usually, a given characteristic can be obtained from more than one mode, vehicle, or service, while a given mode, vehicle, or service normally contains more than one characteristic.
3. Modes, vehicles, and services in combination may possess different characteristics than if used separately.
4. The characteristics themselves are objectively measurable; however, people may value the same characteristic differently.

Like all axioms, these postulates cannot be proven. They can, however, be explained, interpreted, and compared with the traditional approach.

The first postulate states that people are interested in the characteristics of vehicles and transport systems. The private car is appreciated by many because it has a series of attractive characteristics, such as speed, flexibility, comfort, and the ease of carrying along one's burdens. It is not appreciated with respect to its high cost, high rate of accidents, and contribution to environmental problems. The many characteristics associated with the automobile illustrate the second postulate.

Lancaster's first two postulates convey the commonsense idea that a car is a collection of characteristics. All cars share some characteristics, but not in the same degree or performance. Manufacturers implicitly adopt the Lancasterian approach by trying to discover which characteristics appeal most to prospective consumers and then attempting to design vehicles to provide those features. In contrast, the old paradigm presents a schizophrenic view of a 1957 Chevrolet and a 1991 Mercedes as either identical products or goods that have nothing in common. Similarly, the characteristics paradigm recognizes similarities among certain types of bus operations and rail services, while the traditional paradigm views them as either identical or completely different.

The third postulate is illustrated by considering two modes separately, say, bus and walking. The bus offers little flexibility—it will not take you from your living room to work. Walking may get you there but may take a very long time. By combining bus and walking, flexibility is enhanced and travel time decreased.

The fourth postulate is illustrated by three people who travel by different modes from Main to High Street. An executive pays $8.00 for a fifteen-minute taxi ride; a retiree pays 60 cents for a thirty-minute bus ride. Their choices are different because they value time differently, not because they disagree on how long the trip takes or what the fares are. A college student makes the same trip in twenty minutes by bike, indicating a greater preference for exercise and economy and a lesser regard for personal safety than the other two travelers.

Transport projects and choices are thus viewed as the production and consumption of sets of characteristics. This distinction is much more important today than in past eras when characteristic sets of all goods and services were severely restricted by the available production technology and by consumers' very limited incomes. In modern economies, products and services are highly differentiated and small differences in characteristics often mean either a market niche or bankruptcy for a firm. In our context, they can mean success or failure for a transport strategy.

Many modern firms have been implicitly operating on the above four propositions for some time, even though Lancaster's writings have had a limited audience in economics and possibly none at all in the business world.[2] Yet Lancaster's four principles are seen in action in modern supermarkets; the consumer chooses from the varying characteristics sets embodied in perhaps forty kinds of salad dressings, sixty varieties of soup, and thirty variants of lunch meat. The principles are also evident on the auto dealer's lot, where the cars offer a fantastic number of combinations of size, power, design, fuel economy, interior, color, and other features.

The characteristics approach is also found in the more candid accounts of how executives conduct important facets of their businesses. Akio Morita (1986), for example, describes in a very Lancasterian fashion the Sony Corporation's search for characteristics of sound and image transmission devices that consumers value, along with the ensuing search for ways of producing those sets of characteristics. John Love (1986) relates the development of the McDonald Corporation in much the same fashion. McDonald's attention to numerous characteristics (many involving rather subtle differences in service and design features apparently unrelated to food itself, along with taste, texture, color, and variety of foods) emerges as the chief explanatory factor in its phenomenal growth story.

Examples of the implicit use of the characteristics approach are harder to find in public transport. They are often limited to some design features of the more sophisticated metro (rapid rail transit) systems. Too many transit agencies and the public bodies that direct them believe their service is satisfactory if it is possible to go from A to B by a public mode plus a few complementary long and dangerous walks. They pay little attention to the adequacy of the characteristic set offered to the transit user, and transit is too often the citizen's choice only when no affordable alternative is available.[3] Similarly, planners seldom question the adequacy of the characteristic sets implicit in the solutions they propose and implant, or ask if better characteristic sets could be had at equal or lower cost.

The "product-oriented" paradigms and models of urban transportation continue to implicitly dominate planning and policy in most countries. Our mental images still tend to be formed around distinct modes or products, such as cars, buses, and trains, rather than around characteristic sets, such as capacity, travel speed, energy efficiency, and so forth. The inadequacy of the product-oriented approach contributes to the conceptual confusion regarding the urban transport problem, and consequently to the inadequacies of the systems currently found in our cities.

Nowhere is this more evident than in the case of a related paradigm—cost–benefit analysis. This technique grew out of the economic analysis of water projects in the United States in the early years of this century. With some oversimplification, a typical water project might correspond to a unique natural site for a dam, a uniform product (electricity) used by rich and poor alike, and financing from government funds. The relevant question was whether or not the benefit (the economic value of the electricity) exceeded the costs of building the dam and the transmission facilities. Environmental and secondary impacts in the economy were either unknown or considered positive, such as the reduction of pollution from burning coal, and economic development of poorer regions.

The question could be answered by summing up the monetary benefits and the corresponding costs, then "discounting" and comparing them. The discounting process applies an interest rate (called the "social discount rate") to costs and benefits received in future years. The economic logic for discounting is seen by the following example: if $91 is invested at 10 percent interest, it will be worth $100 a year from now (ignoring rounding errors); conversely, the present value of a benefit of $100 to be received a year from now is $91.

Once discounted, the benefits and costs are added and compared, yielding a single-number decision rule. Dividing the benefits by costs yields the benefit–cost ratio, B/C; subtracting costs from benefits yields the net present value, $B - C$. If B/C is greater than one or $B - C$ is positive, the project is considered economically viable. Alternatively, the project's internal rate of return (r) can be calculated from the same data (through successive approximations); the project is then considered viable if r is greater than the social-discount rate. There are some additional complications, such as the economist's efforts to compensate for the distortions introduced by taxes, subsidies, and unrealistic exchange rates, but they need not concern us here.

The analysis is appropriate to such simple circumstances; if they exist, the cost–benefit approach may be used as a decision tool. Faith in this method has eroded over time, however. In recent decades, government agencies have required "environmental impact statements" and the like in addition to (or in place of) cost–benefit analysis. Lawmakers have required such studies because they do not believe cost–benefit analysis provides sufficient basis for decisions. They believe that major projects have important impacts that cannot be expressed in dollars and cents and they want to know what those impacts are before making a decision. Economists and other professionals have also criticized the cost–benefit paradigm for neglecting cultural values, ethics and distributional questions (see, for example, Elizabeth Anderson 1988, Daniel Bromley 1982, Douglas Maclean 1986, and Amartya Sen's (1987) more general comments on the role of ethics in economic analysis).

This criticism is especially strong in such areas as education, health, welfare, and urban transport, where nonmonetary characteristics are especially important.[4] A brilliant analogy describing the underlying problem has been provided by E. J. Mishan (1988: 154–55), one of the most ardent and competent defenders of cost–benefit analysis. He likens many cost–benefit studies to a horse-and-rabbit stew, made with one horse and one rabbit. The horse represents the nonmonetary impacts and dominates the flavor, but the analyst measures only the rabbit. Mishan suggests that the analyst provide the decisionmakers with some descriptive information in addition to the benefit–cost ratio, such as the number of people affected by the noise produced by a proposed airport.

Mishan's sensible suggestion fatally undermines the cost–benefit paradigm by removing the myth that it provides a technical decision rule independent of the "unpredictable political process."[5] Under the narrow, traditional perspective where only the rabbit is quantified, if the benefit–cost ratio is slightly greater than unity, say, 1.3, the project is considered economically justified. But no decision rule emerges if the analyst admits there is a horse in the stew by stating that several negative characteristics and two positive characteristics were ignored in calculating B/C = 1.3.

Some analysts attempt to circumvent this difficulty by assigning a monetary value to the nonmonetary characteristics. This implies imputing a dollar value for such characteristics as human life, noise, pollution, comfort, travel time, flexibility, and punctuality. Some of the arguments used have been rather clever and have on occasion required that the analyst dedicate considerable time and a bit of mathematics to the cause. But only a few true believers would confuse the process with science.

The following examples will suffice for the reader to understand how economists have tried and failed in their attempt to monetarize the nonmonetary.

Economists often calculate the value of human life as the discounted present value of a person's future earnings. (To be coherent, they should subtract the person's maintenance costs, but that would make the value of the lives of young children and retirees negative—an obvious inconvenience.) Another approach is to see how much people are willing to pay for life insurance and compare that with the risk of dying in the same period; still another is to see how much the courts have awarded survivors in lawsuits. It would be too much to expect that these different approaches would produce similar values without fudging the numbers, but people in rich countries will be comforted to learn that all these methods provide a much higher value for their lives than for those of people in poor countries.

Some economists have assigned a monetary cost to noise by using statistical correlations between noise and decreases in property values. Estimates for the elasticities of housing values to traffic noise range from −0.14 to −1.05, and for aircraft noise, from 0 to −2 (Alexandre and Barde 1987). The numbers mean that a 10 percent increase in traffic noise would decrease property values by something between 1.4 and 10.5 percent (the higher number being 7.5 times greater than the lower), while the effect of a 10 percent increase in aircraft noise ranges from a zero to a 20 percent decrease in property values (the higher number being infinitely greater than the lower one).

British traffic authorities assigned 24 percent of the total costs of traffic in 1982 to "pain, grief and suffering" *(sic),* as reported by Stephen Plowden and Mayer Hillman (1984: 32), who, tongue in cheek, opine that the 24 percent is rather low. They do not satisfy our curiosity as to how the authorities arrived at that figure—one subject I would prefer not to investigate.

These are excellent examples of what Antônio Silveira (1984: 32) calls the Morgenstern indeterminacy—numbers that are not numbers. Analysts who attempt to assign monetary values to nonmonetary urban transport characteristics are not using a measuring stick with real numbers on it; they are using a numerical silly putty that can assume almost any value whatsoever, depending on the assumptions and quirks in a particular data set.

A related line of persistent criticism of cost–benefit analysis[6] is that it fails to help researchers and decisionmakers "get a handle" on complex problems. This occurs since the method starts when the project is "ready" for evaluation. "Evaluation" in cost–benefit analysis means to accept or reject the project or rank the projects if two or more alternatives to the status quo are considered and have benefit–cost ratios greater than one. The question of formulating projects, that is, how a project got to be a project, is a chapter missing from cost–benefit manuals. It is difficult to overstate the importance of this point, since *no meaningful evaluation can be conducted separately from project formulation.*

As Tabor Stone (1971) shows in his discussion of the process of formulating urban transport projects, a project does not appear spontaneously. Substantial expenditures and many person-years of effort may go into it, and the result cannot be easily or inexpensively modified. The typical one-stage cost–benefit study is one conducted after the important decisions have been made. All too often, this includes a political commitment to proceed with the project. A benefit–cost ratio greater than unity "justifies" a decision that has already been taken; if the criterion makes the project unacceptable, the decisionmaker is given no alternatives for dealing with the underlying problem. In either case, little or nothing is produced to educate the population or decisionmakers regarding the advantages and disadvantages of the available alternatives.[7]

Project formulation is not missing from cost–benefit manuals simply because the authors forgot to include it. It is omitted because the logical starting point for project formulation is to ask what the problem is. A social problem such as urban transport can only be defined in terms of the characteristics thought to be deficient and the people who have the problem. Cost–benefit analysis is based on the traditional "goods" approach to consumer theory—it can look at a product, but not at characteristics. Furthermore, cost–benefit analysis takes the social-discount rate as its point of reference, rather than the characteristics of the transport system, the city, or urban residents and transport users. Cost–benefit analysis thus has nothing to offer at the problem-definition stage.

The second logical step in project formulation is to ask what strategies are available for dealing with the problem. This also requires an analysis of the characteristics of the modes and vehicles that might be used to deal with the characteristics of the problem. Again, the product-oriented cost–benefit approach has nothing to offer.

These two deficiencies of cost–benefit analysis are not an exhaustive list—others will be discussed in Chapter 10. But they are serious enough for us to judge the method inappropriate for use as a policy guide in urban transportation. Some researchers, however, have been reluctant to disconnect cost–benefit's life-support system for lack of a better alternative.

What I am proposing is a new paradigm, based on the characteristics approach. A formal presentation and real-world applications of this method are deferred to Chapter 10, since we must first develop a greater understanding of the characteristics of modes, cities, and users (Chapters 3–9). However, it will be helpful to outline the essential features of the characteristics approach at this point.

The method begins with a definition of the problem in terms of the characteristics that are considered deficient. This includes an examination of the relevant features of the urban setting, the existing transport system, and transport users. The next step is a systematic search for alternatives that provide better transport characteristics and are within the financial limitations of the public sector and transport users. The third step is to check for coherence, and the fourth, to search for less expensive ways of providing similar performance. The goal of the analysis is to find the technically appropriate solutions and to describe the advantages, disadvantages, and costs of each. The choice among these technically appropriate options is made by the public authority, after a period of public debate.

In this process, we think of urban transport options in terms of the production, cost, and use of characteristics sets (Lancaster's first postulate). Traditional "modes" such as cars, buses, or trains are particular sets of characteristics. A given set of characteristics can usually be obtained from more than one traditional mode (Lancaster's second postulate); the concept of a transport mode loses its static, rigid nature and becomes more dynamic and pliable. Modes can be modified or combined to enhance positive characteristics and to reduce negative attributes (Lancaster's third postulate). Even the characteristics of a mode may take on new meaning under this approach, as alternative definitions and measurements may be more relevant or informative than those conventionally used. Only certain solutions are technically appropriate, since the others do not offer the characteristics necessary to solve the problem or are too expensive to implement. But if there are two or more options in the technically appropriate set, the analyst usually cannot affirm that one is "optimum." Normally, the alternatives in that set differ somewhat in cost and performance across characteristics. From Lancaster's fourth postulate, we know that people value a given characteristic differently. Although the analyst may offer an opinion, city council members (or other representatives) usually have a more legitimate mandate to make that value judgment.

The discussion becomes more concrete when we consider the eighteen characteristics of urban transport modes in Table 1. The first

Table 1
Qualitative Performance of Transport Modes

	Mode			
Characteristic	Walking	Cycling	Transit	Car
Characteristics Important to Society				
Greater capacity/area	S	S	S	P
Greater energy efficiency	S	S	S	P
Less air pollution	S	S	S–I	P
Less noise	S	S	S–P	P
Better aesthetics	S	S	S–P	I–P
Less vulnerability of system	S	S	P	P
Greater sustainability of system	S	S	I	P
Less public expense	S	S	S–P	I–P
More healthful	S	S	I–P	P
Fewer serious accidents	S–P	I–P	S–I	P
Characteristics Important Primarily to Individuals				
Lower costs to users	S	S	S–I	P
Better personal microenvironment	S	S	P	S
Greater flexibility	S	S	P	S
Higher frequency	S	S	S–P	S
Greater punctuality	S	S	S–P	S
Greater comfort	S–P	S–P	S–P	S
Better orientation	S	S	S–P	S–I
Ease of carrying things	I–P	S–P	S–P	S
Less total travel time				
(Approximate ranges)				
Up to 400 meters	S	S	I–P	I
400–1,500 meters	I–P	S–I	S–P	S–I
Beyond 1,500 meters	P	S–P	S–I	S

Source: Adopted from Wright (1988:72).

Notes: S = Satisfactory or Superior; I = Intermediate; P = Poor; common variations in performance that are dependent on highly variable and specific circumstances are indicated by a range (e.g., S–P = performance ranges from superior to poor on this characteristic); grades represent somewhat favorable circumstances for the modes but with no special compensation for disadvantages each mode typically faces.

ten are termed *public interest characteristics* since they affect society via externalities, demands for public funds, or secondary requirements for economic resources. Externalities are unintentional but direct effects that the actions of individuals and firms have on the welfare of other individuals and firms. An example is the use of the automobile by large numbers of people, an action that creates accidents, congestion, noise, and pollution. This direct, unintentional impact distinguishes externalities from the secondary effects resulting from, say, public transport budgets, or imports of vehicles and fuel. Both externalities and secondary effects, however, involve the public interest.

The characteristics with important societal implications are capacity/area, energy efficiency, pollution, noise, public expense, aesthetic values, health, accidents, vulnerability, and sustainability.

The second category is composed of eight characteristics that affect individuals as such, that is, their effects are the sum of their impacts on each individual. They do not involve externalities, secondary effects, or public funds. These characteristics of individual interest are: costs to users; personal (social–psychological) environment, including the choice of one's traveling companions; flexibility; frequency; punctuality; comfort; ease of carrying packages or other burdens; and travel time for short, medium, and long distances.

Table 1 shows the performance of four modes of urban transport—walking, cycling, transit, and the private car—with respect to these characteristics, using qualitative grades. The rest of this book is dedicated to discussing the characteristics in detail, the caveats that apply to the grades, and how the information can be used in formulating and evaluating transport strategies and projects.[8] A preview is given at this point to introduce some important concepts and to offer some preliminary insights regarding the nature of urban transport.

In the first, public welfare category, the nonmotorized modes receive satisfactory or superior ("S") grades across all characteristics except accidents, which, significantly, are caused primarily by motorized vehicles (bicycles do cause accidents, but these are normally not fatal unless motor vehicles are involved). The private car (and its public counterpart, the taxi) has a uniformly negative effect on society through all ten public interest variables, as indicated by its string of poor grades ("P"). However, those who believe that transit is "the" solution to the problems created by the automobile will be disappointed by the mixed performance of the public motorized modes across the ten characteristics.[9] Even more discouraging for those who see transit as the single solution for urban transportation problems is the second group of characteristics. This group explains individual modal choices, and here transit loses to the car on every characteristic except cost to users. Walking and cycling again do quite well on all characteristics except the ease of carrying things, the time required to travel longer distances and, depending on the circumstances, comfort. Cycling can even partially overcome these three deficiencies if circumstances are favorable (for example, with simple adaptations, the bicycle can carry the rider's minor burdens or even considerable cargo).

Some caveats are in order. First, the nonmotorized modes have few poor grades, but they have important limitations. Second, the list of characteristics is not exhaustive: others, such as status and image, or the turning radius of vehicles, may be considered when relevant. Third, the classification and the grades themselves may be questioned.

For now, however, our interest lies in seeing how much useful information may be extracted from the table even without incorporating such subtleties. The following five findings are among the most important:

Walking and cycling are the modes with the highest number of satisfactory to superior grades, with cycling capable, in favorable situations, of getting an "intermediate" grade for accidents and "satisfactory" or "superior" for the other seventeen characteristics.

No mode gets perfect grades on all eighteen attributes. Cycling's poor grade on accidents is serious enough to curtail its use in many urban situations. Walking can be a difficult way to go longer distances and may involve considerable discomfort if the weather or other circumstances are unfavorable. Some people are also hampered by limited mobility. Transit is often inflexible, infrequent, and costly for the user, city hall, or both. Its personal environment leaves something (often a lot) to be desired: the user has little choice with respect to traveling companions, smoking versus nonsmoking ambients, or the options among music, conversation, and silence. If we were to disaggregate the transit category, we would also find great differences among the several public transport modes with respect to many characteristics. This indicates that variety is needed in transit modes to provide users with attractive options.

There is a phenomenon we will call the "Henry Ford paradox," in densely populated areas such as Manhattan and Tokyo and many large cities in developing countries that have some 10,000 persons per square kilometer (26,000 persons per square mile), as opposed to less than 1,000 persons per square kilometer for most American cities. The next finding is Henry's paradox: people use cars to get around faster than is possible by other modes; as many people become able to afford cars, however, gridlock appears and expands, transportation worsens for everyone, and society suffers from the negative effects of the associated urban environmental damage and the worsening of other public interest characteristics. The automobile, like many famous people, cannot handle success.

By a judicious combination of the nonmotorized modes and transit, it is possible to overcome some of the limitations of both, giving the user a better characteristics package than either mode can provide separately (Lancaster's third postulate).

The table is based on a reasonably favorable situation for each mode, but without compensation for problems they typically face. The last finding is that performance often varies widely, even from superior to poor, indicating that public policies can significant improve or worsen the relative grades of transit, walking, cycling, and cars.

Despite the caveats, the nonmotorized modes are clearly an important part of the urban transport environment. Yet most people in high-income countries (including many of their transportation "experts") have not thought about the present and potential importance of walking and cycling as modes of transportation. Many may not even remember that they are indeed forms of transportation. And neither auto industry executives nor public transportation enthusiasts appear to have reflected sufficiently on the consequences of their assumptions that the vehicles they promote represent *the* solution to the urban transport problem. Even our perfunctory analysis of the table should provide both groups with considerable food for thought.

The important insights to be gained through an unpretentious reflection on Table 1 indicate the power of the characteristics paradigm. The power comes from analyzing the characteristics of modes rather than the modes themselves.

In addition to the information on modal performance across characteristics, we also know (or can quickly learn) something about the characteristics of specific cities and their transport users. This gives us three sets of characteristics: one for modes, one for users, and one for the city. In some cases, a very few key bits of information may be sufficient to decide on general strategies or to exclude specific programs or projects. In other cases, a limited amount of information on a few characteristics may reveal a given strategy as the only one appropriate, or show a given project to be inferior on almost all counts to other options. In still other cases, the range of options with similar characteristics may be rather large, but one has far lower costs.

There is an implicit structure in our analysis, conferred by the characteristics of transport modes and their adequacy for different cities and users. When selecting projects or policies, the relevant transport modes and priorities are those whose characteristics match up with those of the city and its transport users, that is, the intersection of the respective characteristic sets of modes, users, and city. The characteristics of modes are similar in almost any geographical location, but the characteristics of cities and their citizens differ considerably. These differences permit us to discover the most appropriate options for each urban area.

As an illustration, suppose we are dealing with a large city in a less-developed country, where most families' monthly earnings are less than the corresponding cost of owning and using a car. The population density is quite high, say on the order of that of São Paulo, with 9,158 inhabitants per square kilometer (23,719 per square mile) in 1975. This density may be compared with 4,488 persons/km^2 (11,624/mi^2) for London, or 1,207 persons/km^2 (3,126 persons/mi^2) for Atlanta (Chile 1985; U.S. Department of Commerce 1988).

High population densities reduce the space for parking and circulation of vehicles, leaving two basic choices: (a) to promote high-capacity modes; or (b) to encourage the minority who can afford cars to acquire more of them and to use them intensely. If option (b) is chosen, cars will occupy virtually all the available road space, generating congestion, decreased mobility, and worsened performance on all the socially important characteristics.

This conclusion follows from basic traffic engineering data, but to fully appreciate its meaning one should visit Mexico City, Manila, or São Paulo for a few weeks, and accompany some typical breadwinners from different social strata on their journeys to and from work. Nonetheless, most politicians and planners in cities in developing countries ignore this larger picture and press ahead with the car-oriented strategy—they are, after all, car owners themselves.

The alternative strategy of favoring high capacity modes, however, is still the only one that will improve the circulation of people and vehicles. The set of high-capacity modes is composed of walking, cycling, and public transportation, although we might be able to improve the car's performance somewhat through carpooling and shared taxis.

In many cities in less-developed countries, cycling is not a viable short-term option, due to high accident rates caused by the existing street design, traffic conditions, and driver behavior. All these factors would have to be significantly modified to allow reasonably safe cycling. As a first approximation, then, we know that our strategy should favor improved facilities for pedestrians and circulation of public transport.

Although more detailed analyses are reserved for later chapters, these illustrations show that the perception is likely to be quite different from the characteristics approach than from product-oriented approaches. The latter have a well-established tradition of building more expressways for cars and adding a few kilometers of subways each decade. Such "products," looked at in isolation, may seem attractive, but they are, for different reasons, incapable of improving the general level of mobility in densely populated cities. As we have seen, cost–benefit analysis is not based on characteristics analysis and cannot define the city's transportation problem or generate the necessary strategies and projects.

Our thesis is that urban transport problems can only be meaningfully defined in terms of deficient characteristics, and solutions can only be considered adequate if they alleviate those deficiencies. This in turn requires consideration of who is affected by the problem. The characteristics paradigm is thus both problem- and people-oriented, rather than absorbed in the methodology itself or focused on a particular mode or vehicle as a preconceived "solution."

Since reality is complex, urban transport analysts, like all other physical and social scientists, attempt to sort out the main causes and effects through models that simplify reality. This process of simplification is based on the use of assumptions. In transportation economics, such model building can be traced to the 1826 edition of Johann Heinrich von Thünen's *Isolated State* (1966); Thünen used a mathematical model to study appropriate technology and the location of production in agriculture as a function of transport costs.

Models like Thünen's isolated state or Newton's equations are extraordinarily useful since they describe the underlying forces of complex phenomena in a simple way, yet furnish a means of understanding and utilizing the most pertinent information. This is the goal of the characteristics paradigm presented herein. This paradigm is proposed as a substitute for (or at least a necessary complement to) existing paradigms, including the conventional approach to cost–benefit analysis. The fundamental argument is that, in the complex environment of urban transportation decisions, many key mathematical models, including the simple formulas used in calculating cost–benefit ratios and the like, employ inappropriate simplification and thus often fail to capture the essence of the real-world issues. Since the conclusions of mathematical models are derived from their assumptions, inappropriate assumptions produce erroneous results; commonly, the models exhibit circular reasoning or assume away the problems.

As shown by William Milberg (1988), many economists have

become so accustomed to dealing with optimization and equilibrium that they build their models to obtain one or both these features, neglecting key attributes of the real-world problem. So many assumptions may be employed that one ends up with a model of the world economy that has no business firms. Transport studies have been plagued by an urban version of fishery economics, where, incredible as it may seem, the experts have assumed away the problem of finding fish (Wilson 1990: 12).

Of course not all modeling results are negative. Substantial progress has been made in modeling the demand for urban transport using the Lancasterian principles (Ben-Akiva and Lerman 1986; Ben-Akiva and Morikawa 1990; Manheim 1979). Simon Lewis and colleagues argue that even large-scale models would work well if users understood the models' intrinsic limitations, if enough time, data, and competent modelers were available, and if the best statistical techniques and packages were used (1990: 262–63).

Yet the use of larger-scale models has proved profoundly disappointing. Don Pickrell (1990) finds predictions of ridership levels wide of the mark in the vast majority of U.S. urban rail-transit projects, with actual ridership being only about one-third of predictions. J. S. Gutman and R. G. Scurfield (1990) find similar errors for nearly all rail projects reviewed in other countries. S. T. Atkins (1987) speaks of a crisis in transport modeling: declines in funding do not permit cities to maintain either research teams or data sets. One also recalls Atkins's earlier remark that such models may be a set of excessively complicated and costly tools for producing doubtful answers to the wrong questions (Mackinder 1979: 2).

An equally important restriction on both cost–benefit analysis and the more arcane modeling efforts is their failure to inform decisionmakers or citizens of the principal characteristics, costs, and options for urban transport. In contrast, a major component of the characteristics approach is providing such information.

More important, the characteristics approach furnishes a vision of the urban transport system as an organic whole. Cost–benefit analysis and mathematical models necessarily focus on the rabbit that can be precisely quantified with existing data and mathematical models, neglecting the horse; their topics and results are predictably marginal to the important decisions at hand. As an example, many engineers and politicians have become infatuated with urban trains, since steel-wheel-on-steel-rail technology has a very low coefficient of rolling resistance compared to rubber-tired buses. As shown in Chapter 4, the relevant coefficient is not the one that is generally used, nor is its effect as important as is often implied for intermodal fuel-economy comparisons in an urban setting. Similarly, some otherwise well-informed people have begun to think that ultrafast magnetically levitated trains (mag-levs) will soon become an urban transport option. Although mag-levs may someday be employed for certain interurban uses (Johnson et al. 1989), they are ill-suited to urban transportation. Passengers have a rather modest tolerance for acceleration and deceleration between stations spaced a few hundred meters apart: the mag-levs' ultraspeed cannot be used.

For reasons that defy logical explanation (but probably have to do with the peculiar culture of academic pecking orders), an inordinate amount of transportation research has been dedicated to narrow mathematical models, with relatively little attention given to the qualitative dimensions of the urban transport problem. All too frequently, however, the qualitative features are much more important, while the mathematical models omit the key variables. The empirical evidence (if any) is usually based on something as precarious as a regression equation or an idealized cost curve that has little or no predictive value in real-world circumstances. Such approaches often confuse correlation with causality, as illustrated in Darrell Huff's classic work, *How to Lie with Statistics* (1954). At best, their scientific validity is limited to disproving rather than proving something, that is, the opposite of what their users normally attempt to do. Qualitative understanding, or insight, precedes useful mathematical formulation; it is important even when the phenomena analyzed are sufficiently complex or imprecise to make acceptable quantification impossible (Briggs and Peat 1984).

In the ensuing chapters, I attempt to balance qualitative insight with basic engineering data and real-world cost experiences to reveal both qualitative interrelationships and the approximate magnitudes involved. This combination illustrates how policies and factors such as street design, priorities, and load factors may affect the value of a given "technical parameter" by, say, a factor of six. Qualitative questions are analyzed, such as the changes expected in operations and costs with different forms of public and private management, although "objective" costing equations would show them to yield the same results.

This approach yields valuable insight regarding the advantages and disadvantages of different strategies, what will work well and what will not, and which policies are affordable for both users and the public sector.

A final dilemma involves the relation of the analyst to paradigms and data. John Briggs and David Peat (1984) show that "objectivity" in the strict sense does not exist: science is an act of perception, with the associated subjectivity. Gunnar Myrdal (1969) argues that, in the social sciences, the closest authors can come to objectivity is to make their biases explicit. This runs counter to much methodological training in academia. Many instructors, for example, still counsel their students to avoid the use of personal pronouns and to employ passive verbs in their writing. They feel that personal pronouns reveal the author's presence in generating and interpreting the data and make a text appear "less objective" or "less scientific."

The guise of objectivity is a particular danger in the study of urban transport, where qualitative factors are often crucial but seldom explicit, and some key phenomena have been subjected to little systematic research. The present volume, like other works, contains the author's perspectives, along with some personal observations on topics that are important but insufficiently investigated. I attempt to make clear in the text when personal and casual observation is used, and the reader should apply the appropriate discount. My use of *we* and *our* is not the majestic plural, but an invitation for the reader to share the adventure of thinking about the nature of urban transport and the options we have available to us.

Our basic tools are the characteristics of transport modes, cities, and transport users. They will permit us to define the transport problem of specific cities and users and to formulate alternatives for dealing with them. But first we must understand them more fully.

Part II

Characteristics
of Transport Modes,
Cities, and Users

Chapter 3

Capacity of Transport Modes and the Use of Urban Space

OUR EXAMINATION of the public interest characteristics of transport modes begins with their respective capacities in relation to the urban space they require. It is perhaps customary at such a juncture to present a classification of modes; that is a strong reason for not doing so here. Method and emphasis are two other motives for my decision to defer formal definitions and discussion of individual modes to Chapter 7: characteristics should have preference over modes.

We are interested in finding better sets of transport characteristics that a city and its transport users can afford. Modes may be modified or combined to furnish those characteristics; they are not ends in themselves. Lancaster's second proposition states that we can normally get a given characteristic from more than one mode, and any mode has more than one characteristic. Transport policies may alter the performance of a given mode on its associated characteristics. Modes are neither static collections of characteristics nor ends in themselves—they are merely the tools we have to use in conjunction with public policies in order to produce sets of transportation characteristics.

This makes the concept of a transport mode quite elastic. In the typical U.S. scenario, a taxi with a single passenger or a van transporting only the driver is similar to a private car. In Venezuela, a taxi with five passengers or a van with eight may approximate a minibus. In Germany or Australia, a bus pulling one or two articulated trailers on a fixed guideway is much closer to a rapid rail system than to the slow buses mired in congested mixed traffic found in most major cities.

The characteristics approach has the advantages of being intuitive; it also makes our classification of modes in Chapter 7 much more simple and useful. Until then, however, I will discuss only a few of the more common modes as they are understood by laypersons in their daily activities. These modes are private cars, buses, trains, bicycles, and walking.

Trains are also called "metros," especially when they have significant underground (subway) sections. I will usually discuss urban passenger trains; they have frequent stops, in contrast to longer distance "commuter" trains that link stations in nearby cities and have few intermediate stops. The term *commuter train* can be misleading, since commuting refers to the journey to work, regardless of the mode used, but English is a flexible language.

Transit refers to public transport, generally a bus or train. *Cycling* refers to pedal bicycles, unless *motorcycling* is specifically used. Other terms will either be familiar *(taxi, streetcar)* or be accompanied by a brief explanation in the text.

Our goal is to understand transport characteristics and how they vary with circumstances and public policies. Both the characteristics and the policies are somewhat familiar to most urban residents. The characteristics approach builds on this familiarity and casts basic technical data in a new perspective. This process frequently leads to challenges to the conventional wisdom of both laypersons and specialists. As Briggs and Peat (1984) have found in physics and chemistry, a new viewpoint changes our interpretation of the data, and may even change the data themselves.

Capacity is the first characteristic discussed; it is often a major restriction on the choice of modes, and it is strongly associated with several other characteristics, such as energy efficiency, pollution, and cost. Capacity also provides an excellent illustration of how a different perspective can change our interpretation of data—in this case, basic traffic engineering data.

Based on conventional experience in the United States, authors such as Clarence De Silva and David Wormley (1983: 2) consider buses to be a low-capacity mode, transporting at best some 5,000 people per hour per lane. From such a perspective, these data appear reasonable and correct. Nonetheless, there are places in the United States and several other countries where buses carry unidirectional flows of

20,000 to 39,000 people/hour per lane (Thomson 1984; Transportation Research Board 1985: 12.50; World Bank, 1975: 74). This has profound implications for densely populated cities, especially those unable to afford expensive metro systems.

Traffic engineering manuals cover flows of vehicles quite adequately for conditions found in the United States and similar settings. They are usually based on the considerable research carried out in the United States in the postwar period. Since our concern is with movements of people rather than vehicles, however, the capacity manuals provide only a useful starting point, and caution is in order when applying them in circumstances where the underlying assumptions are inappropriate.

The capacity of a mode in relation to the area it occupies is an extremely important characteristic. The movement of people and goods requires space for streets, sidewalks, railways, stations, parking lots, railyards, and other equipment used by the traveler, transport authorities, and transport firms. This space is particularly valuable in urban areas, whether one interprets *value* as a monetary expense or as the intrinsic worth of space for parks, trees, housing, manufacturing, commerce, and other activities. The more space a mode requires to transport a given number of people, the less is left for other uses. If additional space must be acquired, say, for the rights-of-way for a new expressway or passenger-train line, the public sector may have to pay high compensation to present owners for the loss of their property. Such outlays can be a substantial portion of the overall expense for a major transport project.

In many core areas of American cities, about half of the potentially usable space is taken up by streets and parking lots, a figure that reaches two-thirds in the pathological case of the central business district of Los Angeles (Stone 1971: 46). In contrast, Bangkok has only 9 percent of its central area in road space, London, 22 percent, and New York, 24 percent (Goldsack 1983: 36). In most central areas of cities in developing countries, streets and parking occupy less than half the available space, but their requirements are still substantial. Any addition of space for transport activities usually implies the loss of precious "green areas," demolition of buildings, or both.

A useful, although imperfect, means of measuring a given mode's transport capacity is to count the number of people it can carry by a given point during an hour and divide that number by the width of the mode's right-of-way. The result is expressed as persons per meter per hour. Since area rather than width would appear in the denominator if we multiplied by a constant distance, this number is interpreted as the mode's capacity in relation to the area it occupies.

On occasion, the ratio of capacity to area is measured per fifteen-minute peak, or per day, instead of per hour. The daily capacity is obtained by multiplying by a factor that reflects the degree of peaking. The maximum daily volume so calculated usually falls within the range of 2.5 to 8 times the hourly capacity, instead of 24 times, as would occur if human behavioral patterns were ignored. The daily capacities can be increased if some of the peak-hour passengers shift their travel to off-peak periods. Again, the data change as the question we pose changes, and hardly in a linear, arithmetical fashion.

The capacity per area of a way is intuitively understood as the maximum number of people who pass a given point in an hour. Fewer can pass if there are lateral barriers, stops at intersections, or other negative factors present. The number also varies considerably with spacing between vehicles, speeds, the type of intersection and traffic control, the number of people in the vehicles, and the quality (or level) of service.

For individually controlled vehicles operating on shared rights-of-way, such as cars, trucks, and buses on roadways, there is a relationship between speed and traffic volumes. For favorable conditions, some representative magnitudes are given in the following paragraphs. Unless otherwise indicated, they are based on the Transportation Research Board's 1985 edition of the *Highway Capacity Manual*. (For additional transportation engineering concepts and data, see Khisty 1990b).

A passenger-car equivalent (pce) corresponds to a stream of cars with no trucks or buses on the roadway. On multilane freeways with high design standards and traffic volumes below 700 pce per hour per lane, each vehicle is able to change lanes, pass other vehicles, and operate at a reasonably high speed, such as 97 km/h (60 mph). These free-flow conditions correspond to the level of service *A*. As more vehicles enter the highway, maneuvers become progressively more difficult. The average and maximum speeds are forced downward as slower cars interfere with the other cars in the same lane, and drivers have difficulty changing lanes to pass slower vehicles. The level of service drops progressively with increased traffic. In approximate figures: service level *B* corresponds to 92 km/h (57 mph) and lane volumes of up to 1,100 pce/h; level *C* to 87 km/h and 1,550 pce/h; level *D* to 74 km/h, and up to 1,850 pce/h.

At level *D*, there are only about 6 car lengths between vehicles. A slight increment in volume to about 2,000 pce/h causes service to fall to level *E*, with speeds around 48 km/h (30 mph); distances between cars drop to about 4 car lengths. Flow becomes highly unstable; the first unfavorable event causes an abrupt decline in both speed and flow. Such events include a few additional drivers entering the freeway, poor visibility, a stalled car in any lane, an accident, an object on the roadway, rain, snow, or ice. A drop to level of service *F* characterizes stop-and-go traffic, and the highway can easily degenerate into a parking lot. This maximizes the density, or number of cars on a given stretch of highway, but reduces the flow to zero.

The essential point is that a high level of service *(C)* can be maintained until 1,550 pce per hour occupy the lane; a reasonable level of service can be maintained under favorable conditions up to some 1,850 pce/h. From that point on, additional traffic or any other unfavorable circumstance can result in gridlock on a major freeway that had average speeds of nearly 87 km/h (53 mph) a few minutes or weeks before.

Some caveats are in order before using the above data to determine the capacity of a roadway to transport people.

The data refer to the special case of a high-standard, multilane freeway on level terrain. Each lane is 3.7 meters (12 ft.) wide, and there is a half-lane of lateral clearance (shoulder). To translate the pce figures into numbers of vehicles, a discount is made in accord with the formulas of the *Highway Capacity Manual* to account for the greater space requirements of trucks and buses. With 20 percent trucks in the lane, the level of service *A* flow falls to 600 vehicles (120 trucks and 480 cars) per lane per hour; maximum flow at level of service *E* is reduced to 1,700 vehicles per hour. For a highway with 20 percent trucks on mountainous terrain, the figures drop to 250 vehicles/hour at level *A* and 700 vehicles/hour at level *E*. The number of vehicles a lane can handle decreases further as the percentage of trucks and buses increases. In developing countries such as Brazil, expressways may have over 50 percent trucks and 8 percent buses (Wright 1989a).

The per-lane capacities of two-lane highways (two-way traffic) are only about half those of multilane highways, since modest increases in traffic make passing very difficult. On city streets, capacities are further reduced by traffic lights and intersections, and vehicle flow becomes limited by the capacity of the intersections rather than by the capacity of the streets.

The capacity figures should be adjusted for vehicle occupancy and parking needs but seldom if ever are. In many countries, the average occupancy factor for cars is 1.5, a modest figure, but still considerably above the 1.15 workers per vehicle that prevails for commuting trips in the United States (Pisarski 1987: 53)—the latter figure approaches the theoretical minimum of one occupant per car. In urban areas, parking can occupy nearly half the available street space (along with considerable off-street space). In contrast, a luxury bus on a freeway may carry about 54 seated passengers, while occupying only 1.6 times the space of a passenger car. On city streets with standing permitted, 80 or more passengers can be transported in a bus.

An implicit assumption in the above capacity analysis is that all car occupants are actually taking a socially useful, desired trip. The driver of a private car should not be counted while in the role of a bus or taxi driver, as occurs when one takes a spouse or child somewhere and returns alone. The "useful" occupancy rate for such a round trip is 0.5, not 1.5. Unfortunately, the useful car occupancy rate is seldom if ever calculated, hiding part of the automobile's inefficiency in the use of urban space.

Considering a very high freeway flow of 2,000 passenger cars/hour per lane and the U.S. commuting occupancy ratio of 1.15, the maximum car-based movement of people during rush hour is 2,300 persons/lane. Dividing by the lane width, we obtain a mere 629 persons per meter per hour (p/m/h). If we add the space for cloverleafs, medians, shoulders and so forth, this figure shrinks to between 400 and 500 p/m/h. On city streets, these capacities shrink further—much further. [For those American readers who have not quite caught on to the beauty of the metric system, a meter is slightly over a yard (1.0936 yards). Additional conversions are provided in the text on page xv.]

We may now compare the capacity of several transport modes under varying conditions in Table 2.

On city streets with a car occupancy factor of 1.5 (more than the 1.15 figure for commuting in the United States), cars are able to transport only about 143 persons per meter per hour at a speed of 24 km/h (15 mph). Their capacity can reach 251 p/m/h as congestion lowers speed by a third to 16 km/h; this flow is only 7 percent of a sidewalk's capacity to transport 3,609 pedestrians per meter per hour, and only 17 percent of a bikeway's capacity of 1,476 p/m/h. Cars (or taxis) with an average of 4 passengers per vehicle carry 669 p/m/h, and minibuses 492 p/m/h (both at 16 km/h); they have less than half the capacity of bikeways and less than one-fifth the capacity of a walkway. Even larger, 30-passenger buses with 1,640 p/m/h at 11 km/h barely surpass the carrying capacity of bikeways and have less than half the capacity of walkways. *The capacities of walking and cycling are greater than those of any other mode except rail transit and buses on express corridors.*

Although the private automobile and single-passenger taxis

Table 2
Personal Transport Capacities and Average Speeds of Selected Modes

Mode or Type of Way	Capacity of Way (persons/meter/hour)	Speed (kmph)
Nonmotorized modes (1.22 m wide)		
Walkway	3,609	3
Bikeway	1,476	13
Mixed traffic, city street (7.3 m wide)		
Cars with 1.5 occupancy factor	143	24
	251	16
Cars with 4.0 occupancy factor	381	24
	669	16
Minibus (10 passengers)	492	16
Bus (30 passengers)	982	14
	1,640	11
Expressway		
Cars with 1.5 occupancy factor	885	64
Cars with 4 occupants	2,362	64
Minibus (10 passengers)	3,937	64
Bus (40 passengers)	6,562	64
High-capacity urban rail		
Metro (22,500 passengers/line hour)	5,577	34
Urban rail (22,500 passengers/line hour)	5,577	48
Metro (40,000 passengers/line hour)	9,915	34
Urban rail (40,000 passengers/line hour)	9,915	48

Note: Most figures are calculated from basic data given in World Bank (1975: 74). Capacities for cars with 4 occupants are those for the occupancy factor of 1.5 times 2.67. A wider (13.4 m) street for mixed urban traffic would increase the capacity figures for cars by about 10 percent. Taxis with similar numbers of passengers have capacities and speeds similar to those of the private car.

always perform poorly with respect to capacity, extensive carpooling and vanpooling could have a very significant impact on capacities and service levels. The key word is *could*—we have noted the figure of 1.15 occupant per car for commuting in the United States. There are, however, important experiences with carpooling and vanpooling in the United States, and extensive use of multipassenger vans and similar vehicles as forms of public transport in other countries (see Chapter 9).

The 40-passenger bus operation used in Table 2 actually has a higher transport capacity than the flow for high-capacity rail when the latter's capacity is taken as 22,500 passengers per line per hour. The rail and bus comparisons are based respectively on Mexico City's metro and the I-495 bus lane leading to the terminal of the New York Port Authority, with a bus passing every 6 seconds (World Bank 1975: 75). Table 2 also presents an alternative capacity of 40,000 passengers/ hour per direction for rail lines, somewhat below world-record levels but far above the maximums transported by most high-capacity rail systems.

In the United States, record peak-hour passenger flows on bus lanes include 32,560 passengers per lane per hour on the approach to New York's Lincoln Tunnel; 21,600 on New Jersey's I-495; 13,000 on the Oakland Bay Bridge in San Francisco; 10,000 on the Shirley Highway Busway in Washington, D.C. (Transportation Research Board 1985: 12.50). There is extensive Latin American experience with bus lanes that carry hourly flows of 15,000 to 25,000 passengers/ lane, with boarding and exiting of passengers at stations located along the lane and additional passing space provided at the stations (Dall'Orto 1989; Nelson and Hills 1990; Szasz and Germani 1985; Thomson 1984; Wright and Sant'Anna 1989). On Brasil Avenue in Rio de Janeiro, flows of 39,000 passengers per hour occur on express segments at speeds of 70 km/h (44 mph) (Thomson 1984). Although the capacities for buses in Table 2—along with those for other modes—need to be interpreted with caution, they should not be dismissed as unrealistic, nor should buses be classified as low-capacity modes based on the limited experience of cities in developed countries.

As noted, the rail capacities of 22,500 and 40,000 passengers per line per hour in the table are not world records. Under crush loading, sections on subways in New York, São Paulo and Tokyo have transported peaks of about 60,000 passengers during the peak hour. The 1985 *Highway Capacity Manual* (chap. 12) registers the probable record north of the Rio Grande at 62,000 persons transported in one hour in 1960 on the Eighth Avenue Express section of the New York subway. No other urban train section in the United States or Canada ever approached that figure. Chicago's record of 16,500 (Lake-Ryan section) dates from 1978; Philadelphia's 10,600 maximum on the (North) Broad Street subway, from 1976; Boston's 13,000 on the Red Line from 1977/78; San Francisco's 8,000 on BART Transbay from 1977; Washington's 13,000 (Blue-Orange Lines), from 1980; Atlanta's 4,250 (East Line) from 1980; Cleveland's 6,200 (West Side) from 1960. Toronto's Yonge Street Line registered the Canadian high of 36,000 back in 1974; the record on Montreal's N Line is 28,200, which was set in 1976.

Only one of these records surpasses the record bus figures by a substantial margin, that of New York's subway. The Toronto and Montreal maximums are somewhat below the Rio de Janeiro bus lane record and about equal to some bus lanes in São Paulo. All the other train records are below the flows that occur every workday on the Santo Amaro—9 de Julho bus priority lane in São Paulo. This corridor routinely handles 15,000 to 20,000 persons/hour in one direction during peak hours and could reach 30,000 if necessary. Even so, it operates at volumes only slightly above those of the Assis Brasil and Farrapos corridors in the much smaller Brazilian city of Porto Alegre (Nelson and Hills 1990; Szasz and Germani 1985; Wright and Sant'Anna 1989).

These figures undermine the "hard sell" efforts often used to impose metro systems on cities with the argument that buses are incapable of providing the capacity that the sellers' mathematical models predict will be needed in the immediate future. The models are based on assumptions that produce enormous flows between A and B, none of which is likely to occur. In fact, a number of these models employ some variant of a geometrical growth rate for population and trips— if carried far enough into the future, any such model would have the entire world population traveling on the proposed line. But even more realistic mathematical forms, such as the logistics curve (that eventually flattens out and approaches a limit), can also yield high figures. In a typical instance, the train capacities cited in the sellers' arguments are based on theoretical calculations of the number of passengers that could be crammed into a train and the shortest headway possible between trains. As the above figures indicate, the theoretical capacities of trains are unlikely to be needed very often.

The "hard sellers" usually bias the results further by comparing the theoretical capacities of trains with poorly designed buses that operate in congested mixed traffic. They omit the real-world examples of peak-hour flows in North and South America that place bus capacities on the level of intensely used train systems.

None of the high-capacity bus services operates under anything approximating ideal conditions. If those conditions were present, it might be possible for buses to equal or surpass New York's subway record. This would require some combination of the following measures: (1) placing the stops or stations for boarding and alighting of passengers off the lane; (2) providing passing space at stations; (3) crowding more people into each vehicle; (4) using large buses with articulated trailers; (5) redesigning the vehicles with wider doors, floor-level platforms and entrances rather than street-level stops with steps for entering the bus; and (6) reducing headways further.

Some experiments in the 1960s at the General Motors proving grounds simulated express services with 2.5-second headways, equivalent to 1,450 buses per lane per hour. At 53 km/h (33 mph), the headway had a distance equivalent between buses of 37 meters (40 yds), still (minimally) adequate for safety. With 50 passengers per bus, those figures translate into 72,500 passengers/hour (Transportation Research Board 1985: 12.49).

The General Motors experiment was light-years from accounting for the difficulties of real-world bus operations, but it also omitted a number of the capacity increasing measures listed above. In Brazil, large, articulated buses carry 180 passengers per unit; other configurations have a tractive-unit bus with two trailers, capable of operating like a train on a fixed guideway, with 220 passengers per unit. On concrete track, the Essen (Germany) and Adelaide (Australia) O-Bahn bus convoys have a rated capacity of about 35,000 to 40,000 passengers per line per hour with 6 persons per square meter of floor space (Araújo 1989: 42); crush loading could nearly double that figure by placing 12 persons/m^2 in the vehicles. Although the O-Bahn has never had such high passenger demands, it appears the system could challenge record rail volumes, with some sacrifice of reliability—not to mention comfort (the rides with record-breaking train volumes were not comfortable either).

The chief practical limit for bus capacity is likely to be the same one faced by train systems—not enough people want to travel on the same section at the same time. What buses could theoretically do with seated passengers, actual train and bus systems do with crush loading. In developing countries, as many as 12 or 13 persons per square meter of floor space have been counted in transit vehicles (New York's subway record levels probably approached these densities also). These levels may persist over time since people often have no other suitable option. In richer countries, the Yogi Berra principle usually goes into effect: "That place is so crowded no one goes there anymore."

I do not believe it is desirable to have near-record volumes on either buses or trains. Crush loading is not a pleasant experience. A better strategy involves spreading out the demand among slightly different routes for better, more flexible service.

The capacities of walking and cycling cited in Table 2 refer to a particular speed and a given set of other conditions. However, the sketchy analyses we have of these modes indicate that the same level of service concepts described above for motor vehicles also apply to walking and cycling. The 1985 *Highway Capacity Manual* (Transportation Research Board 1985: chap. 13) provides such an analysis for walking. A walkway can handle about 394 pedestrians per meter per hour at level of service *A*, with a speed of nearly 5 km/h (3 mph). As the flow of pedestrians increases, slower walkers and those moving across the flow reduce the average speed until, at level of service *E*, the walkway's capacity is reached at 4,921 pedestrians/m/h, at 2.7 km/h average walking speed (a larger, slower flow than in Table 2).

Little research is available on the concepts of capacity and service levels for cycling. Most bikeways are narrow, 1.22 meters wide (4 ft.) or less. Narrow bikeways have lower capacities per area than wider ones, due to lateral obstruction and difficulties in passing. Their capacity is also decreased if flows occur in both directions on the same pathway, rather than separately, on unidirectional bikeways.

With few bikes on the track, nonathletic cyclists can maintain speeds of 12 to 20 km/h (7.5 to 12.5 mph) under favorable conditions; these speeds decline as more cyclists enter the track, as occurs with motor vehicle flows. The *Highway Capacity Manual* (Transportation Research Board 1985: 14.3) cites a range of reported capacities from 500 to 2,530 bicycles per hour for narrow bikeways (1.22 meters or less). The figures for cycle speed and flow in Table 2 present intermediate levels of service and capacity.

The above data give the range of capacities of some of the more widely used modes of urban transport and prepare the way for the discussion of the effects of these modes on the urban environment in the next chapter. Additional modes and their capacities are discussed in Chapter 7; the additional modes are usually intermediate cases related in fairly obvious ways to the more common modes.

Chapter 4

Energy, Pollution, and the Urban Environment

SIX CHARACTERISTICS of personal transport modes affect the urban environment and the quality of life in both the short and long run: energy efficiency, air pollution, noise, aesthetic values, vulnerability, and sustainability of transport modes. There are some obvious interrelationships among these characteristics, so that a given mode may have a similar performance, either good or poor, across most of the six attributes. Other, more subtle relationships are revealed in the course of our discussion.

Energy Efficiency

Energy efficiency in personal transport is measured as the energy used to transport a passenger over a distance of one kilometer (passenger km), expressed in kilocalories per passenger km, kilowatt hours per passenger km, or megajoules per passenger km. In general, space-efficient modes (those modes with high capacities in relation to the area they occupy) are energy-efficient modes.

Unfortunately, conventional measures include only the on-site, direct energy used by the vehicle itself; on occasion I will use such figures for lack of more adequate data. Off-site and indirect energy use is quite important in urban transportation, however.

This second kind of energy is used in the:

transportation of energy to the vehicle;

production of the vehicle and its infrastructure, including earthworks, concrete, and steel tracks;

production and refining of the energy consumed by the vehicle; and

complementary modes, equipment and other supporting activities.

Jalal Salihi (1973) provides a clearer idea of these concepts by comparing a theoretical electric car with a conventional gasoline-powered car; both weigh 1,432 kg (3,150 lb.). In heavy urban traffic, the electric car requires 2.23 kilowatt-hours (kWh) of coal at the generating plant to power the car for 1.6 kilometers (1 mile). Generation and transmission losses reduce this to 0.71 kWh of AC energy fed into the car's battery charger at the owner's house and, after losses in the battery, motor, transmission, and accessories, a mere 0.23 percent of road energy is actually available at the wheels. This corresponds to only 10.3 percent of the original coal-produced heat energy, and omits the energy losses in mining and transporting the coal.

The same distance in a comparable gasoline-powered car requires 3.26 kWh of crude-oil energy. Only 15 percent of the energy in the crude oil is lost in refining and distribution, yielding 2.77 kWh of gasoline energy in the tank. The internal combustion engine dissipates most of this energy as heat and, with the demands of accessories and transmission, only 0.23 kWh makes it to the tire–road interface. This amounts to a mere 7.1 percent of the heat energy in the crude oil entering the refinery. Even that low percentage would decline slightly if we counted the energy expended in extracting the crude from the ground and transporting it to the refinery.

Although the numbers vary with the type of vehicle and operation considered, the example illustrates a valid principle: thermoelectric systems are wasteful in getting energy to a motor, but once it is delivered they use it reasonably efficiently; gasoline and diesel systems, in contrast, place the energy in the vehicle tank efficiently, but then waste almost all of it. Salihi's hypothetical electric car is about half as wasteful overall as the gasoline car.

Off-site and indirect energy is even required for nonmotorized transport. Petroleum is often employed to produce the food that furnishes the energy pedestrians and cyclists use. This is not trivial for agricultural systems that rely heavily on petroleum for tillage, fertilizers, pesticides, herbicides, processing, packaging, and distribution; the moderate-speed pedestrian or cyclist, however, requires less energy than the most efficient motor vehicle (U.S. Department of Transportation 1974: 46).

Herbert Levinson and colleagues (1984: 172) provide one of the few available intermodal comparisons of indirect and total energy use, based on data from the Toronto transport system. They define indirect energy as that used in construction, maintenance, and vehicle manufacture, which I will call CMV energy. This is expressed on an annual basis with an assumed service life, and corresponds roughly to the production of a vehicle and its infrastructure (see list above of indirect and off-site energy usage). Levinson's group defines direct energy to include that lost in generation and transmission. For Toronto's electric vehicles, these losses are rather modest in relation to those in Salihi's example, since power comes from Niagara's nearby hydroelectric plants. Off-site losses with diesel fuel and gasoline are small in both cases.

The Levinson group calculates CMV and total energy in relation to transport generated, where total energy = CMV energy + direct energy (including off-site loss).

The trolleybus uses 0.26 megajoule of energy per seat km, of which 12 percent is CMV energy. The respective figures for the other modes are: subway, 0.42 mJ (69 percent); streetcar, 0.43 mJ (49 percent); diesel bus, 0.54 mJ (7 percent); commuter rail, 0.66 mJ (14 percent); 12-seat van on arterial, 0.75 mJ (16 percent); 5-seat car on arterial, 1.55 mJ (20 percent).

The CMV energy for electric rail systems is a high percentage of total energy use, reaching 69 percent for subways. Under crush loading, subway total energy use falls to 0.10 megajoule/passenger km, against 0.11 for trolleybus, 0.17 for streetcar, 0.22 for diesel bus, and 0.33 for commuter rail.

As Levinson and colleagues explicitly state, such figures should be interpreted with caution. The data depend heavily on the conditions in Toronto, including the use of hydroelectric power. Thermoelectric power would be less generous to the electric systems (the diesel bus would appear at or near the front of the list), and specific applications require adjusting the energy consumption to a per passenger kilometer basis, to reflect load factors.

There is a wide variation in direct energy expenditure per passenger km among modes and countries; circumstances vary widely in different areas of a city. Table 3 shows a wide variation in the passenger km per liter of fuel obtained in the United States in the early 1970s. The lower figures in the table usually refer to averages actually witnessed, while the higher figures refer to available seat km, using the same or similar figures for the vehicle km traveled. The data for buses marked with asterisks are taken from recent observations of actual operations in Brasília, referring to on-site use of diesel fuel. The sources of the other data do not indicate whether off-site losses are included.

We can extract some important conclusions from the table despite the obvious problems with the data. First, energy efficiency could be vastly increased by elevating the average vehicle occupancy or load factor. A compact car with four passengers getting 13 km/l (31 mpg) in urban traffic generates 52 passenger km/l, better than the average energy efficiency of American trains or buses with their current low occupancy ratios.

Second, if average real occupancy figures are used for all modes or, alternatively, if the available seat figures are used for all modes, trains and buses are several times more efficient than are private cars.

A third conclusion—one that requires supplementing the table with additional information—is that the United States uses urban transportation energy very inefficiently relative to most other countries. This occurs for three reasons: reliance on the least energy-efficient means of surface transportation (private cars) for a much higher percentage of surface transportation; low energy efficiency for all modes due to low load factors; and longer average distance for trips and more trips due to low population density and zoning practices that isolate residences from commerce, industry, and other sources of trip generation and attraction.

Table 3
Ranges of Fuel Efficiency for Several Transport Modes

Mode	Passengers		Available Seats	
	km/l	*mpg*	*km/l*	*mpg*
Intracity bus	32–100*	75–259*	92‡	217‡
Intercity bus	35–107*	82–252*	191	450
Suburban train	85	200	170	400
Commuter train	43	100	85	200
Automobile	11	25	51	120
Airplane	6	14	29	68

Note: Data represent extreme values cited in U.S. Department of Transportation (1974: 11, 13, 45), except for those marked with an asterisk, which are empirical Brazilian data from the Federal District for intracity buses (Wright 1987b: 299) and interstate buses (DNER 1986). The latter refer to actual passenger km per liter of diesel fuel. (A passenger km is equivalent to transporting one passenger over a distance of one kilometer; 10 passenger km may represent 5 passengers transported over 2 km, or one passenger transported for 10 km.) Figures marked with a dagger were adjusted upward from original by using load factor of 100 percent instead of 45 percent.

By means of comparison, the average energy efficiency of urban buses in Brazil's Federal District (indicated by the figures with asterisks for intracity buses in Table 3) is more than three times the U.S. average; it exceeds slightly what U.S. buses would register if all their seats were occupied. The corresponding average for Brazilian interstate buses is superior to that of the most efficient U.S. trains. The Brazilian figures include only direct, on-site energy use, but as the Toronto figures showed, the picture would not change significantly if they were adjusted for indirect energy use.

A few intermodal comparisons for the United States are presented in Table 4. Transit buses are only slightly more efficient than automobiles due to their very low load factors and the relatively high load factor of 1.7 considered in the table for cars. This latter value is probably not representative of U.S. urban transportation, since it includes social, recreational, and intercity trips that raise the previously cited 1.15 load factor for cars on the journey to work. If the load factor for transit buses could be increased to the 20- to 30-passenger range, their fuel efficiency would surpass the figure for completely loaded cars, along with those for commuter rail and rail transit.

These figures show that public transportation is more energy efficient per passenger km of travel than the private car. This is especially true in cities such as those in Latin America and Asia where high load factors for transit are common. The difference is rather small in U.S cities where transit vehicles have low load factors; there may even be extreme instances where buses and trains run nearly empty on very

Table 4
Energy Use by Passenger Vehicles in the United States, 1985

Mode	Load Factor (passenger km/vehicle km)	Relative Energy Use (intercity bus = 1)
Intercity bus	41.8	1.00
Intercity rail	19.1	2.12
Commuter rail	35.6	2.19
Transit bus	12.7	2.43
Transit rail	23.1	2.77
Automobile	1.7	3.20
Air—certified route	89.3	3.82

Source of data for calculations is American Public Transit Association (1989: 64). Note that pkm = passenger × kilometers, and vkm = vehicle × kilometers.

low-density routes and are less fuel efficient than private cars.

The data also show that trains offer an appreciable energy advantage over buses only in special cases. When trains are powered by diesel engines, they are normally less energy efficient than buses. The most efficient conventional electric trains with high load factors are normally more energy efficient than diesel buses, if they are located near a hydroelectric plant. Electric buses (trolleybuses) are typically more energy efficient than urban trains.

The encouraging energy efficiency of buses contradicts the oft-assumed superiority of trains. The conventional view is based on the steel-wheel-on-steel-rail technology's very low coefficient of rolling resistance—only a tenth of that for vehicles with rubber tires (Vuchic 1981: 122). The steel-on-steel advantage has been popularized with graphic examples of trains transporting 125 tons for a kilometer on a liter of fuel, while a truck moves only 30 tons over the same distance on a liter of fuel (Adas 1985: 239).

Such examples remind me again of Darrell Huff's (1954) magnificent little book, *How to Lie with Statistics*. Averages for trains are high since they transport huge quantities of iron ore, coal, and other products that have high specific gravities. They move them from point A to point B, rather than collecting them in a variety of places and delivering them to many other points. Trains do this very efficiently, but are not very efficient at moving small amounts of light goods between many places of origin and many destinations. This is one reason trucks move almost everything else and are at times more fuel efficient in doing it (International Road Transport Union 1974).

In urban transport, the train's low rolling resistance is largely canceled out by its greater dead weight, requiring more energy for acceleration between stations. In urban areas with high population densities, stations are normally located at distances of only 300 to 600 meters apart (328–656 yards); they are seldom over one kilometer apart. The Moscow metro is an exception, with a 1,600-meter (1 mile) average between stations (Grava 1976: 241–67), but even there shorter spacings are used in the central areas. A train must expend a great deal of energy to accelerate its huge dead weight after each stop and, even with the most modern systems, only a small part of this energy can be recuperated during braking; the rest is dissipated according to the second law of thermodynamics.

A typical U.S. transit bus with around 44 seats weighs 12.6 metric tons (t) (Francis and King 1989). The weight of a typical rapid rail transit vehicle ranges from 19 t for a 35-seat car to 38 t for a much larger, 83-seat car (Vuchic 1981: 346). The bus has 286 kg of dead weight per seat; the small rail car, 542 kg/seat; the large rail car, 458 kg/seat. With all seats filled, no passengers standing, and an average passenger weight of 70 kg (154 lb.), the bus has 4.1 kg of dead weight for each kg of passenger weight; the small rail car has 7.8 kg; and the large rail car, 6.5 kg. The advantage for the bus increases if bus and train load factors are low, and decreases if they are high, since trains have a higher ratio of standing room to seats.

The advantage of lower rolling resistance of steel-on-steel is further reduced by the rather small absolute values involved. J. D. Walter and F. S. Conant (1974: 252) list a rolling resistance coefficient for bus and truck tires equivalent to 8 to 12 kg of drag per ton of load, against 1 to 3 kg of drag per ton of load for steel-on-steel. For automobiles, the drag from rolling resistance is less than that due to slip in automatic transmissions.

Since 90 to 95 percent of the rolling resistance of rubber tires is due to hysteresis within the tire itself, improved radial tires and higher tire pressures can further reduce resistance. Manufacturers have increased their recommended tire pressures considerably in the last decade, but the expected gains are modest since the drag itself is small. A 20 percent decrease in rolling resistance results in only a 2 to 6 percent decrease in fuel consumption (Walter and Conant 1974: 244–45). Higher tire pressures cause additional damage to highways, although this is a significant factor only for trucks and other heavy vehicles.

The relevant figure for rolling resistance, moreover, is not drag per ton, but drag per passenger. A bus with all seats occupied weighs 356 kg/passenger, yielding a rolling resistance of 2.85 to 4.27 kg of drag/passenger; the small rail car has 0.61 to 1.84 kg drag/passenger; the large rail car, 0.53 to 1.58 kg drag/passenger. The bus has a disadvantage of only 1.6 times in the most favorable case, and 8 times in the least favorable case.

These examples show that the relevant measure of drag/passenger does not yield a factor of 10 for the difference in rolling resistances of steel and rubber; rather, this factor varies with the load factors of bus and rail and the specific configuration of the rail line—wheel combination. Only under conditions of crush loading or low occupancy ratios for buses relative to trains do trains derive the full benefits of lower rolling resistance; even then, the advantage is reduced by the train's relatively higher energy expenditures during acceleration.

Air Pollution

Airborne pollutants generated by urban transportation are now recognized as a very serious health problem in all developed countries and in many developing countries. This does not imply that all the effects can be precisely quantified; scientists naturally do a better job of measuring levels of specific pollutants than of specifying their effects on health and the environment. Scientists are also hampered by a lack of resources for the easier task of monitoring pollution levels. In the mid-1980s, for example, the Global Environment Monitoring System (GEMS) network, linked to the United Nations Environment Program and the World Health Organization (WHO), had information on sulphur dioxide concentrations for only 54 cities worldwide. Exactly half of these cities had pollution levels near to or exceeding the maximums WHO considered tolerable. For suspended particulate matter, only 41 cities were monitored, and 37 had borderline or excessive levels (French 1990: 9–11).

The effects of airborne contaminants are difficult to separate from other causes of illness, since many serious effects only appear after long periods of exposure. Without proper measurement and monitoring, it is often unclear if transport vehicles or other sources of pollution are the main culprits. Nonetheless, the toxic effects of lead, carbon monoxide, sulphur, nitrous oxides, and other contaminants found in transportation fuels are well known to medical science. Measurements currently available indicate that clearly unsafe conditions often prevail, and transportation almost always plays a significant role in generating pollutants. Transport's role is dominant in the contaminants in some locales.

Occasionally, it is possible to establish a reasonably clear pattern for a given pollutant. C. Arden Pope (1989), for example, measured particulate matter with aerodynamic diameter of 10 micrometers or less (PM_{10}) in Utah Valley and associated it with hospital admissions for pneumonia, pleurisy, bronchitis, and asthma. The principal source of PM_{10} was a steel mill that was closed for part of the study period. The effects of the pollutant could be more successfully isolated since only 5 percent of the area residents smoked, because of Mormon religious teachings. During the winter months, hospital admissions doubled with the plant open as compared with the times it was closed, and days of high particulate readings saw a tripling of children admitted to area hospitals with the respiratory problems listed.

It is impossible to conduct such precise investigations of individual transportation sector pollutants, since transport produces a range of contaminants that mix with others from nontransport sources. Yet in many regions transportation vehicle emissions are a major source—perhaps the major source—of air pollution, and they have observable effects on health. The effects become particularly intense in large cities such as Los Angeles, Mexico City, Santiago, and São Paulo where mountains retain contaminants rather than allowing them to be dispersed by the winds.

The metropolitan area of Mexico City is an especially interesting case, since it may be both the world's most populous urban area and its most polluted. There, the shares in total emissions of transport vehicles and (in parentheses) some percentages for private cars are: 55 percent (31 percent) of nitrous oxides; 83 percent (48 percent) of hydrocarbons; 12 percent of sulphur dioxide; 12 percent of particulates; 98 percent (67 percent) of carbon monoxide; and 100 percent (80 percent) of lead (Quadri 1989: 13).

Transport-generated pollution in the form of ozone can be highly visible. Ozone is also known as smog and is not related to the ozone in the stratosphere, which protects the earth from excessive exposure to ultraviolet rays. Ozone is not emitted directly by vehicles; it is formed by subsequent complex reactions of sunlight with emissions of nitrous oxide (NO_x), hydrocarbons (HC), and, to some extent, carbon monoxide (CO). Ozone is thus formed only in the presence of sunlight, especially intense sunlight.

One of the ironies of life is that motorized transportation can make a sunny tropical city look as overcast as London. On a holiday morning when little traffic is circulating, residents of Santiago, Chile, are often blessed with a panorama of blue skies and beautiful, snow-capped mountains. On weekday afternoons with identical meteorological conditions, the sky appears heavily overcast and the mountains cannot be seen. Santiago's old, poorly maintained diesel buses are among the chief offenders, as clouds of hydrocarbons accompanied by nitrous oxides billow out of their exhaust pipes. Smog in Los Angeles is another example of humanity's ability to downgrade a relatively pure natural environment, while occasional "thermal inversions" seal São Paulo's abundant pollutants in its mountain valley. Such phenomena can transform an already serious problem into severe respiratory crises for more sensitive individuals.

Airborne pollutants are also one of the major causes of damage to buildings, historical monuments, home furnishings, clothing, vehicles, crops, forests, lakes, and water supplies. Some of this damage has been reasonably well publicized, such as that occurring to the Black Forest in Germany, the Acropolis in Greece, and many ancient Italian and Egyptian monuments. However, the less publicized acidification of lakes and water supplies and damage to crops and other vegetation may already represent a major biological crisis. Half of Canada's eastern lakes are acid-sensitive and 150,000 of them suffer biological damage, while air pollution has reduced crop yields in countries as diverse as the United States and China (French 1990: 17–24).

Transport-generated pollution must be combatted at the source: wearing gas masks twenty-four hours a day is not a practical solution. (In Manila, however, some people may be seen on the streets with painters' masks over their mouths; some women walk for blocks holding handkerchiefs over nose and mouth, looking delicate and out of place amid the clouds of diesel fumes; some of the jeepney [minibus] drivers tie small towels over nose and mouth and look like Jesse James).

Precise sources of pollution must be identified, along with their intensity and the alternatives for reducing emissions to much lower levels. Harmful emissions are related to the quantity and type of fuel used and the combustion process employed. The problem can be treated as point-specific (for example, downtown Los Angeles or Mexico City), from a regional perspective (Norway suffers from acid rain produced primarily by pollutants from its European neighbors), or even a global viewpoint (the "greenhouse effect"). Although this list of factors seems rather obvious, it contains both opportunities for and barriers to improvement that are frequently overlooked by those who approach the problem with preconceived solutions, such as universal prescriptions of passenger trains or electric cars.

Social Options

Our concern is with social options for decreasing the level of a negative characteristic, air pollution, in terms of both absolute levels and per person kilometer of travel. There are basically five paths available.

Path 1. Switch from motorized vehicles with low load factors, such as private cars, to nonmotorized transportation and vehicles with higher load factors, such as trains and buses. As a complementary strategy, increase the load factors of vehicles from any mode where they are low relative to their respective capacities. Population densities, street designs, and personal preferences may make this option difficult to adopt in some countries or cities, so it should be used in conjunction with Path 4.

Path 2. Increase the distance each vehicle can travel per energy unit of whatever fuel it now consumes. The two shock waves of energy price increases in the 1970s provided a great stimulus for research and development in this area. Saddam Hussein may have provided another.

In some Western countries, concern with emissions produced legislation that forced the automotive industry to research and design more fuel-efficient cars even before the first fuel-price shock. Annual fuel consumption per passenger car in the United States decreased from 2,710 liters (716 gallons) in 1975 to 1,949 liters (515 gallons) in 1987, a reduction of 28 percent (Motor Vehicle Manufacturers Association 1989: 52). Most of this economy was derived from a 42 percent increase in average fuel efficiency to 8.2 km/l (19.2 mpg) in 1987, despite the presence of older, less efficient vehicles in the fleet. Average consumption for new cars reached 11.6 km/l (27 mpg) in the United States in 1988, only slightly below the respective German and Japanese averages of 12.0 and 13.0 km/l (U.S. Department of Transportation 1990: 3.11). Many Brazilian cars (my own included) average 10 km/l on ethanol (ethyl alcohol).

Although research on fuel efficiency continues for all modes of transport, much impetus was lost as fuel prices fell during the 1980s. Politicians, economists, and the media fell back on their traditional assumption that whatever existed at the moment was economic law and would continue indefinitely. In the United States, the extremely low price of gasoline during the decade of the 1980s (about $1 a gallon or 26 cents a liter) meant that an increase of 50 percent in the average car fuel efficiency (from 8.2 to 12.3 km/l) yielded an average annual savings of only $180 per car. As fuel efficiency increases, the financial incentive drops even further; the same absolute increase, from 12.3 to 16.4 km/l, results in an annual savings of less than $90 for the average car. Even in other countries, where fuel is often twice as expensive at the pump, the financial incentive for the individual motorist to invest in a more fuel-efficient vehicle is rather minor.

The preference of many drivers for more spacious and powerful vehicles cancels out part of the engineering advances that, other things constant, could increase fuel efficiency of gasoline engines by perhaps another 30 to 40 percent in the next 10 to 15 years. Overall fuel efficiency, however, lags behind engineering advances now commercially available, as older, more energy-intensive cars are replaced only very slowly by the newer, more fuel-efficient models. Radical decreases in weight and power could increase fuel efficiency by (say) three times. Such vehicles, however, would be unsafe if used in high speed, mixed traffic with existing cars and trucks. There is no clear way to get from "here" to "there."

Potential "breakthroughs" in fuel economy are occasionally announced in the media. Most of them die a natural death—the vehicles are either figments of some mad scientist's imagination or look suspiciously like entrants in a soap-box derby.

Two more-serious contenders are the "lean-burn" gasoline engine and the Hansen cycle for ethanol engines. The lean-burner uses computers and sensors to inject 20 parts of air to each part gasoline into the engine's combustion chamber, a 36 percent improvement on the current 14.7 to 1 ratio (Brown 1991: 13). This is a significant gain, but not so spectacular as some news accounts that have placed the lean-burners' fuel economy at 26 km/l (60 mpg). Those figures represent ideal conditions, not urban traffic conditions, and the lean burner does not work at high speeds. These claims should also be kept in perspective: some models currently on the market—and the 1948 Crosley—get about 19 km/l (45 mpg) under ideal highway conditions. They do not come near those figures in urban traffic, and they are small, light vehicles, often well down on the list of consumer preference, for the reasons listed earlier.

The manufacturers are also cautious. Honda will install its lean-burn engine in the Civic VX to test "customer acceptability"; Mitsubishi, only in the MVV model sold in Japan, giving it an opportunity to correct problems before plunging into the international market. The second potential breakthrough is the proposed Hansen cycle for engines using ethanol as fuel (Demetrius 1990: 161–5). Hansen's system uses exhaust and radiator gases to preheat the fuel–air mixture, with combustion occurring at much lower temperatures, reducing engine wear to minimal levels, and virtually eliminating harmful emissions. Thermal efficiency becomes double that of conventional motors, and the cost of ethanol production is reduced since 70 to 80 proof alcohol can be used instead of the current 190 proof required by present Brazilian alcohol-powered vehicles. I would not like to predict whether Herbert Hansen's idea will become commercially viable or prove to be an alcoholic version of cold fusion.

Diesel engines are more fuel efficient than gasoline engines; in part for that reason they offer fewer perspective gains in efficiency. Bus manufacturers also face the difficulty of reducing the weight of buses in proportion to the reductions achieved by cars. One improvement in the offing is the use of fiber-reinforced material in carbon design in a West German bus, with a 30 percent reduction in weight (Lee 1989). The vehicles passed tests for fatigue, vibration, crash, overload, and extreme temperatures and should soon be available for commercial use (no word on the cost). The Germans have also developed a more efficient gearbox that decreases fuel consumption on in-line passenger service by 15 percent, and an energy regeneration system for braking. The latter did not pass tests and is being subject to additional research and development (Schneider and Meibner 1989: 44–48).

Even without these potential advances, some increases in fuel efficiency are possible as current bus models replace older ones and, in a second wave, more efficient motors become available over the next decade. In some European and other countries with state-of-the-art bus production (such as Japan, the United States, and Brazil), each change will probably be responsible for less than a 10 percent increase in fuel efficiency. In countries where obsolescence prevails, greater gains are possible, if resources are available to import modern vehicles or upgrade local factories. In many developing countries, better maintenance and tuning alone could probably result in a 5 to 10 percent gain in fuel efficiency.

Electric trains with conventional motors and suspensions present a similar pattern (Vuchic 1981: 129–52). Upgrading obsolete systems can present substantial gains in energy efficiency as improved materials and controls are incorporated. As a guess, this might amount to some 25 percent in energy savings for the really bad systems. Part of the heat energy generated in braking can be captured for later use in propulsion. Regenerative braking, however, requires complex controls and creates operational problems. It does not appear that other improvements in conventional systems will provide any major gains in energy efficiency in the next decade or so, and we are talking about a mode that is already among the most fuel efficient in terms of on-site tractive energy. Since energy costs for traction are a very small proportion of total expenses of operating trains, here, too, financial incentives for continued fuel efficiency are small.

Linear induction has become a practical alternative to traditional rail technologies, but the jury is still out on energy efficiency. The urban transport version of the linear induction motor is used with a conventional steel-wheel-on-steel-rail suspension. The "motor" is a linear metal band laid between the tracks, pulling the rail car along by applying a magnetic force to a plate in the bottom of the rail car. This system eliminates both motor and transmission from the rail cars and reduces the total height of the vehicle. The lower height requirement is a particularly important feature where tunnels are involved, as in Vancouver. Linear induction also permits the trains to climb grades about three times steeper than the 3 percent limit of conventional steel-on-steel traction. There are at least two of these linear induction systems currently in commercial operation: the Skytrain in Vancouver, and one patterned after it, the Detroit People Mover. Detroit's rail cars have 424 kg (935 lb.) of dead weight per seat, somewhat below the 458 kg for the large and the 542 kg for the small rail cars cited earlier (Nelson 1990). Some of the weight reduction, however, may be due to lighter materials unrelated to the linear motor.

Another revolutionary development, magnetic levitation, has received more attention from the media, but has little promise for urban transportation. Magnetic levitation has been developed on the theory that conventional suspension systems make it impossible to achieve hyperspeeds with steel wheels and rails due to instability problems. If a redesigned suspension system were to overcome that limitation, mag-lev might lose its current appeal.

The mag-lev vehicle is suspended slightly above the guideway and can attain hyperspeeds of 500 km/h (311 mph) or more. These speeds are incompatible with the frequent stops and starts of urban transport, since the accelerations and decelerations are not acceptable for passenger comfort, aside from requiring exceptionally high and frequent energy inputs. The heavy magnets and wind resistance make mag-levs require more energy than other forms of rail travel. Their potential use in urban settings is limited to connections between distant stations with considerable volume of passengers, such as airport to downtown, or commuting trips between neighboring cities.

Path 3. Make each fuel burn more cleanly in the motors that conventionally use it. Poorly regulated motors burn more fuel and generate a disproportionate amount of pollution per liter of fuel consumed. Diesel buses in developing countries are often the most visible offenders, producing clouds of black smoke filled with hydrocarbons and particulates. A few poorly regulated buses can produce as much of these pollutants as the rest of the fleet combined. However, unseen emissions from gasoline and other fuels are often even more toxic. Improved car engines with catalytic converters can reduce emissions of hydrocarbons and carbon monoxide about 85 percent and nitrous oxides by 62 percent (French 1990: 27).

Path 4. Modify street design, traffic rules, vehicle operation and other features to encourage more efficient use of vehicles, particularly those with high occupancy rates. Although seldom if ever mentioned in studies of transport energy efficiency, this may be the most important path of all (see Chapters 7 and 9).

Path 5. Switch to fuels or motor–fuel combinations that reduce emissions of materials regarded as particularly harmful. This requires substantial research and development, but is not necessarily out of reach for developing countries. Brazil pioneered in this area for a number of years, becoming the first country in the world to completely eliminate lead by adding 10 to 20 percent ethanol to its gasoline.

This path is mined with secondary effects, however. In the case of ethanol, some of the by-products of refining sugar cane to obtain ethanol were thrown into local rivers, transforming them into open sewers. Citizen reactions could not be contained even by the military regime then in power. One unique protest was organized by professional soccer players in Piracicaba, a major cane-producing region where I once lived. The players wore black armbands at their games in mourning for the "death" of the local scenic river. Over time, the by-products were found to be useful both as an organic fertilizer and as a supplement in cattle feed. The rivers stopped receiving them and are now recovering.

Unfortunately, no one has yet discovered an economical way to avoid burning the sugarcane fields in preparation for harvest. The burning has adverse affects on soil, wildlife, and air quality. It also carries soot into neighboring cities, creating problems for both modern industries that require stringent quality controls and for families that want clean homes and clothes. And, like many other fuels, ethanol produces carbon dioxide (CO_2) upon combustion. Although scientists disagree regarding the existence and severity of the "greenhouse effect" or global warming, the possible dangers are not to be taken lightly. Carbon dioxide is a worrisome product, along with other undesirable substances produced during the combustion of ethanol, such as aldehydes.

The United States and some other developed countries have phased out the use of leaded gasoline through large investments in energy-intensive refineries, but unleaded gasoline also contains harmful substances such as benzene. Nonetheless, the worst option is to do nothing. Many countries continue to produce leaded gasoline, despite knowledge that even small amounts of that toxic metal can cause permanent mental retardation and decreased motor coordination in children. Progressively larger amounts can lead to similar problems in adults, or even insanity and death. Mexico City has one of the worst problems with lead in fuels, and public health specialists worry that the entire population has suffered mental and physical damage as a result (French 1990: 15).

The main urban vehicle fuels at present are gasoline, diesel fuel, and electricity. Nonleaded gasoline produces carbon monoxide (CO), nitrous oxides (NO_x), hydrocarbons (HC), and benzene. Diesel fuel produces aldehydes, CO_2, hydrocarbons and particulates, with less CO and more NO_x than gasoline.

Carbon monoxide is sufficiently toxic to cause death to a person seated inside an idling car in a closed garage and in some other environments. Lesser concentrations in congested urban traffic also cause temporary impairment of physical and mental capacities, particularly in cities surrounded by hills or mountains, on streets where buildings partially block winds, and in garages and tunnels. The ozone produced by reactions of HC, NO_x, and CO on sunny days is prejudicial to health, besides being unsightly. Benzene is a highly toxic, colorless, volatile hydrocarbon. One of the better known aldehydes is formaldehyde (HCHO), a powerful irritant to the respiratory tract, eyes, and nose, and a suspected carcinogen. Particulates, a major contributor to lung disease, find their way into just about everything, including the lungs, where they deposit toxic metals.

Fuels such as gasoline also have undesirable evaporative emissions. In general, little is known about the degree to which evaporative emissions may present a significant hazard to human health and the environment. Control measures are possible at both pump and vehicle. The pump is the logical choice and, for obvious reasons, the one favored by automakers and opposed by fuel companies; neither solution is particularly easy or inexpensive to implant.

At the vehicle site, electricity is a source of very clean energy. But a serious environmental problem may be created somewhere else if the electricity is obtained from nuclear energy or from burning coal. Coal produces fewer hydrocarbons and less carbon monoxide than gasoline and diesel fuel, but slightly more particulates and sulphur oxides. The latter create highly offensive odors, along with irritants to eyes, nose, and respiratory tract. Sulfuric oxides are responsible for the production of acid rain in areas that may be located far from the combustion site, with negative effects on health, buildings, infrastructure, and the environment. Poisonous gases are produced while charging batteries used on electric cars and vans. While not a problem for trains and trolleybuses, it is a potential health hazard when cars are recharged in the family garage, although the hazard is controllable through ventilation. Electric cars also present the problem of disposing of a lead-acid battery after every 24,000 km (15,000 miles) of use. Recycling or more advanced batteries may someday lessen that constraint, but perhaps not by very much or very soon.

Hydroelectric energy cannot be increased substantially in most developed countries, since the more useful sites already have dams and power stations. Many reservoirs have a silting problem that can lead to a long-term decline in production of energy. Nuclear energy plants are now regarded more as a menace than a solution; companies have been reluctant to build them of late due to their high cost and the difficult and fantastically expensive problem of disposing of the radioactive wastes.

Solar and eolian energy have a very promising future for many uses, quite aside from present applications of solar energy, such as heating water at our house in Brasília (Flavin and Lenssen 1990). For transportation, large solar collectors may someday generate electricity that will be sent through transmission lines in a very conventional fashion to power electric trains, trolleybuses, and streetcars. They could also furnish energy to charge the batteries of electric cars. Unless there is a major and unexpected technological and economic breakthrough, however, these applications may take many decades to become more than a topic for experimentation and academic curiosity.

Point-specific micro use of solar energy is possible in small, light cars outfitted with a solar roof plus battery. On a sunny day the cars generate enough energy to travel around a bit, and July was for that reason chosen for the solar car competitions among graduate schools of engineering in the United States in 1990, in preparation for the world competition in November in the cloudless Australian Outback, south of the Equator.

Most of the university vehicles managed to run the specified distances on most days of the competition. The University of Michigan's Sunrunner won the race largely by finishing each leg of the eleven-day race and by careful use of batteries. At the risk of understatement, these cars offer little in the way of safety or performance and cannot be expected to operate reliably on rainy days, at night, or in winter in temperate climates. They lack lights, heaters, air conditioners, and other features powered by internal-combustion engines in conventional cars—any one of those accessories requires more energy than is available to propel the solar car. Solar cars are prohibitively expensive; mass production might help lower costs, but perhaps not enough to allow the average family to own one.

Some engineering advances are possible at reasonable costs to make gasoline, diesel, and coal burn more cleanly. Thermoelectric plants can be cleaned up by several methods. Selective catalytic reduction can reduce nitrous oxides by over 80 percent; scrubbers can capture 95 percent of SO_2; and electrostatic precipitators and baghouse filters can capture almost all particulates (French 1990: 24–25). None of these processes is inexpensive. The scrubbers collect industrial wastes and should probably be replaced by more efficient (and expensive) technologies.

Internal-combustion engines can also be cleaned up if enough money and effort are invested. In the United States, toxic automotive emissions of lead, hydrocarbons (from incomplete burning), and nitrous oxides have been cut to a range of zero to 25 percent of their former levels over the last two decades in areas where strict environmental measures have been taken. The sulfur content of diesel fuel can be reduced. Still, electricity, especially if used in public vehicles, offers an overall advantage in regard to pollution. It helps less with the reduction of the production of CO_2. The advantage of electricity from thermal sources will lessen if the greenhouse effect is shown to be a crucial problem.

There are several alternative fuels available for use in internal-combustion engines in addition to ethanol. Methanol is chemically similar to ethanol, and is produced from natural gas, coal, wood, and biomass garbage. Its combustion produces formaldehyde, and methanol has the additional disadvantage of being very toxic. Storage and filling tanks present significant dangers of spillage, fire, and explosion. Both ethanol and methanol have lower energy densities than gasoline or diesel fuel, and engines may not start reliably on these fuels in cold climates or on cold days. These alcohols can, however, be used in both gasoline and diesel engines. Diesel engines adapted for use of alcohol require an additive. Although several additives are available, the least expensive still adds a significant amount to the cost of alcohol-based fuel. Again, the Hansen cycle is to date the only candidate for a major breakthrough.

Compressed natural gas burns much more cleanly than gasoline or diesel fuel and presents no danger of explosions or other localized environmental problems. It is obtained from petroleum sources, and may be more abundant and better distributed than coal (Flavin and Lenssen 1990). Finding commercially viable deposits is another matter, and natural gas requires bulky storage tanks on vehicles, along with central, high-pressure storage and tank-filling equipment. This limits its current suitability in transportation uses to fleets that stop at one location for fuel (for example, urban buses). Given the present limited supply of natural gas, buses should be the prime contender for using it, especially where they transport a high percentage of the population.

Hydrogen is now becoming a technically feasible fuel; research has progressed considerably in the last decade, but separating it from other chemical elements is energy intensive under current production technologies. The tragic burning of the Hindenburg in 1937 provided an excessively memorable illustration of how dangerous hydrogen can be in a transportation vehicle.

The above data provide us with a basic understanding of some of the options for reducing pollution in urban transport. They also show the relation of pollution to energy use and other characteristics of transport modes, such as capacity.

Noise

Excessive noise can cause problems ranging from minor irritants to permanent and irreversible deafness. In some cases, the associated vibrations may damage buildings and other structures or make them unsuitable for activities that require quiet ambients or precision instruments.

The definition of what constitutes an "excessive" level of noise depends on the degree of diminished hearing and interference with other activities considered "acceptable," and on the costs and inconveniences associated with reducing exposure to noise.

Frequency and sound level are two fundamental concepts in measuring and interpreting sound and in understanding the sources, controls, and potential damages of noise to humans (Goldstein 1978: 3–58). Frequency is the number of compressions and rarefactions of sound waves per second, and is commonly measured in Hertz (Hz). Frequencies in the range of 16 to 20,000 Hz may be heard by humans, although most speech-related frequencies are in the lower 500 to 2,000 Hz range. The sound level can be measured in a number of ways. We will use only the most common, a logarithmic scale to the base 10 that expresses an absolute pressure range from 1 to 10 million on the A-class decibel [dB(A)] scale. This scale ranges from 0 dB(A), which marks the threshold of hearing for a young adult, to 140 dB(A), a level that might be experienced by a person standing near a shrill siren or a jet during takeoff.

The most damaging effects of excessive noise are temporary and permanent hearing losses. Such losses are measured by the magnitude of the increase in the threshold of the sound level necessary for a person to detect a sound. Any increase in the threshold level above 0 dB(A) is considered an impairment. American audiologists classify an impairment as a handicap when the subject is unable to detect a sound level of 25 dB(A) (Hodge and Price 1978: 167–91). However, the data (which may not be particularly reliable) indicate that even without exposure to excessive noise, about 40 percent of the population aged sixty to sixty-five years present a hearing handicap.

As stated, noise-induced impairments are interpreted as handicaps when they exceed the 25 dB(A) level. It is possible, however, that part of an impairment or handicap may be due to noise that has not been detected as a source of damage. With the exception of impulse sound (for example, from explosions, traumatic injury, and the like), deafness is a process that can develop almost imperceptibly over many decades. It is at best a precarious exercise to attempt to measure over an individual's lifetime the exposure to an amazing diversity of types, frequencies, and levels of noise. This explains the difficulty audiologists face in establishing a reliable quantitative relation between exposure to noise and permanent hearing loss.

This problem is reflected in the wide range of standards adopted for maximum permissible noise levels. The U.S. Occupational Safety and Health Act of 1972 recommends that daily eight-hour exposure to noise not exceed 90 dB(A); the U.S. Air Force regulations specify 84 dB(A); the U.S. Environmental Protection Agency (EPA), only 75 dB(A) (Taylor and Wilkens 1987: 4.8). Given the logarithmic scale, these differences are very large. The Air Force's 6 dB(A) reduction from the standard of the 1972 act corresponds to halving the sound level (Goldstein 1978: 10; Hodge and Price 1978: 176–77); in turn, the EPA's suggested limit represents less than half the sound pressure of the Air Force standard, yielding a fourfold difference in recommendations among official standards in the same country.

Significantly, neither the U.S. codes nor those of other countries specify what degree of hearing loss is to be avoided or the percentage of the population to which it applies (some individuals tolerate higher levels than others without perceptible hearing loss). The standards, however, tend to become more stringent over time as concern for the quality of life and the environment increases.

There are some indications that good hearing might be a normal condition for old people if they were not exposed to considerable noise over the course of their lifetimes. Cross-cultural studies do not necessarily separate noise-induced hearing impairments from other sources of impairment, such as heredity and illness. Nonetheless, it is intriguing that some peoples with low noise exposure in their cultures have been found to enjoy excellent hearing into old age as a normal attribute. Elders of the Mabaan tribe in southern Sudan and in the Finnish Lapp community hear as well as adolescents there, detecting low conversational tones at a distance of 100 meters (Faruqui 1985: 188–89).

A similarly suggestive study indicates that noise-induced damage can occur earlier and be more severe than audiologists once thought. Half of a group of Wisconsin farm students aged 12 to 18 years who were regularly around tractors and other noisy machinery suffered hearing losses of up to 10 dB(A), and 15 percent had losses of up to 20 dB(A) at 6,000 Hz (Broste et al. 1989: 619–22). These losses far exceed those of control groups. They also affect the left ear more frequently and severely than the right, a significant finding, since tractor drivers turn their heads to the right to observe the contact of the implements with soil and crops at the rear of the tractor, exposing the left ear relatively more.

The Broste study implicitly questions standards that specify only noise levels maintained for eight hours a day as potential causes of significant hearing loss, for the following reasons: First, many tractor operations do not require full throttle, so that exposure times to noise levels of over 90 dB(A) (the equivalent of a chain saw) are probably only a fraction of student hours as drivers. And, second, assuming that the students in the study were not habitual truants, exposure for eight hours per day to tractors and other noisy machinery occurred only during some weekends and holidays during the school year, along with part of the summer vacation months.

Even under the conventional interpretation, persons exposed for eight-hour daily periods over forty years are at risk of a noise-induced handicap for sound levels above 80 dB(A) (Hodge and Price 1978: 174–75), or above 75 dB(A) according to the doubly cautious EPA. Noise-induced handicaps affect from 6.5 percent to something over 15 percent of the population exposed to daily eight-hour levels of 85 dB(A) over a period of about four decades (Kryter 1985). The percentages increase with higher sound levels until 55 percent of the exposed population develops noise-induced impairment at 115 dB(A). At this point, given the 40 percent baseline impairment, 95 percent of the exposed population would be hearing handicapped in their sixties.

Significant incidences of hearing handicaps thus start in the 75–80 dB(A) range, if not lower. They increase fairly dramatically above 90 dB(A) (Melnick 1978: 101–2). For frequencies in the 3,000–4,0000 Hz range, these losses may be registered almost entirely in the first five years; those in the lower frequencies accumulate in a linear fashion and take about forty years of exposure to approximate the level of early losses of higher frequency audition.

Temporary hearing losses can also occur at the same noise levels, but hearing is often fully recovered within seventy-two hours (Taylor and Wilkens 1987: 4.8). A biological alarm mechanism warns of the more severe dangers, as physical discomfort begins in the 105 to 110 decibel range for most speech-level frequencies, and pain is experienced at 120 dB(A) (Goldstein 1978: 7; McDonald 1987: 38).

Intermittent sound levels in these ranges may be experienced in urban traffic by persons near an accelerating motorcycle without a muffler (a common occurrence in developing countries and West Philadelphia), or a line of honking vehicles. Prolonged exposure may be experienced by workers in some older factories where bus "shells" are mounted on truck chassis and considerable hammering and riveting occur.

Most transportation noises are at much lower levels for those on board or near vehicles: passenger cars, 65–85 dB(A); buses, 80–86 dB(A); trains, 75–95 dB(A); trucks, 80–90 dB(A). Most correctly outfitted motorcycles operate at 78–88 dB(A), but some reach unacceptable levels of about 104 dB(A). At the start of motorcycle races, levels of 115 dB(A) or more are reached. Motorcycles whose mufflers have been tampered with probably come near that high value also (Buna 1987: 6.4; Kryter 1985: 197–205; Taylor and Wilkens 1987: 4.9).

Motorcycles are clearly the most serious noise offenders, especially if subject to improper use and modification. Trucks normally produce their highest noise levels on expressways rather than on city streets; motorcycles are not so confined. Buses, trucks, and automobiles regularly produce sound levels that border on causing permanent harm to hearing; in some case, even by conservative interpretation, they reach levels that may cause moderate degrees of hearing impairment in many individuals.

In front of apartment buildings located near freeways, noise levels of 84 dB(A) have been registered, with 51 to 70 dB(A) inside the apartments (Mills 1978: 234). In developing countries, the author has witnessed buses and trucks with worn, poorly adjusted brakes that, when vigorously applied, produce enough noise to cause nearby pedestrians physical pain. Diesel trucks in urban areas are typically the worst source of noise, after motorcycles and jet planes.

Workers in vehicle factories, drivers of exceptionally noisy trucks and buses, airport ground crews, paramedics in ambulances, and highway patrol personnel with long hours at the roadside are probably the only persons at high risk of suffering significant temporary or permanent hearing handicaps as a result of traffic noise alone (Taylor and Wilkens 1987: 4.8). For many of these people, the risk can be attenuated by noise reduction at the source or receptor: modern jets are quieter than earlier models, and workers can use ear mufflers or ear plugs. Bus drivers, paramedics, and police officers, however, have to be alert to other sounds and cannot use earplugs; they face moderate risk of some hearing impairment.

Again, the conventions used to evaluate noise-induced hearing problems estimate the adverse effects in a conservative fashion. These effects vary across age and sex groups, and among individuals of the same group. An exposure that produces little adversity for one individual may be seriously damaging for another. Furthermore, most research has concentrated on certain low frequencies thought to be most important (2,000 Hz and below). The evidence cited indicates that losses accumulate rather quickly for higher frequencies and that these are equally important in speech differentiation and other auditory capabilities (Hodge and Price 1978; Webster 1978: 223).

The audiological research tradition is also heavily skewed toward measurement of the ability to hear simple speech forms against a quiet background. Intelligibility is diminished in more representative work and domestic settings, however, by background noise and competing messages. Finally, severe impairments occur at levels of hearing loss below the 25 dB(A) considered as a handicap by audiologists. In a child, for example, these lower levels of loss may impede normal speech perception and development (Mills 1978: 238). The conservative bias in the definition of a handicap is due to legal disputes involving litigation for occupational hearing loss. An audiologist's testimony that a worker is handicapped is the more forceful by using the conservative interpretation, a key factor if the employer is to be required to provide compensation for the damage. But a person may be hearing-handicapped even if the impairment does not reach the conservative standard.

Hearing handicaps are not the only serious problem caused by noise. Fairly low levels of noise can interfere with sleep patterns, starting at only 30 dB(A). Since the façade of a house reduces the sound level by about 10 dB(A) even with windows open, this corresponds to 40 dB(A) outside the residence, a level likely to be exceeded even by local passenger car traffic (and certainly by the motorcycle that delivers my neighbor's newspaper at 5 A.M.). Half of the young adult population awakens at levels of 50–55 dB(A), corresponding to about 60–65 dB(A) outside. This level can be produced by passenger cars alone if the roadway is near, and certainly by heavier vehicles and by motorcycles. A sound level of 80 dB(A) awakens most adults from deep sleep (Mills 1978: 236); such levels are caused by horns or nearby motorcycles, trucks, and buses.

The effects of moderate degrees of sleep deprivation are not documented with any precision, but for many people and situations they include lowered ability to concentrate and perform physical and mental tasks, irritability, and increased use of sleep-inducing drugs and tranquilizers (Vallet 1987: 5.3–5.6). More serious degrees of sleep deprivation may provoke depression, physiological alterations such as nausea and digestive problems, and, in extreme cases, more serious mental disturbances. Directly or through sleep deprivation, "excessive" noise levels have been associated with quickened pulse, increase in blood pressure, constriction of blood vessels (all factors in heart disease and strokes), abnormal secretion of hormones, tensing of muscles, nervousness, fatigue, decreased job performance and increases in absenteeism, headaches, instability, argumentativeness, anxiety, and stress among children (Faruqui 1985: 190–91; McDonald 1987: 37).

There is little evidence to indicate that typical levels of traffic noise alone cause any of these symptoms to a significant degree. However, high levels of traffic noise do occur, including sirens in New York and other major cities, motorcycles, drag racing, honking touched off by in-car alarms on residential streets, and railroads or freeways located near apartment buildings. One of the most dramatic examples of this is the Costa e Silva elevated freeway that winds through downtown São Paulo at little more than an arm's length from numerous apartment buildings. Noise levels are so loud that local residents' protests forced traffic authorities to close the freeway from midnight to early morning; residents now face only eighteen hours per day of deafening noise.

The second major problem that noise imparts at sub-deafening levels is interference with other activities. External noise levels exceeding 50–55 dB(A) for a building with windows open (or 60–65 dB[A] outside with single-pane windows shut) cause interference with the ability to hear conversation, radio, and television. Such levels are frequently exceeded by urban traffic, and their effects are particularly intense in warm climates in cities in developing countries. Since air conditioning is rare to non-existent, windows cannot be closed, and floors are more likely to be covered with reverberating surfaces such as cement and hardwood than the more absorptive carpets found in temperate climates.

Traffic noise also causes considerable interference with schooling in developing countries. Teachers are unable to make their students hear, the students cannot concentrate, and both groups have an additional irritant to deal with. Businesspeople cannot communicate effectively with each other, their employees, or clients. Worship in churches and temples in downtown areas becomes difficult. Firms that require a high degree of concentration from their employees cannot locate in high-traffic areas. Furthermore, such extraneous noise is more likely to be regarded as irritating and disruptive than noise that is perceived to be intimately associated with one's task (Pendakur and Pyplacz 1984: 471–75). The driver of a truck or bus may find the noise from a diesel motor less distracting and resent it less than those engaged in nonrelated activities.

A few years ago I encountered a graphic example of traffic noise while in Santiago for a meeting of experts on energy questions called by the local United Nations' staff. Traffic authorities had installed a decibel meter near our meeting place on Providencia Avenue. In contrast to the hand-held meters used by most researchers, this one looked like an acrylic post, and provided a visual reading of sound levels. With no noisy traffic, all lights were off. As noise increased, the bulbs lit up in ascending order: first, the green bulbs near the bottom, then the yellow ones in the middle, and finally red bulbs toward the top. When the traffic light at the corner turned green, drivers accelerated their vehicles and the post lit up like a Christmas tree. A nearby church had installed a second set of doors to dampen the traffic noise, an option not available to most local workers, shopkeepers, and newsstand owners.

Many commercial and banking establishments in Latin America and many other developing regions have fronts that are completely open, that is, the "door" is nearly as wide as the storefront. The owner closes shop in the evenings by pulling down a rolled-up steel door or steel curtain (the curtain permits window shopping and surveillance from the outside after hours). Commercial buildings, schools, and most churches have low ceilings, while the walls are either shared with the neighboring buildings or adjacent to them. These factors require that street-side windows be kept open to take advantage of natural lighting and to maintain a satisfactory pattern of temperature and air circulation. These practices are economically and ecologically sound, reducing the demands for artificial lighting, air conditioning, and ventilation, but traffic noise imposes a more serious problem than in similar buildings in colder climates that have closed fronts.

Conversations with shopkeepers and workers on Providencia Avenue revealed that they usually ended their days with headaches and other noise-related problems. I asked a nearby *carabinero* (military policeman—at that time in Chile there was always a carabinero nearby) what the decibel meter was used for. The carabinero replied that someone at headquarters made tables and graphs from the data, but he had no answer to my ensuing question of what the tables and graphs were used for. There is a high probability that such material will merely accumulate in a file somewhere, unless society becomes sufficiently interested in attenuating noise to start making changes in vehicles, regulations, street design, sidewalks, and other facilities.

I witnessed an interesting sequel upon leaving my meeting that evening. Some young children were passing by the decibel meter on their way home from school. Now and then one of the boys would suddenly break away from his mother's grasp and run to the post and scream. By getting closer to the meter than the motor vehicles, the boys were equally effective in making the lights glow. There is a message here for the safety of schoolbus drivers and parents who pick up their children as they vent their pent-up energy after a day at school. Many irritating family squabbles would probably be avoided if both parents and children walked or cycled home instead of riding in a car or school bus. (I have often wondered how the fellow at carabinero headquarters interpreted the schoolboys' street-side message on his tables and graphs.)

The effect of noise is obviously interwoven with other traffic-induced pollution and vibration, contributing to the decay of buildings and damaging their appearance. Too often, these effects encourage those who can afford to move their residences and businesses to abandon these areas. The tax base erodes, buildings decay, and urban blight takes over.

Traffic noise is thus seen as a significant problem for both individuals and cities; this is reflected in the rare opinion polls that address the issue. In England, 26 percent of the adult sample stated that they were bothered by motorcycle noise while indoors at home, and 15 percent were bothered "quite a lot" or "very much" (Plowden and Hillman 1984: 63). Often no action is taken: residents feel that nothing can be done about it or that the solutions are too expensive to implement. This perception is often incorrect. Some effective controls are low in cost, and others are an unplanned side effect of projects and strategies designed to improve other characteristics of urban transportation—a synergistic effect from doing something right. Some possibilities include:

The use of very high fines or impoundment for serious offenses, instead of ignoring the problem or applying light fines. Strict zoning ordinances may also work (for example, banning motorcycles from residential streets or limiting their use to the hours between 9 A.M. and 5 P.M.). Exceptionally high sound levels are so disruptive to sleep and all other activities that they should not be tolerated. A few well-publicized cases of impoundment of noisy motorcycles, for instance, might rapidly eliminate the worst offenses and end tampering with mufflers. Similar measures should apply to bus companies that permit vehicles to circulate with badly worn brakes or other equipment that produces painful noise.

Some minimal regulation (or even a bit of jawboning) to encourage vehicle manufacturers to transfer to developing regions the techniques required in their home countries to make trucks, buses, and cars run more quietly.

Increasing the distance between source and receptor.

Using materials that partially block, deflect, or absorb noise.

In the future, vehicles may be built with noise-cancellation devices. These instruments derive noise from the vehicles themselves and phase their sound waves 180 degrees out of synchronization to those of the vehicle, thereby canceling out a substantial part of the noise. One of the principal companies involved in the manufacture of such devices, however, views urban traffic as too variable to be an easy target for their "noise buster" (Noise Cancellation Technologies, Inc. 1987: 42–43).

It is easier to increase the distance between source and receptor when designing new towns and thruways than when dealing with existing cities, although improvements are usually possible. On narrow streets, motor vehicles can simply be prohibited; alternatively, traffic may be restricted to local private cars and delivery vehicles, with speeds held down by specially designed narrow paths, sharp curves or traffic humps. The Dutch pioneered with these "erf" (or "backyard") environments, and they are spreading to other cities in Europe, Latin America and elsewhere (Chapter 9). Planners and traffic authorities use such measures to create large islands removed from heavy traffic, using the intervening buildings to further dampen noise from traffic on nearby streets.

Some residents on noisy residential streets have persuaded traffic authorities to adopt the erf idea on a micro scale, blocking off one end to avoid noisy through traffic. In Curitiba, Brazil, residents of a suburban street eliminated late-hour drag racing by ripping up the pavement on alternating sides of the street and planting small gardens, replete with grass, flowers and palm trees. This unconventional, "island-lane landscaping" project transforms a two-lane residential street into a one-lane winding path at key points, holding vehicle speeds below 20 km/h (12 mph) and permitting two-way traffic elsewhere. It was designed by the technical staff at the municipal traffic agency and paid for by local residents.

Successful solutions such as those cited feature appropriate engineering rather than intensive, expensive, and ineffective policing. The superiority of engineering over policing is expressed in everyday language in some communities. Traffic humps, for example, have gained picturesque names in Dutch and Portuguese, such as "sleeping policemen," and even "the mayor's stomach."

Since narrow streets provide very little transport capacity or parking space, the negative impact of closing them on private car circulation is small. Delivery vehicles and buses can still be available in the vicinity, and electric buses or even low-speed diesel buses can be permitted in such areas with minimal noise problems. The closing of such streets also reduces noise problems for residents and business-people who have intense traffic on the other side of their dwellings, since they can relocate noise-sensitive activities to the quieter side. Residents with cars must use adjacent streets, neighborhood parking lots, or, in some cases, a special one-way path at the side of the mall, driving their vehicles at pedestrian speeds.

Diesel buses may also be distanced from buildings and pedestrians by locating their stops in the middle of avenues rather than at the curb, since pullaways can generate dB(A) values near 90 (Francis and King 1988: 36). The halving of sound pressure for each doubling of the distance from the source of the noise yields the greatest gains as the first few meters are added; those first few extra meters from the source can reduce excessive noise to more tolerable levels.

Locating bus stops in the median of avenues requires the provision of safety islands and protected crossings for pedestrians. The rider then finds the central stop to be as safe and convenient as the conventional process of boarding on the near sidewalk half of the time and crossing the entire avenue on the remaining occasions.

Noise may also be reduced by something on the order of 10 dB(A) by installing barriers and materials that absorb or deflect sound. As indicated, buildings on one street serve as a shield for buildings on the next street. Residents on some streets benefit if noisy traffic is diverted to adjoining streets (the noise levels on the adjoining streets is usually not raised perceptibly by the additional traffic). An additional—and often crucial—reduction of noise can be achieved by treating the interiors of buildings with materials such as carpeting or heavy glass doors of the type installed at the entrance to the Santiago church. Carpets are less expensive to install and maintain than wood, tile, or many other floor coverings.

Unfortunately, traffic noise is not perceptibly reduced by planting a few trees along a thoroughfare. A forest of evergreens would have the desired effect, but more from increasing the distance between source and receptor than from blockage. Embankments of earth and grass are more effective in absorbing sound; if properly positioned, embankments also deflect sound upward enough to significantly reduce the noise levels in low edifications and on the lower, more vulnerable floors of taller buildings. Walls of cement, wood, or other materials may also be positioned between source and receptor. However, their deployment is usually expensive and limited to special situations due to the visual blockage they create. Special problems are presented by streets that have high buildings on both sides, as sound reverberates, yielding a "canyon" effect that partially cancels the noise-reducing effect of greater distance. Artificial barriers along freeways, such as vertical walls, yield significant noise reductions (of some 4 to 8 dB[A]), but are costly (Harris, Cohn, and Bowlby 1987).

Aesthetic Values

Only one aspect of aesthetics, visual blockage, is subject to cardinal measurement. A slightly broader concept is visual intrusion. This encompasses the size, shape, and appearance of a given transport facility and its associated vehicles as they obstruct the view, restrict sunlight and daylight, interfere with privacy, and create unattractive vehicular movement or headlight glare (Bor 1974: 93). A related problem is severance, which occurs when a thoroughfare cuts a neighborhood into two parts and makes it difficult for residents to cross over to the other half.

Some of these aspects involve questions of taste and, at best, their measurement is limited to an ordinal scale. Nonetheless, visual quality can be an important consideration in formulating and choosing transport modes and projects, and opposition on aesthetic grounds may block certain projects.

As often happens with other transport characteristics, a given mode's performance regarding visual pollution depends on the specifics of the type of project selected. Until at least the 1950s, rail systems were often major aesthetic offenders. Elevated railways were fiercely opposed in most American cities in the early decades of this century, because of their very high levels of noise and visual intrusion. In Europe, even overhead wiring for streetcars was enough to endanger many early streetcar electrification projects (Bottles 1987; McKay 1976). Many aesthetic objections went beyond those of the trains themselves to include noise, marshaling yards, and the sights and smells of industries served by freight trains. The severance effect of urban trackage on neighborhoods is reflected in the phrase "the wrong side of the tracks," to indicate an economically or socially inferior neighborhood. The rails became associated with singularly unattractive urban areas.

The aesthetic disadvantages of rail diminished when urban passenger trains began to have their own facilities rather than sharing them with freight trains. Streetcars became acceptable in Europe when planners found ways to make the wiring less intrusive (McKay 1976: 101).

Engineers have since learned how to reduce the noise of overhead systems—at a cost. Today, only a few negative visual aspects of surface rail remain, such as overhead wiring and signals, so the aesthetics of elevated and underground systems depends largely on the design of stations and facilities. In some cases, citizen and professional groups have fought against elevated trains with the argument that they would destroy the charm of a historical center or detract from the architectonic value of a particular set of buildings. Architects and other professionals, for example, successfully lobbied against the Sür Coester *Aeromóvel* ("Airtrain") in the Brazilian city of Porto Alegre.

The opposite also occurs, however. Elevated monorail structures are a fixture in a number of major amusement parks, world exposition sites, and several Japanese locales, such as airport-to-downtown Tokyo, and in the city of Kitakyusha. The amusement parks and exposition examples are especially revealing. The overhead facilities are part of the attractions, and their elegant, futuristic lines have a positive aesthetic appeal. At least one project, a Disney World monorail circuit, has little or no practical use in the park's visitor transportation scheme; it is simply another amusement park ride, and such rides are not intended to get anyone anywhere. (Actual Disney World visitor transportation consists of walking, horse-drawn carriages, tractors and wagons, and so forth). San Francisco's cable cars have been preserved in large part due to their historic character and their visual charm. Amsterdam's citizens accept the overhead catenaries of their streetcar system; since they expend heroic efforts to preserve centuries-old façades of buildings throughout the city, the catenaries are not evidence of Dutch visual insensitivity.

The Sür Coester *Airtrain* lost a battle on its home turf, but was successfully implanted in Jakarta's principal amusement park where visual appeal is an important factor. Detroit's elevated "People Mover" was designed to provide additional visual appeal for the central area located at riverside. The evaluators from the U.S. Department of Transportation (1980) found no adverse effects of the People Mover on Detroit's historic downtown area. Furthermore, the People Mover's attractive stations are either attached to or placed within the adjoining buildings to enhance the city center's historic, architectonic, and cultural assets. The People Mover is part of a conscious effort to remake Detroit's tarnished image in which visual impressions of urban blight are a major factor.

With automobiles, aesthetics go far beyond the vehicles themselves to encompass the visual blockage and unsightliness of many elevated expressways and interchanges. The commercial strip is also unattractive, with fuel stations, fast-food restaurants, and the like stretching out along heavily trafficked streets and avenues.

In contrast, walking and cycling tend to be colorful and attractive activities. Their efficiency in the use of space allows them to blend in with urban aesthetics even when they require bridges and elevated walkways and bikeways. Some examples include the pedestrian–cyclist bridges near the center of Hamburg; the overhead passageways that link the residential sectors to each other and to the commercial center in Lelystad (Holland); and the early twentieth-century Santa Efigênia iron footbridge in São Paulo, one of the busiest pedestrian corridors in the world.

Modern architectural and engineering design and noise control measures can reduce the visual and auditory disadvantages of elevated structures for all public modes. In most cases, it is possible to make them visually neutral or even attractive. There is also an important, but seldom mentioned, visual benefit from these structures. If there is anything attractive to see in the environs, chances are that one can see it better from an elevated structure, and one can certainly appreciate it better riding or walking than when driving a car. (This is not to say that one should build such structures along the skyline of Copacabana Beach or in front of the Eiffel Tower.)

The private car, however, requires such a vast amount of space that considerable visual blockage occurs when elevated urban expressways are used. Although some such structures have been creatively surrounded with plants in Hong Kong and other urban areas, they remain singularly unattractive and disruptive of the surrounding urban fabric. The associated noise and air pollution further degrade the adjoining neighborhoods.

Vulnerability of Transport Modes and Systems

This characteristic refers to the likelihood of a major disruption of a transport mode or system, as distinguished from a problem with an individual vehicle. Some disruptions are temporary and minor in nature, such as an accident or construction project that blocks a traffic lane and results in a drastic but relatively brief decline in the level of service. Other disruptions may persist for a few hours or days due to electrical failure, flooding, snow and ice, or other weather-related conditions. Electrical failure that reaches traffic lights can affect cars and buses along with electric trains and trolleybuses, and can paralyze traffic for hours. Still other disruptions occur due to strikes, acts of war, or terrorist activities. Finally, a country may be unable to obtain oil, or to transport, refine, and distribute it effectively. Although these questions are closely related to our natural environment, they are considered herein only in the sense of short-term disruptions. Long-term resource availability is treated in the next section under "sustainability."

The automobile is vulnerable to all the factors cited, although less so than transit with respect to strikes. People in countries with high incomes and flexible free-market economies often consider themselves immune to such disruptions. This requires the aid of a short memory and ignorance of current events, including selective forgetting of the problems introduced by the disruptions in oil markets in the 1970s and early 1980s, rationing during major conflicts, blackouts in major cities, and Saddam Hussein. The heavy dependence on petroleum imports implies vulnerability to any event that affects world production and transportation of crude. The recent war in the Middle East emphasized this point for all non-OPEC countries, and contradicts the complacency witnessed among pundits, bureaucrats, and politicians a short time ago.

Transit buses and diesel passenger trains can be partially protected from oil shortages by favoring them in contingency plans for fuel scarcities (unless all buses already use diesel fuel and the only other diesel vehicles are trucks, which have equal priority). The most frequent and prolonged disruptions of public transport in peacetime, however, are those caused by strikes. In the more prosperous Western countries, this typically pits a labor union against the municipal government (or whatever unit of government the union is dealing with). This is, from the viewpoint of economic theory, a situation of bilateral monopoly with no clear market solution. At the extremes, the union wants the maximum in wages and benefits that society will pay to regain service; the government tries to pay the minimum required to contract new nonunion workers or to maintain current workers after having subdued the organizing power of the union. Any wage package in this wide range is possible and is likely to be decided in a political and economic tug-of-war between the union and city hall.

Transport becomes chaotic for days or weeks while users attempt to get to work and continue their other activities by alternate means of transportation. The disruption is proportional to the importance of public transportation in the locale(s) where the strike occurs, and many former transit users do not return to public transportation when the strike is settled. They have mentally labeled it unreliable and, whenever possible, opt for the motorcar, with the attendant negative effects on the urban environment.

In Latin America and many other developing regions, the predominant transit mode is often the diesel bus. The buses are usually owned by private companies or individual operators. Although disputes over wages and benefits do occur, they are usually short lived. The state, which often controls fares and route allocation among companies, quickly intervenes, and the typical result is an increase in transit workers' wages, financed by an increase in fares. Both are usually eroded quickly by inflation; there is no permanent gain by workers or loss by users, and the unfriendly negotiation is usually repeated in a few months.

On other occasions, a transit strike may be politically motivated. Argentina is perhaps the most visible victim of such strikes, but it is certainly not unique. Typically, the conflict develops when a major political party or coalition calls for a general strike out of frustration with the available institutional arrangements for debate, legislation, and policy change, or simply because such a strike has been perceived as an effective instrument for negotiation. To be successful, the strike must paralyze the public transport modes that most private sector and governmental employees use to get to work. Transport workers are thus key targets for unionization and political activism. Since these strikes are normally one-day affairs and are likely to affect the majority of workers, they result in a sort of political holiday. Few workers are likely to suffer punishment for not arriving at work, and transit ridership is usually regained the next day. Both the causes and effects of the transit strikes are different from those of developed countries.

Walking and cycling as transport modes present very low levels of vulnerability. Because the North Vietnamese moved their people and goods predominantly on foot and by bicycle, they were able to resist American military attacks for nearly a decade. An individual bicycle may break down, but a system that relies on it is unlikely to suffer major disruptions. Such a system produces ubiquitous facilities for repairing the individual bikes, in contrast with cities where the bicycle is a recreational vehicle or child's toy.

The only major problem for a bicycle-based system is the presence of snow and ice in temperate and cold climates, which requires special clothing, cleaning of bikeways, and the occasional exchange of two wheelers for more fall-resistant three-wheelers (see Chapter 9).

Sustainability of Modes and Systems

> *A civilization that depends on petroleum to survive is not worthy of that name.*
>
> —Carlos Drumond de Andrade
> Brazilian poet and writer

Sustainability refers to the ability of a country's resources to maintain a particular mode of transportation over the long term. This contrasts with short-term vulnerability, but remains purposely somewhat vague regarding the number of years covered. The "long term" implies a concern with future generations and responsibility for the lives of our children, grandchildren, and great-grandchildren.

From this perspective, the petroleum-based transport systems of most countries rank quite low. Current reserves (reserves are known oil deposits that can be extracted profitably with current technology) are sufficient to maintain current levels of consumption for perhaps 40 years without major real price increases. That statement applies if and only if all goes well for oil production and exports in the Middle East: 565 billion barrels of the 1988 world total of 890 billion barrels of easily exploitable known reserves are located there (U.S. Department of Transportation 1990: 3.2). The United States has only 27 billion barrels of reserves, enough for about nine years' consumption. Western and Eastern Europe and Central and South America are relatively poor in reserves; many other countries have no significant reserves. Only a few OPEC countries have known reserves capable of supporting current production levels for 40 years or more. Kuwait's reserves could sustain nearly 250 years of recent annual production levels (that is, before they were all set on fire), followed by Saudi Arabia with nearly 140 years. All other countries are in the 37- to 84-year range (Sperling 1988: 10). Exports from communist countries are expected to drop to zero in the coming years (U.S. Department of Transportation 1990: 3.7). A recent report by an international monitoring agency finds current world oil stocks equal to 97 days of consumption, indicating how quickly a major disruption in production and distribution could transform a medium-term question of sustainability into a short-term crisis (*Folha de São Paulo*, 5 November 1990: B-2).

Reserves shrink when oil is extracted, and are expanded when new deposits are found. As the easily exploitable reserves are emptied, more money and resources must be spent to find and exploit new reserves, which ultimately means higher prices. Oil can also be obtained from tar sands and shale, but the processes are energy-intensive and plagued with problems of environmental degradation at production and refining sites.

In most countries, petroleum is virtually the only important source of transportation energy. There is also a tendency for the converse to occur. In recent years, industry, commerce, and residences have diminished their requirements for petroleum in relation to other sources of energy, so that the petroleum problem is becoming basically a transportation problem (Sperling 1988: 13–15). In the United States, for example, transportation now accounts for nearly two-thirds of all petroleum usage.

Most developing countries use petroleum almost exclusively in transportation. For the non-OPEC ones, the supply of foreign currency often places a more immediate constraint on their petroleum imports than does the world supply of oil. Countries such as Brazil, El Salvador, Cuba, and Nicaragua have accumulated foreign debt in large measure through petroleum imports. The problem of dependence on oil imports ignores ideological boundaries: neither central planning nor market forces offer an easy way out.

The disparities in petroleum usage among countries are striking. On a per capita basis, the consumption of transport fuels in the richest countries is about 40 times greater than in the poorest countries. Diesel fuel amounts to 20 to 40 percent of transport fuel in most developed countries, but up to 80 percent in some less developed countries (Dunkerley and Hoch 1987: 57–60). Yet middle- or upper-class automobile owners have a pattern of energy use similar to their counterparts in the richer countries.

The perspective of 40 years without large increases in the price of oil depends on maintaining "current levels of consumption" and ways to avoid an ecological crisis. This implies continued improvements in fuel efficiency for vehicles, along with rather modest rates of growth in numbers of petroleum-based vehicles. This is possible— although perhaps unlikely—in North America and Western Europe, where car ownership is already very high and population growth is quite modest and even negative in a few countries. The major question is what will happen in the rest of the world, where few people have cars and population is growing rapidly. In 1987, the ratio of people to registered motor vehicles in the United States was 1.8; for Costa Rica, 34; for Thailand, 96 (National Safety Council 1989: 66). China has about 1.2 million automobiles and a billion people, or 800 people per car (Lowe 1989: 12).

For most of these countries individually, widespread car use would require more resources for manufacturing and petroleum acquisition than are conceivable in view of their meager natural and financial endowments. Mark Hanson (1989) concludes that continued growth of motor vehicle–dominated urban forms is not even sustainable in isolated city settings such as Mexico City and Jakarta. When the less-developed countries are regarded collectively, geometric expansion of the private car is not sustainable over a generation or two, due to the ultimately limited logistic curve of oil production and other resources.

If every family in the developing countries had an automobile, known oil reserves would disappear in a few years. An "upwardly mobile" family in a developing country may find it unfair that Americans and Europeans squander so much petroleum on personal transportation while it cannot have a car. That view is well taken, but hardly an argument for increasing petroleum dependence in poor countries for private urban transportation.

In earlier sections, we saw that the expected increases in fuel efficiency for the next decade or so were rather modest, perhaps in the 10 to 30 percent range. I did not attempt to look much beyond that frame of reference, for rather obvious reasons, but it appears that perpetual motion machines will continue to elude us. If we want gasoline-powered cars to average 80 km/l instead of 8 to 12 km/l, they must be redesigned as mopeds. Mere inertia in the auto industry will produce future cars similar to present ones.

It is also entirely too clear that the concentration of crude oil reserves in the Middle East may eventually revive the effective cartel pricing seen in the 1970s. Taking into account these factors, Lee and colleagues (1990) have estimated that the price of crude oil could fluctuate from $4 to $64 per barrel in coming years. Recent events make the upper end of the range all too relevant.

If there are no major conflicts or other disruptions of economic or ecological systems, petroleum supplies will not suddenly disappear two generations hence, but it will cost considerably more to locate and extract them. Alternative fuels will become economically viable if—or when—petroleum fuel prices increase sufficiently. And we recall that most alternative fuels present their own problems, including, to varying degrees, sustainability. These problems will affect some countries earlier and more sharply than others, reflecting their access to alternative fuels.

Energy is not the only limiting factor from the perspective of environmental sustainability. Vast amounts of iron, coal and other resources are required to support the world's motor vehicle fleet. They too are finite resources associated with numerous ecological problems. Major disruptions in the supply of these factors may affect some or all countries, and global warming may be shown to require short-term actions, as Flavin and Lenssen (1990) argue. Significantly, in all these scenarios, the more a country is dependent on the private car, the harder adaptation will be.

A final reflection: most governments find it increasingly difficult to provide urban transport infrastructure and services; most poor countries do not produce petroleum and cannot afford to import much of it. Most developing countries cannot sustain extensive public transport projects over long periods of time if they require large subsidies for construction and operation. Either self-financing projects must be selected or new sources of revenue must be found. Affordability is another dimension of sustainability.

Chapter 5

Public Expense, Health, and Accidents

O NE UNDERLYING theme of this chapter is health: the financial health of cities and their transport systems; the relation of personal travel to the physical and mental health and fitness of their citizens; and serious traffic accidents, a phenomenon often responsible for more deaths and casualties than war.

The second major theme is the cost of transport to the public sector, interpreted as an expenditure of public funds or as a gain or loss in revenue from selecting a given transport project, strategy, or policy. An understanding of this factor will allow us to discover what a given public outlay will provide the citizenry in terms of transport characteristics.

Public Expense

The acute financial crises of all levels of government in most countries call into question the cost–benefit analyst's traditional assumption that a project is justified if it has an economic rate of return greater than the "social discount rate" (a hypothetical interest rate assumed to represent the real cost of capital to society). A true believer in cost–benefit analysis might affirm that, if risk, externalities, distortions, borrowing capacity, and other factors were properly accounted for, the social discount rate would be the proper guide for public investments.

The *if* is not easily overcome. The concept of the social discount rate is sufficiently vague that there is no agreement as to its value at a given time and place. It has no direct relation to the finances of the local governmental unit that must raise the funds and make the expenditure.

A better starting point is to begin with the commonsense notion that the municipality's funds and borrowing capacity are limited. Its projects should be cost-effective and, in many cases, they will have to be self-financing. This point is so obvious that it is often overlooked: a transport strategy or project must be financially viable. Bus services that support themselves from the fare box (the norm in Latin America and many other developing countries) automatically meet this requirement. Urban rail systems and road building require that the public entity cover its expenses from a combination of general revenue, user fees, and borrowing. If borrowing is chosen, a realistic assessment of the capacity to repay the loans must be made. Comparing an abstract social benefit with an equally abstract social rate of discount is a very imprecise and uncertain way to do this. Too many governmental units and transport organs have gone bankrupt on that principle.

The message is clear: whatever the real or imagined economic benefits to society at large, the financial viability of projects and services must be shown and provided for. Transport agencies or the governments that support them must be able to pay the expenses accrued through the provision of infrastructure and services.

This practical distinction between abstract economic benefits and the availability of local government funds explains our earlier separation of transport costs in public and user expense. This also allows us to analyze separately the effect of user costs in evaluating the demand for transport services. Users' decisions are understandably more influenced in their transport choices by what they pay as individuals than by the municipality's receipts and expenditures on transportation. (The exception is when such expenditures make some modes exceptionally attractive in relation to others.)

The major public finance issue in urban transportation is the cost of building and operating different modes and the options for paying for them. Data in this chapter illustrate the range of investment costs and operating subsidy levels for several modes. More specific analyses of economic policies and the subtleties that distinguish economic cost from financial cost are covered in later chapters. For now, we consider cost much as a city manager might: the expenditure required to implant or maintain a transportation service, or the revenue gained or lost due to a given transport policy.

Two important categories of public-sector transportation costs are investments to implant or expand a project, and the expense necessary to administer, operate, and maintain it. Both categories, investment and operation, vary widely from project to project and from place to place. This cannot be overemphasized: the "typical" cost curves for different modes seen in some manuals are derived from unlikely assumptions and have no relation to subsequent costs in a given city. When they show lower per-passenger costs for building new train systems than for improving bus services, they are usually pure fantasy.

Both the "average" cost and the variation in costs need to be kept in mind when analyzing an urban transportation problem. Having such information available during initial discussions of transport problems and projects helps avoid major mistakes; technical staff, political representatives, and the informed public can avoid committing themselves to inappropriate strategies based on faulty hypotheses about the size of the outlays that will eventually be required.

Investment Costs: Some Ballpark Figures

The following data on investments in new urban train projects illustrate the large variations that occur for apparently similar projects. [Here, and throughout this book, all prices are given in U.S. dollars.] In the 1980s, comparable surface passenger rail lines were inaugurated in three Brazilian cities (Brazil 1987: chap. 5). Porto Alegre's construction costs were about $8 million/km ($12.9 million/mile), Recife's about $21 million/km ($33.8 million/mile), and Belo Horizonte will be the most expensive of the three if it is ever completed (only a short stretch is presently in operation). The São Paulo metro, with its extensive underground sections, cost an estimated $85 million/km; the Rio de Janeiro metro, with a main line entirely underground, cost $115 million/km. Los Angeles Metrorail has a projected cost of $3.5 billion for 29 km of line, an outlay of $121 million/km (Zimmerman 1990: 4). In Tokyo, recent costs for metro systems with significant subway sections are even higher, about $160 million/km ($257 million/mile) (Kikuchi and Onaka 1988: 33).

This twentyfold difference for rail systems has many contributing explanations. The most important is given by Stone: the cost of an elevated transport facility is three times that of its surface equivalent, while an underground structure costs ten times more than the surface version (1971: 112). Even Stone's rule of thumb, however, fails to explain the threefold variation in expenditures for the three Brazilian surface rail systems.

Costs also vary with the choice of route and the peculiarities of natural and man-made features. Porto Alegre and Recife are largely flat; Belo Horizonte has considerable rolling terrain, hills, and mountains. Some rail projects can use an abandoned freight line or the median of a freeway: little or no compensation need be paid for the right-of-way, and earthmoving and other tasks are simplified. Costs are much lower than on routes that require a great deal of demolition, excavating, and compensation to make room for rail lines, tunnels, stations, and access facilities for pedestrians, buses, and cars. In the first phase of the Caracas metro, for example, some nine hundred buildings were demolished (Venezuela 1986). There are fantastic costs associated with such work in highly built-up centers on valuable real estate.

Low-capacity surface rail systems (often described by the misnomer "light rail") can operate with a few short trains and small, inexpensive stations. Porto Alegre's stations might be generously described as plain, and the rail line ends downtown. Additional expenditures would be required to extend the rail lines across the downtown area and into other sectors of the city to give passengers more options for boarding and alighting. Detroit's People Mover has thirteen attractive stations constructed as parts of the adjoining buildings on its 4.6 km (2.9 miles) of exclusively downtown track. Its brochures proudly acclaim that $2 million was spent just on the art (mainly mosaic tiles) that adorns the stations.

The transport authority's "financial package" also has a major effect on expenditures. The Porto Alegre project received partial financing from a World Bank loan and conducted international competitive bidding on most important contracts. The Recife and Belo Horizonte projects received part of their initial funding from private banks and were less successful in opening up bidding. Santiago, Chile, found itself with a unique system whose trains and components could for a time be imported from only one source. Ian Thomson (1983) estimates the final cost of those items at up to four times the figures used in the economic viability study; the national origin of the evaluators and suppliers was the same, one of a number of coincidences in the evaluation and construction of the ensuing system.

The quality of the final engineering project can also be a major factor in determining the total expenditures. The engineering project and the financing scheme influence the extent to which delay and negotiation ultimately run up costs. The authors of a good project investigate the relevant alternatives for decreasing costs on all possible fronts while maintaining desired levels of characteristics (see Chapter 10), and the final engineering project is precise and detailed. Porto Alegre's preliminary studies and plans were a key factor in holding down the costs of bidding and execution.

Stoppage and start-up costs are very high for contractors and are passed on to the public sector. The precarious financing of the Belo Horizonte project has led to numerous stops and starts; at the moment, work is stalled, $600 million has been spent, $300 million more is needed to finish the system, and no funding is in sight.

Some projects are so unfortunate that they are directed more by the construction companies themselves than by a clear, previously elaborated engineering project.

The tremendous range of the costs cited for similar real-world systems indicates that average cost data should be used with *great* caution, whatever the source.

Rail projects clearly involve high costs. The $8 million/km spent on the Porto Alegre project is probably a lower limit. It is true that San Diego spent only $3.4 million/km ($5.5 million/mile) on its "Tijuana Trolley," but that was back in 1978 and on an existing rail line that is still used at night by private freight trains. In contrast, a few years later Calgary, Canada, was spending from $14 to $19 million/km, and a recent proposal for St. Louis calls for about $10 million/km, although it uses an abandoned railway line and a stretch of the city subway (Tapin 1989: 311–22). Low costs require inexpensive rights-of-way and favorable terrain for construction. Few cities have more than one such potential line, and that is usually located where there are few potential riders. Other lines for light surface rail are likely to range from $20 to $60 million/km (a caveat: the higher figure should not be taken as the upper limit).

In built-up areas, expenditures for conventional urban rapid rail systems with extensive underground segments are likely to start at about $80 million/km ($129 million/mile). As the Tokyo example illustrates, some systems run double this figure, and that is not an upper limit either. While *caveat emptor* is applicable to all urban transportation projects, it is especially germane to rail technologies. A very high percentage of recent passenger rail projects in the United States, Latin America, and other countries has been initiated with excessive optimism about costs, construction time, and ridership (Gutman and Scurfield 1990; Pickrell 1990; Thomson 1983).

The investment costs of providing roadways for automobiles also show a great deal of variation. In the Brazilian countryside, a paved, two-lane roadway (one lane in each direction) may cost from $100,000 to $250,000 per kilometer ($160,000–$400,000/mile), depending on the terrain and design standards. It may cost almost as much to rebuild and upgrade a badly damaged, substandard road, while upgrading a two-lane road to a four-lane divided highway may cost about $1 million/km in favorable terrain (Brazil 1987: chap. 5). In urban areas in the United States and other countries, however, the cost of an urban freeway may take a quantum leap to the range of $10–$40 million/km ($16–$64 million/mile). Again, these are not absolute limits: a roadway tunnel leading out of central London may exceed the upper value by a factor of three or four before it is completed (Mackett 1990).

On the other hand, the marginal costs of maintaining an existing street system may be a rather modest part of municipal expenditures. For example, Brazil's 1986 Federal District budget allocated the modest sum of $506,000 for urban roads and streets in Brasília and its satellite cities, with a total population of nearly two million (Distrito Federal 1985: 1–29). This amounted to less than two tenths of 1 percent of the total budget. These costs are admittedly underestimated: most of the Federal District's major highways are funded through the National Highway Department (DNER) and do not appear on the District's accounts; the latter omit the expenditures for personnel (including traffic police), street illumination, traffic accidents, and other items, and the streets were then relatively new and required no major repair or new construction that year. Nonetheless, the example illustrates how some municipal authorities can perceive their costs with private transportation as being quite low when no new construction is immediately involved.

That impression is reinforced by the need to maintain streets regardless of which vehicles use them, making it difficult to "assign" those costs to the private automobile. Even residents without cars in poor neighborhoods in developing countries are capable of lobbying local authorities to pave their streets to avoid dust and mud. The "sunk costs" of building the existing street system are not relevant to the discussion of next year's budget. Inertia is very kind to the automobile.

However, investment and maintenance costs can become imposing when new facilities are contemplated or major repair and reconstruction are required. This is an important variable in developing countries, where cities often have high rates of growth and expansion and major choices must be made regarding the modes that should be favored or neglected. It is also important in more prosperous countries, particularly in the United States, where gridlock has become pervasive on many expressways and urban arteries, and much of the aging infrastructure will require major repair over the next decade (Cervero 1986).

The automobile has indirect high costs for local governments through its effect on the expense–revenue ratio for urban land. The private car has an impressive demand for streets and parking (in addition to its requirements of public illumination, traffic lights, and administration). The urban space so occupied is removed from use in activities that generate taxes, such as high-density residential areas, commercial and professional establishments, and industry. In the Southern California boom areas, municipalities compete for these income-producing activities. The losers are saddled with low-density housing, with the associated expenditures for streets, illumination, new schools, and other services. There is a vicious cycle present: low density implies low land values, which encourage individual residences and spatially extensive commercial and industrial establishments. A high population density elevates land values per square meter: urban land values can thus be higher in very poor countries than in the United States (Gibbons 1990). The small revenue–expenditure ratio of low-density real estate constitutes a "hidden" cost that few in municipal government are likely to observe or act upon.

Another hidden cost of the automobile is the public expense generated by traffic accidents. Much of this expense is borne by the private sector in countries without a national health system and with little public provision of payments for dependents of disabled or deceased breadwinners. However, in European countries and in many less developed countries, the public sector usually pays these bills. Given that accident victims are predominantly composed of adolescents about to enter the labor market and relatively young workers, the economic impact can be substantial. Often, however, it is not calculated. Brazil's national health care system (INAMPS), for example, does not record traffic accidents as a separate, identifiable category even though INAMPS pays for the overwhelming majority of medical, hospital, disability, and pension costs. These are very sizable expenditures: Brazil has an estimated 40,000 to 50,000 deaths annually and perhaps half a million significant injuries in traffic accidents, and nearly two-thirds of hospital beds in trauma and orthopedics are occupied with accident victims (GEIPOT 1987; SIRTO 1987).

Bus systems are typically the least expensive modes of public transport to implant or to upgrade, since they can use much of the existing road and street infrastructure. On some routes, bus service requires little more investment than the vehicle itself, signs for the bus stops, and an occasional shelter. In some areas, service can be upgraded at little cost to a semi-exclusive bus corridor simply by prohibiting other traffic along the route. In most instances, however, street alignments need to be improved and some construction is required to permit other vehicles to share the roadways. In Brazil, the costs of upgrading an avenue to serve as a semi-exclusive bus lane have been around $1.5–$2.0 million/km ($2.4–3.2 million/mile), or $3.5 million/km ($5.6 million/mile) or beyond if provision is made for mixed operation of diesel and electric buses (Wright and Sant'Anna 1989). A lane on each side of the avenue is reserved exclusively for buses by physical barriers between intersections, and shared at crossings with other vehicles. Passing space is normally added near stops.

Such lanes lower the cost per passenger of investment and operation of buses by increasing the speed and transport capacity of each bus. Again, a caveat: considerable variation in expenditures for bus lanes occurs from one locale to another. Costs increase if high compensation is needed for rights-of-way or if a number of large stations are to be built. Busways are usually more expensive if they offer exclusive rights-of-way, including separate facilities for access and exit; Anthony Armstrong-Wright (1986) cites costs ranging from $2 million to $7 million per kilometer ($3.2–$11.2 million/mile). In general, exclusive busway costs per lane are similar to those of expressways. Since they require only one lane in each direction plus passing space at stops, however, the same passenger transport capacity is obtained at a fraction of the cost required for a system dominated by private cars.

Expenditures for shelters at bus stops are unlikely to be a significant part of bus-lane or busway investment cost. This statement does not apply if shelters are upgraded to the status enjoyed by some of the better urban rail stations, or if Detroit's dedication to art is to be imitated at bus transit stations.

Facilities for walking and cycling are the least expensive transport infrastructure available. Pedestrians and cyclists can circulate on just about any surface that happens to be available, and the annual investment costs for these modes are normally extremely low in all countries. A World Bank study (1975) found the construction costs for sidewalks and bikeways negligible in relation to the number of users (less than 0.05 cent per passenger km in the early 1970s).

The variation is also great in this category, however. An effective and near-cost-free measure for protecting nonmotorized transport may involve nothing more than closing off a street by placing some physical barrier at the entrance. Examples taken from Rio de Janeiro and other Brazilian cities include mounds of dirt covered with grass, concrete cones, wooden posts, steel pipes, and even pieces of old railroad ties and tracks. At the other extreme, some cities can probably spend from $200,000 to $1 million per kilometer in converting an existing street to a very high-class pedestrian mall, or on the construction of a bikeway with elevated sections across major avenues, free-ways, or rivers, as a number of Dutch examples show (Plowden and Hillman 1984: 140–41). Yet even the most extravagant versions of malls and bikeways are typically on an order of magnitude lower than those required for the infrastructure of any form of motorized trans-portation with similar capacity.

The investment costs of additional public transit modes are dis-cussed in Chapter 7; they are normally greater than for bus systems, but seldom as great as rapid rail systems under similar conditions.

Costs of Maintenance, Administration, and Operation

Walking and cycling require very little maintenance and admin-istrative expenditure by the public sector. The only items that involve substantial outlays are public safety and illumination, and these expen-ditures are not specific to the nonmotorized modes. Some exceptions are snow removal from sidewalks and bikeways in colder climates, and expenses incurred with malls for trash collection, landscaping and the like.

The private car is much more demanding of public funds. In the United States, Stone attributes as much as 70 percent of state and local law enforcement activities to traffic-related duties (1971: 34); traffic police, accident investigators, and court officials are equally busy in most developing countries. Other traffic-related expenditures include public illumination and traffic signals, a traffic engineering contingent, a road repair crew, and, in colder climates, a snow-removal and street-salting crew.

The maintenance of public transportation modes can place few or many claims on public funds. Most European transit systems oper-ate at a loss, with fare box revenue covering something around 20 to 40 percent of their costs. Subsidy levels in the early 1980s were at 72 percent in New York, 71 percent in Milan, 70 percent in Brussels, 61 percent in Berlin, 56 percent in Paris, and 30 percent in London (Gold-sack 1982). Robert Cervero estimates that only about one-half of 1 percent of U.S. city bus routes cover their costs, even when "costs" are underestimated by generous assumptions (1990: 188).

In many Latin American countries, bus and jitney services oper-ate without subsidies. Among U.S. bus operators, fare box revenue still covered operating expenses in 1966; by 1985, however, fares were a mere 34 percent of those expenses (Lave 1990). For U.S. transit as a whole in 1988, operating revenue provided 42 percent of total operating costs, with passenger revenue covering 37 percent of those costs and the other 5 percent coming from renting advertising space and other sources (American Public Transit Association 1989: 24–29). For Brazilian rail systems in 1988, fare-box revenue covered 42 percent of the São Paulo metro's operating expenses, compared to 39 percent for the São Paulo state railways, 26 percent for the Rio de Janeiro metro, and something between 10 and 13 percent for passenger trains in other cities (Lima 1989).

These figures indicate that most rail transit and many public bus transit operations are highly deficitary. The ratio of fare-box receipts to expenditures declines to even lower levels if amortization, depreciation, and interest are included: the part of the São Paulo metro's costs covered by fares plunges from 42 percent to 23 percent, for example.

In contrast, bus transport in Latin America and some other countries is typically run by private companies at a profit, although some cities also maintain a subsidized public company alongside the private firms. The ability of private operators to cover costs in Latin America and many other developing countries holds true whether they are subject to economic regulation, as in Brazil, or compete in a market with no such regulation, as in Chile.

Even without subsidies, fares are low. In the medium-sized city of Campina Grande (1980 population of 250,000) in Brazil's Northeast, the fare is typically around 10 U.S. cents per ride. It keeps the operators in business and also covers the municipality's personnel and other expenses in administering the system (Wright and Sant'Anna 1989). In Bogotá, unsubsidized private operators charge fares of 10 cents for buses and minibuses, 25 cents for shared taxis and executive buses, and 45 cents for "superexecutive" buses (Acevedo 1989: 5). The executive buses do not carry standing passengers and generally have longer routes, of the suburb-to-downtown variety. Metro Manila's buses and jeepneys have exceptionally low fares, about 6 U.S. cents for a ride of up to 4 kilometers, and another penny or two for the next 4 kilometers. The owners, however, have gone on strike on more than one occasion to increase fares, alleging that they are losing money. My calculations indicate that they are covering their expenses with diesel fuel, very low wages, and little else; the calculations are supported by the decline in the number of buses and jeepneys in recent years, as some have worn out without being replaced and others have left the regulated public sector for more rewarding private contracts (Benigno 1991: HC-7).

Fares in the United States and Europe vary widely, but are normally several times more expensive, despite heavy subsidies. A fare of 60 cents, charged by the Ann Arbor (Michigan) Transportation Authority in 1989, is a relatively low fare in developed countries. Philadelphia area local fares are $1.25 plus 30 cents per urban zone crossed (Cervero 1990: 190). Comparable or higher fares are charged in many European cities, and most are increasing faster than inflation—Philadelphia's increased to $1.50 in 1991.

The striking differences in profitability and fares of buses across countries have several explanations. The systems operate under vastly different conditions. Load factors are typically high in Brazil, Colombia, the Philippines, and most other developing countries; buses often run nearly empty in Europe and the United States. Labor costs are low in most developing countries, while prices of vehicles and parts are the same or higher than in Europe, resulting in many more older vehicles remaining in the fleets. A bus driver's salary in Brazil during the 1980s ranged from perhaps $200 per month in some locales to $400 per month in others. (Again, all financial data are in U.S. dollars.) With the added costs of benefits and payroll taxes, a bus company's expenditure per driver ranged from $350 to $700 per month. In high-income countries, drivers' salaries may be ten times the lower end of the Brazilian scale, a disadvantage for bus operations in comparison with some rail technologies that demand less labor per passenger.

We will take up the analysis of financially viable transportation strategies in Chapter 11. For now, we merely observe that urban passenger trains are highly unlikely to cover full costs from the fare box in any country; most do not even come close to covering their operating costs. Armstrong-Wright (1986) estimated total costs of bus systems at 2 to 8 cents per passenger km, versus 3 to 25 cents for rail systems. The less expensive bus systems had costs below those of any rail system. Furthermore, most bus systems were in the 2–5 cents per passenger km range, and all rails except conventional streetcars were in the 10–25 cents per passenger km range (these costs are somewhat outdated by inflation, but the relative differences are still representative).

Those who desire to implant and operate rail systems must ensure a substantial and stable financial package and continued support from the public sector; an alternative is to concede special privileges to attract private operators, a difficult option politically outside of Japan. Buses can and do operate in many countries without public funds, although they too are likely to be deficitary where both population densities and ridership are low.

One advantage of bus and jitney systems over rail transit is low vehicle investment cost. Some types of jitneys cost little more than private cars: a 15-passenger version known as a "jeepney" in Manila, with hand-molded stainless-steel hood and fenders, sold for less than $9,000 in 1991. Armstrong-Wright (1986) cites costs for buses in the $50,000–$130,000 range (20 percent more for trolleybuses); conventional streetcars, $300,000–$600,000; modern streetcar, $800,000; and a metro rail car, $1,000,000. These figures are outdated by inflation, but the relative differences among vehicles remain valid. Vehicle prices vary considerably from country to country, depending on the accessories, the exchange rates, and taxes. In West Germany in mid-1990, a 44-seat, 12-meter-long (13 yd.) bus with room for 50 passengers was selling for about $238,000; an 18-meter articulated unit for $292,000; a trolley bus for $374,000–$476,000; a dual-mode trolley-diesel bus for $544,000; an 18-meter tram with 1 joint and 6 axles for $1,632,000; a 28-meter-long light rail vehicle for $2,380,000 (Lindner 1990). Rail cars can cost ten times the price of a standard bus; metro rail cars provide about three times more capacity than these buses, but unless that capacity is fully used, the cost differential in favor of buses remains very large.

When comparing the costs of a new rail system with bus lanes or busways, the full costs of rail cars must be added to the investment in rights-of-way; bus lanes and busways *reduce* the number of buses needed. This occurs since each existing bus can travel at a higher average speed and make more trips per day. With less stop-and-go traffic, wear and fuel expenses also decrease on a per passenger basis.

Health and Synergy

Transport-related stress and exercise affect the health of urban residents. The negative effects of stress on health include increased incidences of headaches, psychosomatic diseases, digestive disturbances, strokes, and heart disease. Medical research on these topics has concentrated on the workplace rather than on traffic. It is possible that traffic is a minor contributor to overall stress among the population. Driving or riding in a car, however, often produces fairly long periods of tension that are involved in anticipating and avoiding potentially dangerous situations, waiting for lights to change, or facing stalled traffic. Bus drivers and fare collectors also face long periods of stress, a factor all too visible in crowded buses in developing countries.

Well-run transit systems permit the rider to relax during the trip, reducing stress, but other effects work in the opposite direction, such as frustration with waiting, unreliable service or schedules, concern over missing a stop, close proximity to strangers (especially those not identified with one's peer group), or, in unsafe areas, anxiety about potential assailants or pickpockets. Walking and cycling are the only modes that provide a significant amount of exercise and, at least in safe neighborhoods, reduce stress through the indirect effect of the physical exercise involved.

The lack of hard data does not permit us to go beyond this qualitative description of the performance of common urban transport modes with respect to transport-induced stress. Several recent studies in epidemiology and physiology of exercise, however, indicate that moderate amounts of nonathletic walking or cycling have a significant, positive impact on fitness and health. Since the nonmotorized modes have a major role to play in urban transportation, integrating walking or cycling into daily urban trips can help overcome health and fitness problems created by sedentary professions and lifestyles, while improving the urban environment and other transport-related characteristics.

Sedentariness is already the rule in more wealthy countries and is increasingly common in less developed countries. Walking and cycling as habitual modes of transport are among the best options people have available for maintaining a minimally acceptable level of fitness.

Most people have shown their aversion to regular practice of strenuous sports. In the United States, for example, a recent survey indicated that the vast majority of those who started an exercise program abandoned it shortly thereafter—the only exception being those who had taken up walking (*Consumer Guide* 1988: 129–31). If walking and cycling become safe enough to be practiced as independent modes and as complements to transit trips, exercise can become a byproduct of one's daily activities, avoiding the need for special equipment, fees, trips to the gym, and other inconveniences that discourage the vast majority of the population from regular participation in sports and strenuous exercise programs. The evidence is recent and summarized below.

Early Modern Concepts of Exercise, Fitness, and Health

The effect of exercise on health and longevity has been the object of debate and disagreement for many years. It was not until the 1940s that doctors began to recommend mild exercise as therapy for patients recovering from heart disease (Paffenbarger 1989). Prior to that time, most physicians recommended extended periods of bed rest for patients who had undergone surgery or even normal childbirth, with the (now recognized) ill effects of extending hospital stays, delaying recovery, and producing complications such as adhesions of scar tissue. Over time, patients were counseled to take a few steps soon after surgery, radically shortening hospital stays. Exercise and physical therapy became standard therapy for many forms of heart disease and other disabilities.

A contradictory phenomenon in life outside hospitals and clinics was the emergence of the concept that exercise contributed to fitness and health only if taken in Olympian doses. Medical science largely ignored moderate activities such as cycling or walking to work or to the bus stop as sources of exercise. Nobody thought to investigate if part of the advantage in longevity (nearly a decade) that women have over men in developed Western countries could be explained by the simultaneous retirement of many older men from employment and activity, while older women continue to perform household chores.

The evidence of the beneficial effects of minimal activity on the recuperation of the ill did not spill over into physicians' recommendations for nonathletic activity for the general population. In Western societies, knowledge had become so fragmented into academic departments and well-defined professions that fitness became the domain of drill sergeants, coaches and athletes. "Authorities," such as the U.S. President's Council on Physical Fitness (typically captained by retired coaches and athletes), have long recommended at least a half-hour per day of vigorous, structured exercise. Coaches demand hours. The ability to perform fixed tasks is still used as the means of attesting fitness levels, as in the widely adopted method of the Royal Canadian Air Force (1975). There has been a strong positive feedback for athletes, as the ever more demanding training regimens yield new records in sports. The message for the nonathletic majority, however, is a negative one: such regimens are too exacting to be imitated.

The Morehouse Challenge

In the 1970s, Lawrence Morehouse, author of several arcane treatises on the physiology of exercise, shocked the "exercise establishment" with *Total Fitness* and *Maximum Performance* (Morehouse and Gross 1975, 1977). The total fitness concept is designed for people who are neither hospital patients nor athletes in training. It is addressed to the majority of citizens who shun prolonged daily periods of rigorous exercise, yet need to establish a "fitness reserve" sufficient to feel well, to tire less easily, and to meet the demands of domestic and work activities, minor emergencies, and casual sports.

The method prescribes a change in lifestyle that involves a minimum of structured exercise. The overweight are advised to adopt a "wide variety diet." To avoid craving, no food or drink are excluded. Rather, this "diet" transforms an average daily 100 food calorie (kcal) surplus—typical of people who are slowly gaining weight—into a 500 kcal deficit through a slight reduction (300 kcal) in overall calorie intake, coupled with burning an extra 300 kcal through increased activity. This modest 500-kcal deficit equals a loss of one pound (0.45 kg) of fat per week, and is checked by stepping on the scales weekly rather than by counting calories. No one should lose more than one pound per week, and the target or "ideal weight" should not be set too low.

Morehouse redefines exercise as increased physical activity. For a previously sedentary person, a minimally sufficient fitness level might be obtained by walking more, using the stairs instead of the elevator, sitting up instead of lying down while watching television, standing up instead of sitting down while talking on the telephone, and stretching to reach things on shelves. For higher levels of fitness, Morehouse recommends three 10-minute sessions a week of limbering up and cardiorespiratory effort. The latter should raise the pulse rate to 60 percent of maximum, meaning exercise at some 110 heartbeats per minute for a forty-year-old (as an average for large numbers of people, the maximum heart rate is 220 minus a person's age, in beats per minute). Optional higher levels of fitness can be attained in eight-week stages by raising the heartbeat to 70 percent and then 80 percent of maximum.

Total Fitness counsels against excessive exertion for the nonfit, diets that lead to rapid or excessive weight loss, jogging, deep knee bends, sit-ups, and all calisthenics that require brusque, military-type movements. Morehouse criticizes overly vigorous exercise and sports as dangerous and unnecessary for fitness. He also cautions against letting exercise become an additional source of tension in a person's life.

The Morehouse method offers a benchmark for the view that moderate exercise can result in an "adequate" level of fitness and an enhanced quality of life, with additional years of life a likely bonus. Yet the exercise requirements, though undemanding, must be met on a regular basis. Inactivity can cause fit persons to lose 80 percent of their initial conditioning level in a month; conversely, much can be done in a month for an initially inactive person.

Criticism of the Morehouse Method

The early reviews of the Morehouse method contained three types of criticism: three 10-minute exercise sessions a week were insufficient to achieve the calculated weight losses; several isolated statements were inaccurate; and several claims were contrary to results of published studies and prevailing expert opinion.[1]

Regarding the first criticism, the critics erred by counting only the calories expended on the 10-minute exercise sessions. Morehouse's pound-a-week-fat-loss calculation (equivalent to 3,500 kcal) started from a fat-producing 100 kcal per day surplus and built a daily 500-kcal deficit through a combination of reduced calory intake and higher expenditures resulting from changes in total lifestyle activities. The 10-minute formal exercise sessions play a minor role in creating this deficit. Since Morehouse's text is quite clear about this, the misinterpretation is indicative of the degree to which entrenched errors in thinking can make some critics unable to understand a straightforward argument—or even to perform simple arithmetical operations.

The critics fared better without producing substantive damage when claiming that some statements were inaccurate. For example, Morehouse errs in placing the percentage of the body composed of water at 90 percent. His substantive point, however, is still correct: one should pause to drink water during exercise or sports in order to replenish lost fluids. This was also a heretical point of view among athletes and coaches until quite recently.[2]

The third type of criticism was substantive in nature: Morehouse's theories were unsupported by epidemiological studies. That support, however, has recently come in a very strong form in three separate studies, each coordinated by a renowned epidemiologist.

The Harvard, Dallas, and MRFIT Studies

Ralph Paffenbarger and colleagues (1986) conducted a landmark study of Harvard alumni that found a strong and statistically significant correlation between moderate exercise and reduction of all-cause mortality ratios, along with a significant positive effect on longevity. The still-ongoing study is based on an examination of physical activity and other lifestyle characteristics of nearly 17,000 male Harvard alumni aged thirty-five to seventy-four during a follow-up period of twelve to sixteen years. Paffenbarger's calculations of activity levels are based on the total weekly number of calories spent in walking, climbing stairs, and sports. A significant positive effect on survival ratios and longevity is found for even very moderate exercise (500–1,999 kcal/week) and a slight additional benefit for expenditures of over 2,000 kcal/week.

The highest survival ratios are found among regular exercisers with normal blood pressure who are also nonsmokers and have positive hereditary factors (both parents lived at least sixty-five years). However, roughly half the negative effects of smoking, hypertension and hereditary factors are canceled out by moderate levels of exercise. The expected positive effect of athletic inclination and ability, defined as being a varsity athlete as an undergraduate, is not present. In fact, very active ex-varsity athletes have lower survival ratios than the moderately active ex-athletes and moderate to very active nonvarsity athletes.

The very limited amount of exercise required to produce some benefit is indicated by Paffenbarger's measure of moderate activity, which begins at a mere 500 kcal/week. This could be obtained in three minutes per day of going up and down stairs, plus eighteen minutes of walking.[3]

These results have received support from Stephen Blair and others (1989) in their study of the relation of physical fitness to all-cause and cause-specific mortality in 10,224 men and 3,120 women. Blair's is the only study to date that includes both a large sample of women and baseline data on fitness and health. These data were obtained from a preventive physical examination, a maximal treadmill exercise test at the Institute for Aerobics Research in Dallas, and a long-term follow-up study.

The Dallas results are in agreement with the Harvard alumni study on all aforementioned factors. The Dallas study, however, shows more pronounced effects from the mutual factors considered. This is presumably due to the availability of the baseline fitness data. The study also shows a correlation between moderate levels of exercise and enhanced survival rates in relation to such negative factors as cholesterol, glucose levels, and even cancer. There is a positive, but less pronounced, gain in survival ratios and longevity for additional levels of fitness, up to a certain point. At very high levels of fitness, a negative effect appears among some subdivisions of the sample, in comparison with more moderate levels of fitness. The results are similar for both men and women.

Despite physiological evidence that the overall effect of exercise on fitness is roughly the same for both sexes (Morehouse and Miller 1976: 331–34), previous studies had found no significant relationship between fitness and health for women. This probably occurred since previous studies did not contain a baseline fitness evaluation and, incredibly, ignored the substantial doses of moderate exercise women typically obtain from such activities as preparing food, caring for small children, ironing, and cleaning house. Such tasks require substantial standing and walking and elevate heartbeat levels somewhat over extended periods—precisely the basis of the Morehouse method.

This perspective is coherent with the results of yet a third study, by Arthur Leon and colleagues (1987), the Multiple Risk Factor Intervention Trail (MRFIT). The MRFIT definition of exercise includes an even wider variety of leisure activities than the Harvard and Dallas studies, considering such things as gardening. Moderate exercise is again found to improve survival ratios, and, after a certain point, no benefits are found for additional exercise.

These three studies rely on correlation as evidence, a methodological weakness since correlation does not by itself prove causality. Fortunately, there are underlying factors that do provide the missing causal link between moderate exercise and health. Such exercise provides, among other benefits: a strengthened heart muscle, better muscular and skeletal maintenance, better digestion, more rapid elimination of wastes and toxins, better sleep, lower stress, less depression, a more self-confident, positive attitude on life, increased resistance to disease, faster recovery from illness and surgery, (possibly) lower osteoporosis, and increased lung capacity (*Consumer Guide* 1988: 21–31).

In sum, moderate amounts of walking or leisurely cycling can provide sufficient fitness to improve the quality of a person's life, reduce mortality ratios, and even add a couple of years to the average life span.

Up to a point, the Harvard, Dallas, and MRFIT studies show that more exercise is even better. This does not detract from the benefits of moderate exercise, but rather reinforces them by increasing the probability that a person will ascend to a somewhat higher level of activity. In other words, a person who is moderately fit from activities such as walking or cycling as part of the journey to work will find it easier to participate in sports or other vigorous activities, in contrast with someone with an inactive lifestyle. It is easier to go from 1,000 to 2,500 kcal per week of activity than from 300 to 2,500 kcal/week. Somewhere above 2,500 kcal/week, more exercise provides no additional health benefits and may place the exerciser at higher risk.

These are not the only benefits of habitual moderate exercise, or even the most important. Other benefits have not attracted the attention of the epidemiologists, but they become evident after about three weeks of moderate exercise. They include: "feeling better," increased concentration and productivity at mental tasks, not needing coffee "to get going" in the morning, ability to function normally after an occasional poor night's sleep, and enhanced ability to relax and relate to one's family in the evening—the walk home helps one to leave the day's problems at the workplace.

Since commonsense is an uncommon commodity, a warning is in order. Some members of the exercise establishment and well-meaning amateurs believe exercise must be painful to do any good. They find ways of transforming walking into a form of torture, such as using rubber suits to "sweat off" fat, wearing weights on ankles and wrists, "overloading," or marching at fixed speeds, distances, or times.

Sweat is composed of water, not fat. In hot weather, warm clothes can cause moderate dehydration or even heatstroke: shade is preferable to sun, and clothes should even be light in color—cooler during the day and easier for drivers to see at night.

Weights place unnatural stress on the wrong places: they may restrict the flow of blood, elevate blood pressure, cause skin irritation, or strain ligaments. Hands should be kept free. If briefcases or purses must be carried, they should be kept light or placed in a backpack (or on the rack of a bicycle).

Significant overloads or forced marches, like any exercise program, should be preceded by a thorough physical examination. Most healthy adults can safely build up to walks of thirty minutes, an hour, or more. But the initially unfit might best start with only a block or two on the first day, and add no more than a block each day until they attain that capability. Several short walks are about as beneficial as a single long one. Overloads and structure should cease before stress or boredom gets the upper hand.

Serious Accidents

Traffic accidents are one of the most serious health problems in both rich and poor countries. Typically, they are among the foremost causes of death of males in the fifteen-to-forty-five age group (National Safety Council 1989: 8; Plowden and Hillman 1984: 69; Sobania and Wright 1989; Wright 1986). In the United States, traffic accidents in the fifteen-to-twenty-four age group are by far the leading cause of death. This includes deaths among females who, with lower exposure to traffic accidents and better safety records as drivers and pedestrians, account for only 25 percent of the fatalities in this age group.

The high speeds of motor vehicles are inherently dangerous. Over time, many developed countries have partially compensated for this, lowering their per-vehicle accident and fatality ratios through traffic and vehicle engineering, education, and strict sanctions against improper driving. In the United States, for example, the fatality rate per 100 million vehicle km declined from 34.7 in 1923 to 4.0 in 1988 (National Safety Council 1989: 70–71). Developing countries typically have none of these preventive measures effectively in place, and they have much higher accident rates. Brazil, for example, has about half the population of the United States and only a tenth as many motor vehicles, but its traffic fatalities, at 40,000 to 50,000 per year, are comparable to the 49,000 traffic deaths in the United States in 1988; these totals are nearly as large as the cumulative total of 58,000 Americans who died in the Vietnam war (GEIPOT 1987: 14; National Safety Council 1989: 71).

As the Brazilian Traffic Safety Work Group points out, these deaths are particularly tragic ones (GEIPOT 1987: 13). Heart disease, cancer, and other leading causes of death typically strike people who are nearing the average life expectancy of their countries. Their children are, by and large, economically independent and minimally prepared to deal emotionally with the loss of the loved one. Traffic deaths, in contrast, are concentrated among children, adolescents, and young and middle-aged parents. Few surviving relatives are emotionally prepared for the sudden, violent death of these loved ones, and the economic consequences for these survivors are often devastating.

Injuries that result in permanent disability can be equally traumatic. Unfortunately, the statistical classifications vary so greatly within and across countries that it is hard to present a meaningful quantitative picture of the problems associated with injuries, and I will not attempt to do so here. However, common results of traffic accidents include brain damage, confinement to wheelchairs, blindness, loss of the use of a limb, and extreme or chronic pain. And there are the less traumatic and more numerous minor injuries. For every fatality, there may be from ten to forty injuries of differing severity (the wide range reflects differences in reporting and classifying injuries).

Due to their endemic and dispersed nature, automobile accidents typically receive little attention from newspapers, radio and television. The exceptions are major tragedies, usually involving buses, trains, and airplanes. This conveys a subliminal and false impression that these modes are dangerous compared to private cars. Because such accidents are rare, they are "news." Car accidents happen all the time, and so are not news, even though, at the American or Brazilian rates, they account for over 130 fatalities per day—the equivalent of a major plane crash with all passengers killed.

Despite the media's rather limited attention, most developed countries have dedicated substantial effort to diminishing the magnitude of the problem. On occasion, some developing countries have tried to follow their example, with mixed results. In all cases, government regulation, research, and even the media focus on ways to improve car and truck safety, with less attention paid to traffic engineering and almost none given to the overall nature of the urban transport system. Broadly speaking, public and private sector efforts have concentrated on improving the safety of the vehicles themselves through such measures as the installation of padded dashboards, energy absorbing frames, seat belts, better lights and brakes, and air bags; and working on the "human factors," through improved driver education, the study of perceptions and reactions, attempts to control alcohol abuse, law enforcement, and similar measures. Better roads and traffic control, including four-lane divided highways with controlled access, have made a major, though largely unnoticed contribution, almost as an unintended secondary effect of efforts to improve traffic flows. Other than this, traffic engineering has received little systematic attention. It is sometimes remembered after a number of tragedies have occurred at a particular intersection, and local residents prevail upon the traffic authorities to "do something about it."

I have no major quarrels with the work being carried out in vehicle design or with the research on human behavior. However, my argument is that major breakthroughs, especially in developing countries, require a different, yet complementary, approach to the problem. Traffic safety should not be considered in isolation, but as part of the urban transportation system. It is, among other things, a consequence of the amount of travel, the choice of transport modes, travel patterns, street design, and the conditions that influence the use and safety of each mode.

As noted, the United States reduced its fatality rate per vehicle kilometer by almost 90 percent between 1923 and 1988 through investments in improved vehicles, education, and policing. Yet the total number of fatalities in 1988 (49,000) was nearly three times that of 1923 (18,400), and the death rate of 19.9 per 100,000 population was actually higher than the 16.5 registered in 1923 (National Safety Council 1989: 70–71). The 19.9 figure represents a considerable decline in relation to the historic high of 30.8 fatalities per 100,000 population registered in 1937, but it has been creeping upward since the modern low of 19.0 was reached in 1983.

The reasons for this unspectacular record are simple: more people are traveling longer distances by private car and motorcycle, the two most dangerous motorized modes and the ones that cause a disproportionate number of deaths to pedestrians and bicyclists.

The differences in safety for several forms of motorized transport in the United States are illustrated in Table 5 for 1987. The safest mode is the transit bus, with only 2 passenger deaths in nearly 37 billion passenger km of travel, followed closely by school buses and, progressively less closely, by intercity buses, scheduled airlines, and trains. In other developed countries, urban passenger trains are often slightly safer than transit buses; the U.S. figure for trains is relatively poor since it includes intercity services. Cars are one hundred times more dangerous than transit buses, and motorcycles, over four thousand times more dangerous. Motorcycles are also over forty-two times more dangerous than cars.

Similar relationships across modes hold for other countries, although the absolute numbers may be quite different. In England, bus travel in 1979 produced only 34 passenger deaths in 52 billion passenger km, a ratio of only 0.07 death to 100 million passenger km. Rail travel in Canada is thirty times safer than by car (Whitelegg 1983). In Brazil in 1985, 37 billion passenger km of intercity bus travel resulted in 342 bus passenger deaths, a ratio of 0.9 death to 100 million passenger km (Wright 1989a). Although this is over ten times more than the British figure, intercity travel in Brazil is still twenty times safer by bus than by car.

Table 5
Death Rates for Some Motorized Transport Modes in the United States, 1987

Transport Mode	Deaths per 100 Million Passenger km	Risk Relative to Transit Buses
Motorcycle	25.5	4,270.8
Passenger cars	0.600	100.6
Passenger trains	0.082	13.8
Scheduled airlines	0.048	8.0
Intercity buses	0.044	4.6
School buses	0.018	1.6
Transit buses	0.006	1.0

Source: Calculated from data in National Safety Council (1989: 60, 87). Data for cars include drivers and passengers; for taxis, only passengers; data for trains include commutation.

There are some fairly obvious—although widely ignored—reasons for this extreme variation of risk across modes. Buses are very valuable investments, and accidents can bring lawsuits against the owners. Accidents are therefore a poor business practice. Management often equips buses with tachometers to provide the fleet manager with evidence of excessive speed and other driver errors at any point on the route. A bus can be seen more easily than other vehicles, and its movements are normally more predictable. In the event of an accident, buses are large, sturdy vehicles. Their passengers are much less likely to suffer severe or fatal injury than occupants of smaller vehicles. The driver is seated at a relatively high position and enjoys a better view of the road, pedestrians, and vehicles than do other highway users. Unlike automobiles, buses are seldom entrusted to sixteen-year-old boys. The bus driver is normally an adult with many years of driving experience, selected and kept on for having a good driving record. Drivers receive both formal and on-the-job training, and are under supervision. Suspension or dismissal is expected for use of alcohol, other drugs, or unsafe behavior on the job.

Urban trains also have many of the above features, plus, for many systems, an exclusive right-of-way on a fixed path, with controls to avoid collisions. In such circumstances, they are often even safer than buses.

Motorcycles, at the other extreme, offer at best a helmet as protection against the impacts of accidents. They overturn very easily, not only on impact with other vehicles and fixed objects, but on contact with irregular or slippery surfaces. In Great Britain, two-wheeled motor vehicles were responsible in 1981 for a fourth of all traffic fatalities, although they logged only 3 percent of its vehicle km (Plowden and Hillman 1984: 53–78). In the fifteen-to-twenty-four-year age group, 76 percent of accidental deaths and 36 percent of all deaths are caused by traffic accidents. The great majority of these youths died in motorcycle accidents.

Motorcycles are incompatible for safety reasons with pedestrian and bicycle traffic, and thus must share roadways with cars, trucks, and buses. Their drivers are drawn principally from the worst category in all statistical studies of traffic accidents: those who are predominantly young, male, given to "showing off," adverse to using helmets, with higher incidences of using alcohol and drugs than other road users (Plowden and Hillman 1984: 53–81).

Motorcycles, even more than cars, represent a danger to pedestrians and bicyclists. The earlier cited 52 billion passenger km of bus travel in Great Britain accounted for only a third as many pedestrian fatalities as the same amount of travel by car, while motorcycles kill five times more pedestrians per kilometer driven than cars (Plowden and Hillman 1984: 5; Whitelegg 1983). Motorcycles thus kill fifteen times as many British pedestrians than would die from an equivalent amount of travel by bus (give or take rounding errors). And the fatality rate for motorcycles in Britain is a third less than in the United States.

There is little data on motorcycle accidents in developing countries; the casual information I have been able to piece together indicates that their accident rates per motorcycle are far higher than in either Britain or the United States. The relative differences across countries may be as great as those cited for automobiles. The U.S. and British statistics would also worsen if data on motorcycle fatalities were separated from those of mopeds, motor scooters, motorbikes, and other somewhat less dangerous vehicles. The larger the two-wheeled motorized vehicle, the more dangerous to the driver, passenger, and third parties. Mopeds are only a fourth as dangerous to their riders as motorcycles and seldom account for pedestrian deaths (Plowden and Hillman 1984: 54).

The safety ratings of walking and bicycling are more difficult to evaluate. More than other modes, their safety depends on the available facilities. Under current practice in most countries, pedestrians and bicyclists are placed in conflict with other vehicles by inadequate street patterns and other traffic-engineering errors; in such circumstances, they are very vulnerable indeed. Pedestrians account for as much as 70 percent of traffic fatalities in the city of São Paulo—to cite one tragic example—and for about half the traffic deaths in Brazil as a whole (Gold, Grostein, and Pereira 1992). In Great Britain, pedestrians account for 31 percent of fatalities and bicyclists 5 percent (Plowden and Hillman 1984: 44). Little data, however, is available on the crucial question of the safety of the nonmotorized modes when they are isolated from motor vehicle traffic.

Walking presents almost no traffic fatalities if pedestrians are isolated from motor vehicles. Data compiled for Great Britain for 1981 by Stephen Plowden and Mayer Hillman reveal that only two pedestrian deaths resulted from a collision with another pedestrian, and only seven pedestrian deaths resulted from collisions with a bicycle (1984: 154). The authors do not satisfy our curiosity as to how these deaths occurred, but it is easy to imagine an elderly person or small child being struck and killed by a speeding cyclist, and a speeding jogger might do likewise.

Cycling presents a higher degree of danger than walking, even when isolated from motorized traffic. A bike moves faster and has a rigid frame with protruding handlebars, pedals, and brake levers, all of which can inflict injury. Cyclists are also subject to falls and collisions with fixed objects, other bicycles, and pedestrians.

British and Swedish data for 1982 provide some information on bicycle fatalities under current conditions. In that year, bicycles traveled 5.5 billion km with 294 fatalities in Great Britain, a ratio of 5.3 fatalities per 100 million km. Sweden's ratio was 4.1, down from 12.0 in 1973 as a result of changes in urban design and traffic engineering (Plowden and Hillman 1984: 152, 155). Both of these fatality ratios for bicycles compare favorably with the fatality ratios for cars in many developing countries.

Some admittedly sketchy data indicate that cyclists' injuries are common but fatalities are quite rare when bicycle mishaps do not involve motor vehicles. The data are sketchy since police departments in most countries register motor-vehicle accidents rather than transportation accidents, excluding bicycle accidents that do not involve motor vehicles. Hospitals, on the other hand, may have accidental injury files involving bicycles, but these include children's injuries in play not related to transportation accidents. In other words, both hospitals and police count what is easily counted rather than what counts.

A pilot study of hospital emergency room data in North Carolina (Stutts et al. 1990) found that only 10 percent of the emergency room data were also on police files. In the United States in 1987, 525,026 injuries to bicyclists required hospital emergency room treatment. This is a large number, but only slightly above the 460,420 emergency treatments for basketball players in that same year (National Safety Council 1989: 83). Basketball players required emergency attention 1.8 times more than cyclists in relation to the numbers of participants. (The comparison would be more meaningful if we knew the average time spent playing or riding by each kind of participant and the severity of each type of injury).

The North Carolina data showed that off-road locations (such as parking lots and driveways) account for the majority of emergency room cases. Most of these involve children under fourteen years of age, that is, essentially nontransportation accidents that occur irrespective of the level of use of the bicycle as a mode of transport. In that sample of 649 emergency room treatments of pedal cyclists, seven died, and all seven were involved in a collision with a motor vehicle (Stutts et al. 1990: 71).

Although the comparison with basketball is shaky and the North Carolina sample small, these considerations suggest a hypothesis for future tests: pedal transportation is about as safe as playing basketball, if it is completely segregated from motor vehicles. Efforts are needed in both activities to reduce the high injury rates (helmet use is especially valuable for cyclists), but participants may be less exposed to death than when traveling in a car.

There is somewhat better evidence on a related and equally important point: bicycles kill fewer pedestrians than cars. Bicycles caused 0.15 pedestrian death per 100 million bicycle km in Great Britain in 1981, compared to 0.38 per passenger km of travel by car; the figure for cars is two and a half times that for bicycles.[4]

There are two important conclusions here: pedal cycling and walking should not be encouraged where they are in conflict with motor vehicle traffic; and if pedestrians and cyclists can be successfully segregated from motorized traffic, the resulting nonmotorized traffic will be safer than transport by any means other than, possibly, buses and trains. A suitable combination of walking and cycling with buses and trains offers the safest possible overall pattern of urban circulation.

A more detailed description of the measures needed to accomplish this is given in Chapter 9; however, a preview is in order here. I have already cited the reduction of the bicycle fatality ratio in Sweden to a third of its peak level through redesigning streets, relocating parking areas, and establishing more car-free zones. An even more important illustration comes from the central area of Belo Horizonte, Brazil's third industrial city. There, traffic engineers and urban planners redesigned all the main intersections and bus lines in the late 1970s to deal with catastrophic levels of accidents and congestion (Wright 1990: 7–8). The modifications reduced the fatality rate per 10,000 motor vehicles dramatically from forty-five in 1976 to twelve in 1981. The reduction in the fatality ratio, although impressive, understates the improvement that occurred in Belo Horizonte's central area. The statistics are aggregates for the entire city and include high indices of fatalities that continue to occur in the very sizable untreated area outside the city center. If local statistics were available, the results would be even more impressive.

Similarly, in 1983 Curitiba registered five traffic deaths per 10,000 vehicles, the lowest rate among Brazilian cities. This was achieved by simple traffic engineering improvements, implanting priority bus routes and transforming a substantial part of the downtown area into pedestrian malls, punctuated by bus-only access routes.

These measures are doubly important in developing countries. Among the OECD countries in 1979, the Netherlands registered the lowest pedestrian fatality rate per million population, 18.7; Ireland had the worst pedestrian fatality rate at 67.4, with the United States, Canada, and the United Kingdom clustered near 38 (Plowden and Hillman 1984: 201). For São Paulo, my estimates range from 175 to 304.[5]

Plowden and Hillman argue that no measures should be taken to encourage pedal cycling or walking unless suitable segregated facilities are provided. They emphasize that "suitable" does not mean the marginal changes that most bicycling enthusiasts and transport officials have been discussing. I would add that such segregated facilities should be provided—and in many cases must be provided—to achieve better transportation characteristics, including greater safety.

The safety problem, moreover, is much more pressing in countries with low and intermediate levels of motorization. The investments required to enable the majority of the urban population to drive cars are so great relative to incomes and the national resource bases that this will not occur for many decades, if at all. Traffic safety in those countries cannot be increased by discouraging walking and bicycling; rather, it requires reducing the conflicts of motor vehicles with pedestrians and bicyclists.

This leaves unanswered the question of what to do with motorcycles and mopeds. First, it is well to recognize that we are dealing with two distinct types of vehicles. Mopeds equipped with very small motors are somewhat heavier and considerably noisier than bicycles, but they are similar in other respects, including their British accident rates. If the highest speed of mopeds is similar to that of bicycles, traffic authorities have the option of treating them as bikes, and have done so in the Netherlands and some other countries. In Britain, mopeds are defined as two-wheeled vehicles equipped with pedals and having a maximum design speed of 48 km/h (30 mph) and a motor of 50 cc or less. If they are to be treated as bicycles, I would favor reducing the maximum speed by a third, to 30 km/h and decreasing the engine capacity to a level compatible with the lower speed. This, of course, begs the question of noise, but it would permit the more frail, unfit, and lazy to cycle while placing mopeds on approximately the same safety level as bicycles. (I suspect they would still be more dangerous, but have no data on this point.)

Motorcycles constitute a difficult category to deal with in urban traffic. They have an extremely high rate of accidents, impose danger on other traffic and are incompatible with both heavier vehicles and nonmotorized traffic from the standpoint of safety. Some traffic authorities have ignored this and made the unwarranted assumption that education of motorcyclists is the solution. Plowden and Hillman reviewed a number of such projects for motorcyclists and found no evidence that such training lowered accident ratios in relation to motorcyclists who received no training (1984: 59–61). There were, however, indications that the lessons encouraged some youngsters who might have avoided motorcycles to try their hand at riding them and induced their parents to be more complacent about the dangers involved, thus increasing fatalities.

My opinion is that the only useful motorcycle education programs are those that encourage or require people to use safer forms of transportation. Parents who love their children should not give them motorcycles. In countries where youngsters are economically capable of buying their own motorcycles, the state should help the parents keep their children from doing so. Since motorcycles are forty-two times as dangerous as cars and four thousand times as dangerous as transit buses, motorcycle use might be more appropriately regarded as a form of suicide rather than of transportation. Like Russian roulette, motorcycling is to be discouraged.

This raises the question of the means to be employed to discourage motorcycle use and whether this is an unwarranted restriction on individual liberty. Plowden and Hillman suggest that a progressive licensing scheme be adopted (1984: 63–65). A license to ride a moped would be issued to persons aged sixteen or older. An application for a license to drive a small motorcycle would require that the applicant have held a moped license for a given number of years, say five, and the driver's license for the small motorcycle would have to be held for, say, another five years as a precondition for applying for a license to drive a larger motorcycle. This would ensure that no cyclist started out on the heavier, more dangerous vehicles in this class. It would also get youths to, say, twenty-six years of age before allowing them on larger motorcycles. At that stage in life, they could more correctly balance the dangers involved, and most of them might forget about motorcycles altogether.

Other measures involve legal restrictions on the use of the vehicles themselves. Most legal systems permit cities to ban certain types of vehicles from specific streets and zones. Motorcycles are a strong candidate on both noise-reduction and safety grounds. A more radical step would be to ban them from within the city limits and, subsequently, restrict their use to police work, the needs of the armed forces, and in specially licensed sports arenas. Some developing countries that now have few motorcycles should prohibit their manufacture and sale in the domestic market.

There are exceptions, of course, even here. In the Philippines, motorcycles with sidecars (known locally as tricycles) perform yeoman service as public transport vehicles on short routes. A line of tricycles can usually be found along a street leading to the local market, and for about eight cents a tricycle owner will deliver a shopper and her purchases at her doorstep. The tricycles accompany traffic flows better than pedicabs and are thus more suited to operation on busy streets, although both tend to operate on secondary streets. Tricycles also have greater capacity and range; I have seen as many as seven passengers and their burdens on a tricycle.

Even tricycles cannot be described as safe or silent conveyances. Nonetheless, their drivers are experienced professionals who manage to make accidents relatively infrequent, and the drivers belong to associations that fine members who fail to use proper mufflers. In such circumstances, a good policy might be to license only motorcycles equipped and used for such purposes.

With this exception, motorcycles should be restricted to police use and special sports arenas. This is not an undue intrusion on individual liberty. The issues are similar to those involved with mandatory seatbelt use laws now in force in a large number of countries. Those laws have been adopted in precisely those nations that have a long tradition of respect for human rights and due process. Parliaments and courts have understood that a person's failure to use a seatbelt affects society at large through the increased risk of that person's injury or death and the attendant suffering of family, friends, and coworkers. There is also the economic burden of medical and hospital expenses, lost production, and lost support for dependents. With motorcycles, the above arguments are much stronger than for seatbelts, given that the danger to third parties is extremely high in relation to all other forms of transportation. Finally, all major religions condemn suicide and the lack of respect and nurture for life that, consciously or not, characterizes most motorcycle use.

Chapter 6

Transport Characteristics and Individual Preferences

*T*HE CHARACTERISTICS just discussed affect society as a whole through externalities and secondary effects, including their impacts on public finance. We now turn to a second set of characteristics of transport modes—those that affect the transport user's choice of mode of travel. This set is composed of costs to users, the user's personal microenvironment, flexibility, frequency, punctuality, comfort, ease of carrying things, and total travel time. The two sets are related, at times in paradoxical ways, and the more important interrelationships are noted below.

Costs to Users

The cost to the transport user may be viewed initially as the average cost of a trip by car, or the fare paid to ride a bus, train, or taxi. All vary greatly from country to country, in accord with differences in relative prices and governmental policies regarding taxes and subsidies. For the United States, where automobile transportation costs drivers less than in most other countries due to much lower fuel and vehicle taxes, 1986 ownership cost alone was still $7.20 per day; fuel and maintenance costs were 3.9 cents per kilometer (McKnight et al. 1989:

27). The daily ownership cost amounted to over two hours' wages at the $3.35 an hour minimum wage rate; on a weekly basis, the ownership cost amounted to 38 percent of a minimum wage for 40 hours of work. Most American adult workers earn considerably more than the minimum wage and are able to afford cars. In developing countries, the ownership cost alone exceeds most families' total income.

In contrast, U.S. transit fares in 1989 averaged 62.1 cents per trip (American Public Transit Association 1989: 56), yielding a daily expenditure of about $1.55 for 2.5 unlinked trips. In other countries, car ownership and operating costs are typically much higher, while transit fares are similar or lower. As seen earlier, in developed countries transit fares are heavily subsidized, while in developing countries the rare urban trains are subsidized and the ubiquitous buses are usually privately operated, with low costs and no subsidies. In most of Latin America, for example, bus fares normally cover costs and range from 10 to 25 cents per ride.[1] The buses between Brasília and its satellite cities probably have the most expensive "urban" fares in Latin America; until recently, they were about 40 cents per ride (Wright 1987a: 294–96). (For updates, see Chapter 11.)

Average costs to users, however, are not always a good indication of the financial incentive to choose a particular mode for a given trip. Although some companies do reimburse employees for travel expense based on average cost, few drivers calculate it. Marginal cost, that is, the cost of taking an additional trip, is much more useful in explaining modal choice. If we neglect the value of the transit user's time, marginal cost and average cost are the same: both are equal to the transit fare. But for the car owner, average costs include the fixed costs of purchase, licensing, registration, and insurance payments, while marginal costs include only such items as fuel and maintenance. If there is enough gasoline in the tank, the driver may consider the marginal cost of a trip as zero—it requires no out-of-pocket cost. This is one reason transit companies in cities with high car-ownership levels find it so difficult to get car owners to take a bus.

The concept of user cost goes beyond the marginal cost of private vehicle operation or the transit fare, however. Often the car owner has a spouse and children, and the marginal costs of transportation for all family members are involved in decisions on car use. The numerous forms of sharing the vehicle have low marginal costs that work against transit. These joint decisions are intuitive enough, but are difficult to incorporate into mathematical models—perhaps one reason Pickrell (1990), among others, verified that modelers have grossly overestimated future ridership of rail transit projects.

Another factor that works in the same direction is the implicit value of time. On certain occasions, this may involve a real opportunity cost: the inability of the transit user to get quickly from one location to another may result in a lost sale, inability to take a part-time job, or some other reduction in income. If transit is much more time consuming than the automobile, the user will implicitly add the lost income to the transit fare when subjectively calculating the marginal cost of using the two modes or when considering buying a car. On other occasions, no income loss may be involved, but the user might still prefer to take a faster, though more expensive, mode. Some economists go so far as to impute a cost for this loss of time, but the validity of this procedure is questionable and the numerical results vary widely. The difficulty of quantifying these subtle and complex effects is an additional reason that many mathematical modeling efforts and cost–benefit analyses run amuck. The message, nonetheless, is clear enough: if transport planners want to attract car owners to transit, they must make it competitive in terms of time. There are occasions where this is possible (see Chapter 9).

Personal Environment

This characteristic includes a number of social and psychological factors that are extremely important in explaining transport choices; these factors are difficult to include in mathematical models, but are easily understood at a more intuitive level. Here, we will consider the dimensions of privacy, peer selection, microambient control, and orientation.

Stone makes a very perceptive distinction between what I have termed privacy and peer selection (1971: 99). Both vary considerably across cultures and among individuals in a given culture. *Privacy* refers to the ability to keep others from invading one's personal "airspace." Americans, Canadians, and some Europeans have a deep-rooted psychological desire to maintain a minimum distance between themselves and others, particularly strangers. When conversing, they stand about a meter (more than 3 feet) away from each other. Closer approximation is tolerated only when the circumstances require it, as is normally the case with public vehicles. Even then, closeness is often subconsciously quite uncomfortable, and crush loading may be a psychological ordeal, quite aside from any physical discomfort involved.

Anthropologist Edward Hall indicates that some Middle Eastern peoples do not share the concept of spatial privacy (cited in Zinsser 1988: 184–7). Latin Americans do have the concept, and it varies a great deal from country to country, but on average the distance at which they feel comfortable is considerably less than for North Americans and many Europeans. Brazilians typically converse at about half the distance preferred by Europeans; handshakes are accompanied by a pat on the back or shoulders, and so forth.

I witnessed one particularly amusing illustration of these differences in subconscious "personal airspace" some years ago. A petite Brazilian girl and a tall European man were carrying on an animated conversation, in spite of the man's obviously limited Portuguese. The girl kept inching forward in search of the half-meter distance she felt comfortable with. The man kept backpedaling in an attempt to maintain his meter of private airspace until he literally backed into a wall.

Aside from their potential for cultural misunderstanding, spatial tolerances are important in determining such things as what load factors are acceptable in public vehicles and the relative appeal of the private car. In some cultures, four people per square meter of space inside a bus or train are about as many as transit users will tolerate. In others, eight persons may be acceptable and even ten to twelve persons per square meter may be tolerated during rush hours. In the latter setting, discomfort is physical, not merely psychological.

Stone (1971) argued that Americans would prefer (or perhaps need) the equivalent of private cabins in public vehicles. This is probably an exaggerated view of their spatial intolerance; if the advice were followed it would eliminate the capacity and energy-efficiency advantage of transit. But it is clear that some peoples react to crowding more than others.

Peer selection refers to the ability of a person to choose traveling companions that are judged compatible or at least tolerable in terms of values, standards of behavior, and other factors. In public urban transportation, it is generally not possible to travel alone or to choose one's traveling companions. At best, one can hope to keep track of a friend who entered the vehicle at the same time and should be getting off at the same station. The private car permits choice of fellow travelers to a very high degree. Walking and cycling also usually allow some degree of peer selection. But few people are attracted to transit for the opportunity it affords them to meet strangers. The feeling of insecurity about pickpockets and assailants also explains differences in transit ridership and the preference for cars over transit in cities where both car ownership and crime are high. Visible and effective policing, on the other hand, can help attract or maintain ridership. The Detroit People Mover and its stations are probably the safest locales in the downtown area; that factor, along with the tasteful location of stations within key buildings, is an example of how security can be a selling point for transit. It is not enough by itself: there are at times more security guards than passengers in a People Mover rail car; the system registers only 15,000 trips a day (Nelson 1990).

A traveler's *personal microambient control* includes the choice of smoking or avoiding smoke, riding in silence or listening to a particular type of music, or carrying on some other activity, such as reading, eating, or telephoning. Here the performance of the various modes is mixed, but in general the automobile is again the clear winner, followed by walking and cycling, with transit last.

The most important factor on this list is smoking. Some smokers are extremely inconvenienced by having to refrain from smoking for even a few minutes and abstain only if social pressure or sanctions are highly visible. Smoke annoys most nonsmokers and causes considerable discomfort to those who, like myself, are allergic to tobacco. The private car accommodates individual preferences (although not necessarily in carpools, where it begins to assume characteristics of a transit vehicle). Transit agencies have to inconvenience one of the two groups, and this does not help ridership.

Aside from my personal bias, there are good reasons for prohibiting smoking in public vehicles. They begin with the ill effects of "secondary smoking," in which nonsmokers breath the air contaminated by smokers in close proximity. Standards of cleanliness in vehicles, stops, and stations are degraded by ashes and cigarette butts. Burn holes appear in seats, promoting a dilapidated aspect that invites vandalism. The close physical proximity and frequent movement of passengers provide opportunities for minor burns on clothing, arms, and legs. Finally, cigarettes may present a danger of fire in some stations and vehicles or activate their smoke detectors.

A formal prohibition of smoking may be insufficient to terminate it, although in most cities a substantial number of smokers comply with the norms. Prohibitions are more effective if the surroundings present a high visual standard and a visible form of authority is present. For example, I have never seen anyone smoking in the metro stations or vehicles of São Paulo and Rio de Janeiro, although the antismoking movement has made little progress elsewhere in Brazil. On two occasions when I was on a Rio metro platform, however, either guards or smoke detectors must have observed someone, since a brisk order came over the loudspeaker that cigarettes must be put out immediately.

The differences in the other aspects of personal microenvironment are much smaller across modes, and, in at least one case, may actually favor transit. The availability of truly portable radios and headphones enables the transit user to exercise some control over acoustics. In trains, it is often possible to read or jot something down without eye strain or motion sickness, an option not available to the car driver except in a traffic jam. Pedestrians in Curitiba, Brazil, enjoy access to public phones, refreshments, and other amenities on the way to their destinations.

Orientation refers to travelers' sensory awareness of their location in relation to the surroundings. The visual component predominates, although awareness of time and other sensory impressions, such as sound and smell, can also contribute to the feeling of being either lost or in a familiar and comfortable setting. The car driver has the visual information presented by the street design, traffic signals, buildings, and other landmarks, and is able to select the route. Maps are easily obtained if necessary. There is ample use of commercial radio in the United States and other developed countries to broadcast information on traffic conditions, and considerable research is underway to provide more specific and timely information, including routing for individual vehicles, through interaction between roadside devices and motor vehicles. There is an outside chance that these rather expensive devices will become common in some cities in another decade or so and improve substantially the orientation of some motorists. Pedestrians and cyclists, however, have the advantage of a greater intimacy with their environment, aided by their proximity to the physical landmarks and human activity along their paths and the lack of separation that the car's shell imposes on its occupants.

Passenger trains have a mixed record on orientation. Modern metros typically have color-coded diagrams of their routes and interchanges on prominent display in their stations and rail cars, and sometimes also in leaflets for outside distribution. Station names are announced as they are approached. Since most such systems are composed of a very limited number of lines, even visitors and persons with limited map-reading skills can quickly find their way around. The larger underground stations, however, often feature several entrances, exits, and transfer points without any meaningful orientation as to how these relate to the above-ground area in the vicinity of the station. User confusion also occurs at transfer points due to the lack of appropriate visual information. Boston's metro (MBTA) pioneered in this respect decades ago by introducing photomurals in the stations; aside from their decorative function, the murals presented images of activities and places directly over each station (Stone 1971: 104–5).

Many older systems have never been upgraded to provide better orientation. Some of them, such as the "suburban" train stations in Rio de Janeiro, provide only a few written signs on entrances and platforms and garbled announcements of departures on the loudspeakers.

Bus passengers face the most difficult orientation problems. They have the same type of physical surroundings as motorists, but do not control their routes or schedules—unfathomable mysteries to visitors and new residents. Since families in most countries are becoming increasingly mobile, this is a severe disadvantage for transit. In my own travels in several countries, I have seldom been able to use transit buses to get anywhere but from an airport to a downtown station, usually due to the lack of adequate information regarding the options.

An exception is the Ann Arbor Transportation Authority, which provides an illustrated bulletin with intelligible diagrams of each route. In São Paulo, city guides with bus schedules can be purchased at newsstands. The prices are fairly steep, since there are literally hundreds of pages of maps and fine print. I carry a copy of one on all my trips to that huge city, since not even experienced taxi drivers know how to find the majority of the streets. But I have never been able to use the complex information on bus routes. It takes time to find the route, and the bus stop is not indicated. It seldom helps to ask someone nearby; most people are familiar only with the routes they use. Trips that require transfers are an informational disaster.

Long-term bus users develop a better understanding of the routes and options that serve their customary needs, but may have problems getting to an unfamiliar area or street address. Many transit users never become familiar with most neighborhoods in their cities, due in part to the hurdle of finding how to get there by bus. When the bus user alights at a stop or station, no orientation or map is available concerning the location of nearby streets, important buildings or other sites. I have partially overcome this in my own travels by purchasing city maps and carrying them with me. For the bulk of the world's urban residents, however, this is not a viable option. The maps are expensive and unwieldy. Their scales are usually adequate for compressing the city's streets onto a sheet of paper, but are inconveniently small for a pedestrian trying to get around in a specific neighborhood. There is no visual information or color-coding other than microscopic lines and street names. High levels of map-reading abilities are scarce everywhere, and very scarce in many developing countries.

Most bus systems can provide more adequate orientation, by

making the routes themselves more intelligible, and by improving on the visual communications schemes used in metros (see Chapter 9).

Flexibility

Flexibility has two dimensions: the number of routes the traveler may use to get from A to B by a given mode; and the number of pairs of distinct origins and destinations that can be reached by a given mode. The latter is often the more important dimension, and users prefer modes that offer high flexibility with few transfers.

Walking is the most flexible mode, both with regard to routes and pairs of origins and destinations. It is the only truly "door-to-door" form of personal transportation, capable of reaching virtually any street, alley, building, or individual room in any building, often by a large number of alternative routes. Bicycling rates a close second, with the private car in a more distant, but still respectable third. Walking's flexibility is such an important component of urban transport that walking complements virtually all other trips, for distances ranging from a few steps for the cyclist to fairly long distances for the transit user.

Buses are normally constrained to fixed routes. Bus stops and stations also have fixed locations and are limited in number. Routes can, however, be altered and extended quickly, easily, and at modest cost. Trolley buses are limited to paths where their overhead power lines (catenaries) are located, and trains are constrained to the paths provided by their rails. The extension of trolleybus systems requires additional power stations and catenaries; increasing the number of rail lines and stations may require large-scale demolition or burrowing. Streetcars are an intermediate case between the trolleybuses and urban passenger trains.

Transit operations rely heavily on complementary walking to provide a minimally acceptable degree of flexibility. Among transit modes, high-performance trains are the most vulnerable on this account. Their enormous dead weight and the high cost of constructing lines and stations make it doubly uneconomic to have closely spaced stations to serve areas with low population densities. For many urban areas, the distance to a station is often great enough to require a bicycle ride rather than walking at one or both ends of the trip. There is a crucial, but oft-forgotten message here: transit cannot succeed unless there are adequate conditions for complementary, nonmotorized trips.

Frequency

Frequency can be measured in vehicles per hour on a given route, or, inversely, in minutes between opportunities for boarding a vehicle on that route. For walking, cycling and—when nearby parking is available—the private car, the "vehicle" is always available; for buses and trains, it often is not. In Rio de Janeiro, I once rode a "suburban" train whose frequency was once a day, each way. In the same city, a metro train on Line 1 comes by about once every three minutes.

Bus routes also show a great deal of variation. On highly traveled routes, a bus may be available every minute, but intervals are typically much longer. Comparatively, if similar levels of ridership are served by bus and train, buses usually offer more frequent service.

Punctuality

Punctuality is expressed by such measures as the maximum and average number of minutes of delay in leaving a stop or station after the scheduled time. The punctuality of departure of cars, bikes, and walking is under the exclusive control of their users. Their punctuality of arrival depends partially on traffic conditions, but they can compensate for possible delays by leaving earlier. The transit user depends on the operator and, with buses, on traffic conditions.

Modern electric train systems with adequate maintenance and control facilities are very punctual. There is a corresponding high cost that has prevented upgrading some of the older systems. Rio's suburban commuting trains reached a deplorable state in the 1960s and 1970s, for example, and large sums have since been spent to upgrade them. Automatic traffic control is in place on some of the more heavily traveled sections, and the electric trains are reasonably modern and reliable. But other sections still operate in extremely crowded and precarious conditions. Although the state operating company does not release statistics on the matter (for obvious reasons), it is common knowledge that a number of trains on the more precarious sections are simply canceled every day. José Álvaro Moisés and Verena Martinez-Alier (1977) drew together extensive documentation from newspaper reports to show how accidents or long delays, breakdowns or suspension of service on numerous occasions touched off riots by irate passengers who faced dismissal or having their pay docked for late arrival at work. Although a few passengers are usually injured in the rioting, the targets of the violence are the source of the irritation—the trains, equipment, and stations. There is a clear and oft-ignored message here too: where physical conditions are poor, the operator must promptly inform passengers the reason for the delay and its expected duration. If the delay is serious, the operator should quickly arrange for free bus transportation. In the Rio incidents, passengers are often left stranded in overcrowded rail cars in suffocating heat for over two hours with no communication from the operator.

Buses in mixed urban traffic have difficulty adhering to schedules. The operating company can deal with the problem by varying the number of buses (if frequency is high enough, departure punctuality is irrelevant), and controlling departure at the beginning of the route to avoid "bunching" of vehicles at later stops. Unless operators have exclusive lanes or busways, they are at the mercy of congestion, accidents, and inclement weather (another point to which we shall return).

Comfort

Comfort is a subjective perception, yet most of its underlying factors can be objectively measured, such as the temperature, illumination, and noise level within vehicles and stations, and the number of persons per square meter of floor space.

Related amenities are also important. Simple checklists and qualitative grades are usually enough to judge their adequacy, although more sophisticated scales can be developed. Some of the relevant factors are the availability and cleanliness of bathrooms for pedestrians and transit users; the absence of obstructions, holes, or craters in walkways and transitways; places for the pedestrian to rest in the shade and find refuge from inclemencies; access to public telephones and to sources of potable water, refreshments, newspapers, and the like.

Automobiles, especially more spacious ones with heaters and air conditioners, score very highly on such factors, while other modes vary a great deal in their performance. Modern rail systems perform well in this respect, with commuter rail and buses lagging far behind. These are not fixed parameters, however, bus services can offer metro-quality levels of comfort. Pedestrians, transit users, and cyclists are generally (but not always) at a disadvantage, and proper care can diminish that disadvantage. We return to this topic in Chapter 9, but as a preview I observe that engineers are *not* obligated to design highly dangerous crossings or to maximize the size of the puddle in front of the bus stop.

Ease of Carrying Things

Most travelers carry burdens that are intimately related to their reason for traveling. A list of some of the most commonplace items includes purses, lunches, luggage, groceries, books, tools, briefcases, shopping bags, and extra clothes, not to mention small children. A number of vendors must also transport their wares over part of their daily journeys.

The automobile obviously scores very well on this characteristic and transit very poorly. Walking is a very distant last, even with the use of backpacks. Bicycles cannot match the car, but with proper adaptations can be impressive cargo vehicles in their own right.

Travel Time

Total travel time spent getting from A to B is inversely related to average travel speed. In this case, average speed, not maximal or marginal, is the relevant measure. Maximum speeds impress the observer and the media emphasize them unduly, leaving subliminal images that often contrast with the actual average speeds of modes.

The component that has received the most attention is vehicle speed after the passenger boards. This component of average speed varies greatly with traffic congestion and other conditions that seldom affect transit systems with exclusive rights-of-way. Average speed, however, should include other time components of the trip: time to get to the station, waiting time to board the vehicle, transfer time, and time for the traveler to get from the vehicle's stopping point to the final destination.

Alan Pisarski (1987) recently studied U.S. commuting times by different modes based on the 1980 Census. Given his caveats regarding the quality, scope, and utility of the data, the average transit user spends about 42 minutes getting to work, compared to half that, or 21 minutes, for the private vehicle user. The differences are attributable to speeds rather than distance. Average speeds by mode are: private car and motorcycle, 51 km/h (32 mph); railroad, 37 km/h; subway, 22 km/h; bus/streetcar, 21 km/h; taxi, 20 km/h; bicycle, 13 km/h; walking, 2 km/h.

The relatively high speeds for cars reflect the small percentage of travel in city centers in total U.S. commuting travel and overstate the car's advantage with respect to transit in some areas. The very low speed for walking indicates that pedestrians are suffering a great deal of delay and interference from motorized traffic at crossings (healthy adults on unimpeded routes usually walk at about 4–5 km/h or 2.5–3 mph). Some walkers also have limited mobility or may include time spent buying coffee or newspapers, or window shopping when reporting the time spent getting to work.

Private car speeds in more densely populated areas are much lower: 35 km/h (22 mph) in New York (lower still in downtown Manhattan); 44 km/h for the average of five Australian cities; 45 km/h in Moscow; 30 km/h for twelve European cities; 30 km/h for Singapore; 21 km/h for Tokyo and Hong Kong (Newman and Kenworthy 1988: 170). In London in 1980, average surface traffic speed was 20 km/h and falling (Goldsack 1982).

Rush-hour speeds are slower yet, as are average speeds in many cities in developing countries. Mexico City has almost completely gridlocked, and I recently took an hour to travel 5 kilometers by car in downtown São Paulo during the evening rush hour—the speed of a healthy pedestrian. In Manila, gridlock has become an art form, and Bangkok's street network is known as the world's largest parking lot.

These data demonstrate that the private car is not necessarily a rapid alternative to other modes. In densely populated cities, it can easily fall behind the metro. When buses are given exclusive lanes in congested areas, they can also become faster than automobiles, despite stops for passengers' boarding and alighting.

The relative speed of modes should consider the distance to be covered, plus the time needed to get to the vehicle and from it to the final destination (plus parking time for cars). Walking is usually faster than the car for perhaps some 400 meters (437 yds.)—depending largely on the time lost getting to and parking the car. Somewhere between 20 and 400 meters, the cyclist overtakes the pedestrian, having overcome the delay of getting to the bicycle and unlocking it. The car and the bicycle dominate after some 400 meters. In normal city traffic, the car overtakes the bike at around 1.5 kilometers (just under a mile), and transit overtakes the pedestrian at a similar distance. Beyond 1.5 km, walking is seldom speed-competitive if alternative means of transportation are at hand, and the relative speed ranking places cars first, trains second, and either buses or bicycles in third. Nonetheless, if there is considerable congestion for motorized traffic and an exclusive bikeway at hand, the bicycle can easily move into first or second place over much longer distances, and the car may fall back to second, third, or even fourth.

Bicycles seldom appear at the top of the long-distance speed hierarchy since they are usually left out of transportation surveys and, in any case, seldom enjoy an exclusive bikeway over longer distances. Yet examples may be found. John Wilcockson (1980: 14) outpaced cars over distances from 10 to 25 km (6 to 15.5 miles) in his trips on London streets and, in my days as a doctoral student, I regularly left class by bicycle and arrived home, some 3 km away, before my classmates and neighbors, who went by car. Presently, at age 46 and over the hill as an athlete, I can pedal at nearly 30 km/h (19 mph) on level terrain for a half-hour (15 km or 9 miles of cycling); I can maintain 12–20 km/h indefinitely when in street clothes without tiring or perspiring heavily. Even the less-demanding speed is comparable or superior to motor-vehicle speeds in densely populated cities, and can be valid for distances of 5, 10 or 15 km.

Buses often perform well when they are given exclusive use of a traffic lane in a congested area. Urban and intercity buses share such an exclusive lane on Rio's Brasil Avenue. At times, I have been on one of these buses, traveling at 70 km/h (44 mph) and watching the stalled cars on the other lanes. The exclusive bus lane on Santo Amaro and 9 de Julho avenues in São Paulo reduced bus passengers' travel time by 30 to 45 minutes each way, and added about 10 minutes to car trips (Sá and Padovani 1987: 8–14). For some routes and times, the buses outpace cars and taxis, despite the intermediate stops.

The data cited earlier show trains traveling faster than buses or bicycles. High average train speeds, however, require long distances between stations. In urban settings stations are normally only 300 to 600 m apart, and the stops lower the average to, say, the 30 km/h found on both Rio's metro and suburban commuter trains (the latter have fewer stops but inferior equipment). If total travel time is taken into account (adding in waiting and walking), cycling becomes competitive for healthy adults for intermediate distances. On exclusive bikeways, the athletically inclined could probably outpedal the train for any urban distance.

If buses enjoy exclusive rights-of-way, they can compete with trains on overall travel time. Buses can operate at speeds similar to trains while reducing the distances that users walk through greater geographical coverage.

We conclude our analysis of speed with an insightful comment by Ivan Illich (1974). He considers a car owner who travels some 12,000 kilometers a year (7,500 miles) (a reasonable figure for many countries, although below the U.S. average of about 16,000 kilometers a year per car). The motorist spends about 4 hours a day in car-related activities—driving, parking, repairing, and cleaning the car, filling the gas tank, and, most important, working to pay for its purchase and upkeep. That amounts to 1,460 hours per year, yielding an average speed of about 8 km/h or 5 mph, only slightly better than the pedestrian and below that of the cyclist.

A Summary of Modal Characteristics and Performance

A useful way to summarize our analysis of modes is by reexamining Table 1, reproduced here as Table 6. This table should now have a

Table 6
Qualitative Performance of Transport Modes

	Mode			
Characteristic	*Walking*	*Cycling*	*Transit*	*Car*
Characteristics Important to Society				
Greater capacity/area	S	S	S	P
Greater energy efficiency	S	S	S	P
Less air pollution	S	S	S–I	P
Less noise	S	S	S–P	P
Better aesthetics	S	S	S–P	I–P
Less vulnerability of system	S	S	P	P
Greater sustainability of system	S	S	I	P
Less public expense	S	S	S–P	I–P
More healthful	S	S	I–P	P
Fewer serious accidents	S–P	I–P	S–I	P
Characteristics Important Primarily to Individuals				
Lower costs to users	S	S	S–I	P
Better personal microenvironment	S	S	P	S
Greater flexibility	S	S	P	S
Higher frequency	S	S	S–P	S
Greater punctuality	S	S	S–P	S
Greater comfort	S–P	S–P	S–P	S
Better orientation	S	S	S–P	S–I
Ease of carrying things	I–P	S–P	S–P	S
Less total travel time (Approximate ranges)				
Up to 400 meters	S	S	I–P	I
400–1,500 meters	I–P	S–I	S–P	S–I
Beyond 1,500 meters	P	S–P	S–I	S

Source: Adopted from Wright (1988:72).

Notes: S = Satisfactory or Superior; I = Intermediate; P = Poor; common variations in performance that are dependent on highly variable and specific circumstances are indicated by a range (e.g., S–P = performance ranges from superior to poor on this characteristic); grades represent somewhat favorable circumstances for the modes but with no special compensation for disadvantages each mode typically faces.

much deeper meaning for the reader than when it was first presented. The intervening discussion should also have clarified many doubts regarding the relative classifications and the variations in performance.

Walking and cycling have high grades for all public interest characteristics except serious accidents. Much better segregation of nonmotorized traffic from motor vehicles is required before we can responsibly encourage wider use of these modes in urban areas. Walking and cycling in segregated areas, along with improved forms of transit, can enhance overall traffic safety; they perform well on all other public interest variables. Transit without proper integration with nonmotorized traffic has a disappointing performance, although still superior to the private car.

The car, however, performs superbly with regard to the characteristics that influence the transport user's choice of mode for a given trip, provided that family income is high enough to permit this luxury. Transit performs very poorly on all modal choice characteristics except cost. It may even lose on this characteristic in high-income areas if the implicit value of lost time is accounted for.

Only the nonmotorized modes perform well on both public interest and modal choice characteristics. They have important limitations, nonetheless, including safety and walking's handicaps in traveling longer distances and carrying burdens. For cycling, distance and carrying capacity are much less of a limitation. Comfort is at times a problem for both walking and cycling.

The qualitative grades given in the table are neither static nor immutable. They depend to a large measure on public policy. Our goal is to find affordable options for enhancing positive characteristics and alleviating the effects of negative characteristics in the total transportation picture.

Chapter 7

Modes of Urban Transportation

with Howard M. Bunch

MODES ARE A MEANS of producing characteristic sets—a dynamic, elastic concept rather than a static classification. We now consider modes in a more formal sense, including some additional modes and their approximate costs and capacities.

A transportation mode is composed of a given type of vehicle, the travelway it uses, and the complementary equipment necessary for it to operate. The universal mode, walking, is comprised of: pedestrian(s), sidewalks, streets and other paths, traffic signals and signs. Cycling differs by substituting a pedal bicycle and adding the possibility of a bikeway in that same definition. Cars and buses use streets, arteries, and expressways and the same control and signaling devices. Cars and buses differ in the size of the vehicles, ownership, and operating procedures. A metro is composed of: rail cars and tractive unit (some cars have built-in tractive units), the tracks, stations, and yards, systems of signaling and traffic control.

Complementary services, such as administration and policing, are also required, and operational procedures vary considerably. These factors provide finer distinctions and are occasionally used as a basis for more detailed classifications. Many of these elements overlap, however, resulting in a lack of consensus regarding which differences define a separate mode (Vuchic 1981: 65). The complementary services and the way, for example, may be shared in whole or in part with other modes. Policing and roadway intersections are regularly shared by pedestrian, bicycle, car, and bus traffic. Streetcars divide road space with all other forms of road traffic, and buses and trains may share a guideway, as occurs on the O-Bahn, in Essen, Germany.

Even apparently distinctive details are likely to be ambiguous when examined closely: a train or metro generally conjures up the image of a series of large, heavy cars with steel wheels operating on steel rails. The metros in Montreal and Santiago, however, use rubber tires operating on concrete surfaces to enhance acceleration; in Essen and Adelaide,[1] buses operate on fixed guideways and in articulated units. Technical distinctions begin to blur: the O-Bahn buses clearly fit one of the dictionary definitions of a train as an articulated series of vehicles.

Initially, we will classify modes in terms of access (private or public), propulsion (nonmotorized or motorized) and capacity in relation to the area they occupy. A private vehicle is one normally used only to transport the owner (or a firm's employees). A public vehicle is one that transports anyone who wishes to ride, usually upon payment of a fare. The fare may be a flat rate on a fixed route or vary in accord with the route, distance, number of passengers, and other factors. Types of payment and service can also be used to create subclassifications of transit modes, but we will consider them merely as variations in the operational procedures of certain more basic modes.

Based on the private–public, nonmotorized–motorized, and capacity distinctions, the modal classifications are:

Private, non-motorized: walking, cycling, and animal-drawn vehicles. Walking and cycling have high capacities (for example, above 1,000 persons per meter per hour); animal-powered conveyances have low capacities (below 500 persons per meter per hour as a guess—they are seldom studied).

Private, motorized: cars, vans, company buses, motorcycles. Cars and probably motorcycles have low capacities; multipassenger cars and vans, intermediate capacities (above 500, below 1,000 persons per meter per hour); buses, intermediate-to-high capacities, depending on the size of the vehicle and operating conditions. Carpools and vanpools on expressways can move into the lower range of high-capacity modes.

Public, nonmotorized: rickshaws, pedicabs. They are common in Asia and, although neglected in most engineering studies, appear to have capacities intermediate between walking and cars. They transport both goods and passengers, and require much less space than cars for parking but more than bicycles.

Public, motorized: taxis; vans, jitneys, and similar conveyances; streetcars; buses; rail transit systems (excluding streetcars). The
order of each mode in this list corresponds to its approximate
ranking with regard to capacity/area, from the low-capacity,
single-party taxi to the high-capacity rail transit systems.

An Expanded List of Transit Modes

Data on capacity for several of these modes under different operating
conditions were presented in Chapter 3. Here we extend the analysis
to include more public modes and variations in operating conditions
and rights-of-way, a process that requires some brief definitions and
descriptions of the modes involved.

The term *transit* includes any public, multipassenger vehicle
and the associated infrastructure. The most common forms in developed countries are taxis, minibus and bus transit, guided transit, and
rail transit. Many countries also have jitneys, vans, and shared taxis;
these are considered "transit" or "paratransit" only when they carry
fare-paying riders. *Paratransit* is a term used to designate vehicles with
flexible fares and lack of fixed itinerary; for obvious reasons, these are
usually small vehicles. We discuss paratransit in Chapter 9.

Bus Transit Systems

The most useful classification for bus transit systems depends
on the degree of exclusiveness of their rights-of-way (ROWs) and the
presence or absence of guide mechanisms:[2]

Mixed traffic. The lowest capacity and performance of bus
transit systems are found in *mixed* traffic, typical of operation on ordi-
nary city streets. This corresponds to Class III ROWs, that is, those
with no physical separation of buses from other vehicles, either longi-
tudinally or at intersections. Some bus systems have priority signaling
at intersections: a bus activates a signal as it approaches a traffic light:
it receives a green light and other traffic receives a red light. Class III
ROWs include lanes reserved for high-occupancy vehicles (HOVs),
such as shared taxis, carpools, and vanpools, in addition to buses. A
reserved lane is usually indicated only by means of signs and symbols,
such as a white diamond, painted on the surface of the lane itself. Such
lanes are easily invaded by other vehicles and are frequently ignored

and eventually abandoned. They occasionally work adequately on longer multilane freeway sections, but tend to be ineffective on city streets where cars enter and exit at each corner and bus passengers board from the sidewalk rather than the median area. Examples of the first category include a section of I-66 near Washington, D.C., and on I-5 in Seattle. Its problems on city streets are exemplified by a short stretch of Glen Avenue–Fuller Road in Ann Arbor and by the "Little Axes" in Brasília. The Ann Arbor reserve lane is still indicated by signs and fading diamonds, but is ignored by car drivers. The Brasília reserve lane was formally abandoned a few months after implementation; the right lane of a two-lane one-way street was reserved for buses, but all other traffic also entered and exited from the right side. Peak-hour traffic made it difficult for a car entering the street to move over into the left lane or, once there, to get back to the right lane in time to exit (miniature cloverleafs for entering and exiting are spaced at 500-meter intervals). Lane-switching became a major nuisance and probably increased the number of accidents, although to my knowledge no data were published on this aspect.

HOV lanes can work somewhat better if other restrictions keep single-passenger cars out. Examples include routes within a college campus area that lead basically to a bus stop, with no parking or other facilities to attract private cars. In such cases, these lanes may resemble low-grade busways more than reserved lanes.

Bus-only lanes. These are still on Class III ROWs and are like HOVs except that only buses are allowed. Bus-only lanes are difficult to successfully implant due to the protests of other drivers who want to use the lane and the likelihood that they will invade it with their vehicles if police control is insufficient. This reaction is caused by the obvious reduction of road space available for other vehicles; it becomes an almost insurmountable problem for transit authorities when there are few buses on the lane. When bus traffic is intense enough to justify an exclusive lane, there is a tendency to provide physical separation of some sort, transforming it into a busway.

Busways. These may be roadways specially built for buses, or lanes protected from penetration from pedestrians and other vehicles by curbs, other barriers, or grade separation. Physical separation of buses from other traffic between intersections elevates the ROWs to the semi-exclusive Class II. Exclusive (Class I) ROWs are obtained when this longitudinal separation is accompanied by elimination of at-grade intersections. Sometimes Class I ROWs are obtained by the less-reliable alternative of installing gates or other barriers to guarantee exclusivity at intersections. An exclusive (Class I ROW) busway will have its own access and exit facilities along with a special roadway or physically separated lane. Examples of exclusive and semi-exclusive busways are found in Pittsburgh, Houston, Los Angeles (El Monte), and in a number of Brazilian cities, such as São Paulo, Rio de Janeiro, and Curitiba.

Guided busways. Prefabricated concrete slabs with an **L** on each side of approximately 18 centimeters (7 inches) height are placed on compacted soils on each side of the busway. Buses or trolleybuses that enter the guided busway have small lateral rollers mounted on all steerable wheels that press outward against the up-side of the **L**. The rollers take over the steering function from the driver, who controls only the acceleration and braking. At least three types of lateral rollers are available: two types are extended by the bus driver upon approaching the guided section, while the third is permanently positioned slightly to the back of and slightly outside the front wheels. The third type removes the danger of the driver forgetting to extend the rollers or doing so at the wrong time. All of the systems depend on simple mechanical devices, that is, they require no sophisticated or expensive electronic devices.

Guided busways have the advantage of placing the vehicle on a precisely defined path. By eliminating driver error in positioning the bus, the guideway saves considerable space on curves and permits the reduction of the longitudinal lane width to 2.6 m (2.8 yds.), as opposed to the usual 3.7 m (4 yds.). For a two-way bus operation on an avenue, this adds an extra 2 m of badly needed space that can be used for passenger boarding and to widen sidewalks. The reduction in lateral movement yields a much smoother ride and greater passenger comfort. When trolleybuses use the guideways, comfort equals that of the best urban rail systems.

The increased precision also permits the use of platforms for boarding and alighting. If buses are equipped with wider doors and level floors (eliminating steps), boarding and alighting operations can approximate those of rail transit, a major factor in enabling bus systems to reduce or to eliminate rail's advantage of higher capacity to area.

Guideways for buses can be built in existing urban settings much more easily than can conventional urban rail transit. Since buses are able to climb fairly steep grades and turn sharp corners, guideways can be placed in many streets and avenues. They do not have to be continuous, since the bus (or trolleybus) operates in the traditional fashion before entering the guided section, at shared intersections and upon leaving the guided part of the route. Bus guideways can thus be built and used in a piecemeal fashion as funds become available, in contrast to rail transit systems, which require that entire lines be completed before any services can be inaugurated.

Various bus sizes and combinations. In many cities, buses have typically been of a fairly large, standard size. However, minibuses are better suited for tasks such as serving low density and flexible routes, navigating narrow streets, and transporting the handicapped. Articulated buses (with the tractive unit pulling one or two trailers) offer high-capacity service on more densely traveled routes, especially during peak hours. Articulated buses can be seen in many European cities, such as Hamburg, and are common in Brazil's major cities.

Some of the earlier articulated vehicles presented problems with vertical and horizontal swaying in the rear of the trailers. Several manufacturers have developed models that reduce tracking, stability, and swaying problems encountered with towing. At least one has adopted a tractor-trailer configuration similar to that perfected for highway freight transportation (*Mass Transit* 1984: 22–23). In Brazil, an articulated bus with a single trailer unit can transport up to 180 passengers (including standees); European versions with two trailers can accommodate about 230 passengers. If ticket purchase and verification is placed outside the bus, this reduces on-vehicle labor requirements per passenger to metrolike levels.

The bus transit category includes several propulsion technologies aside from the conventional diesel engine. Electric buses, or trolleybuses, are perhaps the best known, but most of the alternative fuels described in Chapter 4 can be used with adapted versions of Otto-cycle and diesel engines. There are also hybrid or dual vehicles; they operate on electricity on sections with catenaries, and use diesel engines upon leaving those sections. Technically, these vehicles present no major problems; they reduce noise and pollution along the more densely populated stretches of a route, without the high cost of electrifying the whole route. The hybrids' investment costs are higher, however, and they are heavier and more expensive to operate than either a conventional diesel bus or a conventional electric bus. Their disadvantages are analogous to those of amphibious vehicles. A plane, for example, can be designed to land and take off from water, but it is not a very good plane and performs miserably as a boat.

Guided Transit

This category of transport includes a wide variety of systems whose distinguishing characteristic is full automation without drivers or attendants on board:

Monorail transit. (Some of the smaller and older systems are not fully automated, but we include the category here anyway.) A straddle monorail system operates on exclusive, Class I ROWs composed of a single rail, usually in the form of a concrete beam that also serves as the conduit for the energy supply and traffic control mechanisms. The monorail vehicle rides astride the beam; the single vehicle and two-car unit are the most common configurations. Suspended monorail systems are rare. They require more expensive support systems and have problems with wear at the suspension points.

Straddle-type monorails are often thought of as rail transit vehicles. Their rubber tires, however, distinguish them from conventional steel-wheel-on-steel-rail systems. By analogy, they may be thought of as elevated trolleybuses with very short axles designed to place them on a narrow, 80-centimeter-wide concrete beam.

A set of horizontal wheels applies counterpendular pressure to the sides of the beam to keep the vehicle from falling off. With other things constant, this increases cost, weight, friction, and energy loss in the monorail operation beyond, say, a guided trolleybus (elevated or otherwise).

Monorail technology requires moving a section of the entire beam to switch lines, a time-consuming process that makes it difficult to develop a network of monorails. As a result, their applications tend to be limited to loops or shuttle-type services within the downtown area, at amusement parks and expos, or airport to downtown, where most monorails now in operation are located (for example, Disney World, Yokohama Dreamland, and the airport to downtown Tokyo).[3] Japan, however, has 8.4 kilometers of double track in Kitakyushu in use as an urban transport mode, with several others in various stages of planning or implementation. The Japanese try to use monorails in urban transport since they can be built in the median of highways, become legally part of the roadway, and qualify for subsidies from highway funds.

Most straddle-type monorails operate with maximum flows up to 6,000 persons per hour per direction, although higher capacities are possible. They are expensive: despite the free ROWs in Japan, the average cost of four recent systems was some $60 million/km ($97 million/mile), with half of that cost for the guideway (Kikuchi and Onaka 1988: 33).

Minimetro systems. Similar to rapid rail transit (see below), except for full automation and shorter trains and platforms (and, in some cases, smaller cars), capacity for minimetros is something on the order of 10,000 to 20,000 passengers/hour per direction. Most of these systems use conventional electric traction, but linear induction (Chapter 4) is a proven alternative. When the technology of minimetro systems is proprietary, it may be classified under automated guided transit (below), rather than as a separate category.

Automated guided transit (AGT). These systems might be better denominated "proprietary AGTs," since ownership is what distinguishes this category from guided transit. AGT systems have, at the upper end, capacities that approach 10,000 persons/hour per direction and monorail-type operation, and, at the lower end, very limited capacity cable car systems that operate at low speeds and have room for only about two or three passengers per car.

The proprietary aspect means that a city interested in one of these systems has to purchase it from the manufacturer. Some manufacturers include Walt Disney, LTV-Vought (Dallas–Fort Worth, airport), Westinghouse (Atlanta, airport; Busch Gardens, Virginia, amusement park; Miami, airport), Otis Elevator (Duke University, campus), Boeing (Morgantown, West Virginia; campus), Sür Coester (Jakarta, city park); Soulé Corporation (Paris-Nord, expo); and TAXI 2000.

The automated facet implies that no operators are on board the vehicle. All operations (including opening and closing doors, accelerating, stopping, and announcing arrival at stations) are controlled from a central command post with the aid of computers. This requires exclusive ROWs, and one common way of obtaining them is to build the system as an elevated structure. This obviously economizes labor costs for in-vehicle operators, but may require relatively more staff in the control room and security functions than alternative rail and bus options.

Almost all AGT systems (including the planned versions) are loop or shuttle operations, and may present obstacles to networking. Some of the low capacity systems, such as TAXI 2000 (Anderson 1988), attempt to introduce flexibility with the use of small units and networking through off-line stations. To date, however, none of the very low-capacity, small-car systems has ever ventured outside of the EXPO or amusement park areas into an urban traffic setting. The cost of the Soulé version is listed in the manufacturer's brochures at $5 to $12.5 million/km ($8–$20 million/mile) without civil works. An intermediate speed and capacity option, the Detroit People Mover, cost $42.3 million/km ($68 million/mile), with $17.7 million/km for the guideway alone (Nelson 1990). With two 100-passenger cars in each train and headways of 2 minutes, the DPM could transport some 6,000 persons/hour. As these systems approach monorail capacities, they are also likely to approach the monorail costs of $60 million/km.

Loop operations have a disadvantage for travelers who want to go to a station or two behind their boarding place: since the train only goes in one direction, they must travel virtually the entire loop to get to their destination. A 5-minute walk becomes a 15-minute ride.

The Sür Coester Aeromóvel (or "Airtrain") is a revolutionary variation on the monorail (Coester 1990; Rogers 1989, 1990; Sür Coester 1988). This experience started with a short experimental stretch in the Brazilian city of Porto Alegre in the early 1980s with governmental support, but is now essentially a commercial enterprise with a more realistic 3.2-kilometer line in operation in a large park in Jakarta, Indonesia. The operation in Jakarta reveals that the Aeromóvel has overcome most if not all the formidable research and development problems involved in establishing a new transport system and, like linear induction, may soon be regarded as a proven technology.

Unlike the rubber tire versions of monorails with their heavy motors and suspension systems, the Aeromóvel runs on two steel rails (1.6-m gauge, although narrower versions are acceptable). It has no motor or other heavy appendices on board. This reduces vehicle weight to about a third that of a conventional rail car while retaining about the same passenger capacity. Wear of moving parts is also greatly reduced by the lower weight. The force to move the Aeromóvel is provided by an inverted sail or plate placed in the hollow concrete beam (monorail) that provides the support and guideway for the vehicle. Large industrial fans are used along the beam to provide low-pressure aeolian power on the sail or plate. Switching, acceleration and braking are controlled by opening and closing ducts, using computer-controlled hydraulic levers. The switching operations mimic those of conventional rail systems, so Aeromóvel routes can be joined as a network much more easily than conventional monorails. If the plates are firmly attached to the cars, serious collisions are nearly impossible; as two cars or units are brought closer together, the plates compress the air between them, automatically acting as a brake.

Some energy is lost due to the inability to completely seal the spaces between the plate and the hollow concrete beam, and between the slit on the upper side of the beam and the shaft that connects the plate to the rail car. These losses probably offset the gains from the decreased weight of the vehicles, leaving the Aeromóvel about as energy-efficient per seat km as most rail transit options (unfortunately, as we saw in Chapter 4, good data on energy usage are hard to find and compare). Each car or set of articulated cars operates as a unit, providing high-frequency service. The cars can go up steep grades (10 percent) and make sharp turns (radius of 25 m or 27 yd.). Since there are to date no urban transportation experiences with the Aeromóvel technology (several cities are considering it along with other options), it is difficult to estimate capacity and cost for the Aeromóvel in an urban setting. Capacity might reach, say, 10,000 persons per direction per hour. The cost of the Jakarta Aeromóvel for all guideway, station, vehicle, and other components was $4 million/km ($6.4 million/mile) (ROWs were free). It is, however, a loop system. As a guess, the firm's cost for a two-way line might be about $10 million/km if we include the cost of stations in urban areas and elevators for the handicapped. Additional costs for ROWs and other local requirements could obviously make the system considerably more expensive.

Rail Transit

This category is very broad, ranging from the low-capacity and relatively low-cost streetcar up through full-fledged rapid rail transit systems:

Light rail transit (LRT). This technology varies from streetcars to more sophisticated rail systems with exclusive ROWs. The word *light* (unless applied to some streetcars) is a misnomer, as most LRT systems have cars with weights identical or similar to those of "heavy" systems. They differ from the latter by having fewer cars in each train and lower frequencies. LRTs are usually predominantly surface rail systems, although they may have elevated or subway sections.

The change from streetcars to higher-capacity forms of rail transit requires complete separation of track from other vehicles and pedestrians. Rapid rail systems enjoy exclusive ROWs: all crossings and interference from other modes are eliminated by grade separation or effective horizontal barriers, so that the rail system can operate in its own controlled environment.

As discussed in the next chapter, the lack of segregated facilities was the cause of the modest capacity and performance of streetcars at the turn of the century. These factors, along with technological obsolescence of the older streetcar systems, contributed to their worldwide retraction during the middle decades of this century, and to their virtual disappearance from the Americas.

Nostalgia, however, can be a powerful force. Quite recently, a group of technicians at the Brazilian Urban Transport Company (EBTU 1988) attempted to conceptualize an ideal vehicle for public transport in Brazil's growing cities. They reasoned that the vehicle should be relatively inexpensive and able to travel in mixed traffic, achieve speeds of 60 km/h, use signalized street intersections, climb moderate to steep grades, have a short turning radius, and have a high transport capacity.

This was a fair description of the semi-exclusive busways that the EBTU had helped implant in several cities, but some technicians insisted that the vehicle be of the steel-wheel-on-steel-rail variety—a streetcar that could later be upgraded into a light rail system and, eventually, a full-blown metro.

There were two main problems. First, rail vehicles can meet any one of those standards, but no single rail vehicle can meet all of them simultaneously. For example, a streetcar can turn sharply, but only at low speeds; it can travel at higher speeds, but these are incompatible with dangerous at-level intersections shared by cars, trucks, and buses; it can carry reasonably high passenger volumes, but only on exclusive ROWs. Also, there is no easy way of "upgrading" a streetcar system to a metro with exclusive ROWs.

The capacity of a system should not be calculated without taking into account interference from other traffic. In many situations, low performance in terms of flexibility, speed, and frequency will also result in lack of passenger demand for the available capacity. Theoretically, line capacities for streetcars are thought to range up to 12,000 persons/hour. Actual peak flows, however, seldom come near this figure due to both interference from other traffic and lack of demand. The peak flow listed in the *Highway Capacity Manual* is 9,000 persons/hour in Pittsburgh, and that was registered over a half-century ago; the San Francisco and Toronto lines managed only 4,900 and 4,200, respectively (Transportation Research Board 1985: 12.16, 12.18). Light rail systems with exclusive ROWs have capacities of up to 20,000 persons/line/hour, based on European experience, but in most settings such figures are unrealistically high. The *Highway Capacity Manual* lists the peak flow on a North American line at 9,000 in

Philadelphia in 1956. Few other light rails achieved even half of that volume, and San Diego registered a 1981 line peak of only 600 passengers/hour.

Rapid rail transit (RRT). These are high-speed, high-capacity systems, capable of carrying 40,000 to 60,000 persons/hour in one direction under conditions of crush loading. Examples include the subway systems of São Paulo, Tokyo, Moscow, and New York.

Rail systems have attracted a variety of additional names, introducing some confusion and several misnomers. *Metro* is commonly used throughout the world to designate both LRT and RRT. Although a bit imprecise, it is a welcome term. *Mass transit* is often used as a synonym for *metro,* an unfortunate choice, since buses, bicycles, walking, or even automobiles are more likely than a metro to transport the masses in any given city. The term *subway* was originally an accurate term that referred to underground rail systems. Semantically, it should not be used to refer to metros of the surface or elevated varieties, but *subway* is often used by laypersons to designate any metro. *Heavy rail* is an unfortunate synonym for RRT, since the trains and rails are usually no heavier than those of LRT systems. And the *rapid* in RRT usually means an average train speed (including stops) of only 30 km/h (19 mph); if the passenger's access, waiting, and egress time is accounted for, speed drops to bicycle levels or below.

Commuter rail systems. These are conventional intercity rail systems, with trains of up to 10 cars, and require correspondingly long stations. They normally offer a low degree of automation and frequency. Some still have diesel-powered locomotives.

In the Americas, most users have a negative image of commuter rail. In the Washington, D.C. area, Moshe Ben-Akiva and T. Morikawa (1990) found that riders would prefer a decent bus. In Rio de Janeiro, trains are crowded with low-income riders who cannot afford bus fares. Many of these users ride the buses for the first few days after receiving their paychecks, and switch back to rail at the end of the month as their money runs out (Moisés and Martinez-Alier 1977).

Some commuter rails, principally in Europe and Japan, feature few stops and exclusive ROWs. They may have cruising speeds of up to 130 km/h, and average speeds of up to 70 km/h. In general, however, speeds are unimpressive: the trains linking Rio to its suburbs are hard pressed to maintain average speeds over 30 km/h, and these speeds are probably typical of most other developing countries and some developed countries. Up-grading is likely to be limited to electrifying a few diesel operations and improving track and geometry.

Regional High Speed Rail Connections

Japan has a number of high-speed rail connections with few stops between a metropolitan area and more distant cities. With the possibilities of using magnetic levitation or another hyperspeed technology, trains may someday outpace air travel on intermediate distances. Presently the fastest Amtrack express train on the Northeast Corridor of the United States attains speeds of up to 200 km/h (125 mph) on some stretches (Nice 1989). Similar speeds are attained in several European countries and the French TGV can attain 300 km/h (186 mph). Experimental magnetic levitation systems have cruising speeds of nearly 500 km/h (311 mph); even these speeds do not approach the possible limits of this new technology. Currently Transrapid International (composed of the German firms of Krauss Maffei, MBB, and Thyssen Henschel) has plans to establish the first commercial mag-lev service by linking Disney World to Orlando's airport. The projected cost of $20 million/km ($32 million/mile) is less than that of many urban freeways. This cost, however, is for an interurban link, does not include ROWs, and is subject to verification in practice. Recent problems with the concession may delay or otherwise endanger the project. Prototypes have included a shuttle that carried 50,000 passengers at a transport expo in Hamburg in 1979 and another that has reached speeds of 495 km/h. Their reduced noise levels make them preferable to steel-on-steel technology in urban and suburban areas.

These systems are, however, unsuited for typical transit operations that involve stops at stations spaced at intervals of 300 to 600 m. The HSST Corporation's brochures present a scaled-down version with a maximum speed of 130 km/h (81 mph); this version is more suitable than the hyperspeed versions for stations spaced a few kilometers apart, but has a gross weight of 12 tons and only 16 seats—¾ ton per seat. Conventional support and guidance systems are likely to be much more energy- and cost-efficient in these circumstances. With closely spaced stops, passenger comfort places strict limits on acceleration and deceleration—especially for standees—eliminating the mag-lev advantage of speed.

Special Function and Exotic Modes

There are several other additional modes that have limited applicability in urban settings but deserve a brief mention.

Boats often provide regular transportation between urban areas separated by a river or large body of water where bridges either do not exist or have insufficient capacity. One of the more important examples is that of the large ferryboats and the faster, smaller craft that shuttle thousands of passengers daily across Guanabara Bay between Rio de Janeiro and Niterói. There are several dozen lesser but still significant examples in Brazil alone. In previous centuries, several European cities also relied on a significant flow of people along their canals. Currently, however, this traffic has faded even in Hamburg and Amsterdam. On occasion, water transportation in developing countries can serve as an economical and efficient substitute for expensive and winding routes of alternate land transport modes.

Inclined planes, funiculars, cable cars, and elevators are modes whose sole redeeming virtues are their local aesthetic or tourist appeal and their ability to scale very steep grades. Passenger stations (often quite informal) are located at the top and bottom of a steep hill. The vehicles normally operate in pairs moving in opposite directions; both are clamped to a moving cable that pulls one car upward and lowers the other one. Energy use is decreased to that required to overcome friction and any excess in upward-bound passengers' weight over that of the downward-bound (the weight of the latter helps raise the upward-bound car). Support and guidance systems are usually of the steel-wheel-on-steel-rail variety; some operate on a single track (two rails) with a double-track oval in the middle for passing, while others have a separate two-rail track for each car.

Salvador, Brazil, has an inclined plane and the oversize Lacerda elevator to provide important passenger links from its "High City" to the "Low City." The seaport of Valparaíso in Chile has a series of 13 inclined planes that serve as links from the sealevel business sectors to the residences located on the surrounding hills. Valparaíso's system dates from the first years of this century; while the stations have become quite dreary over the years, the basic function is still performed adequately. When I was there in 1984, Chile was implanting its market-oriented pricing strategies, and it cost the user 10 percent more to go up the inclined plane than to go down. (Such a policy can be justified either from the demand or the cost side.)

Some years ago, artists' sketches appeared in some books on transportation that depicted future scenarios of people flying between tall buildings with the aid of small rockets or propellers strapped to their backs. Such things might become technically feasible if someone were to invest enough money in their development. Such exotic modes are unlikely to become important urban transport options, however, due to the implied energy requirements, the noise and pollution expected from such apparatuses, and the predictably disastrous effects of transferring surface traffic congestion to urban airspace.

Some attempts to redesign the private car are more realistic, including solar-powered vehicles and small battery-powered electric cars. As shown earlier, however, these cars look suspiciously like an adult tricycle with a cover on it.

Chapter 8

Characteristics of Cities and Their Transport Users

ALL TOO OFTEN, transport modes are discussed in an isolated, purely technological setting. It is forgotten that they have to be placed in the urban environment in a way that is suitable to people in their dual roles as urban residents and transport users. Furthermore, modes must be affordable for both users and government. And in the longer term, they will influence the characteristics of the city itself and even the ways in which their citizens think and act.

A number of characteristics of cities are particularly relevant to transport plans and policies, including:

the population density;

the layout of major streets, avenues, and expressways, varying from a radial design that funnels movement toward the center, to a cobweb or grid that permits and even encourages movements from everywhere to everywhere else;

micro-level features that influence local traffic circulation patterns and traffic safety; and

the visual form, that is, the apparent clarity or "legibility" of the city, reflecting the degree to which people receive orientation or are disoriented by the street pattern, landmarks, and other characteristics of the urban setting (Lynch 1960);

historical, recreational, and aesthetic environments that are to be preserved or created;

the financial situation of the municipal government.

Each of these features is intertwined with the characteristics of the city's transport users, such as the value they place on maintaining the city's landmarks and aesthetic qualities. In addition, users' income levels, car-ownership patterns, and other features are closely tied to transport demand.

City Characteristics

Rather than examining these characteristics one by one, we will consider them jointly in the context of how transportation modes and modern cities have evolved and what their present patterns imply for urban transportation.

From the beginning of civilization until the first decades of the twentieth century, personal travel in cities was predominantly done by walking, occasionally supplemented with pack or draught animals. This applied to both personal travel and the movement of household, commercial, and industrial goods. The street was an extension of the urbanite's home, a place where friends met casually or by design, conversations were held, business transacted (Berman 1982).

Most important cities were located on or near a river front, seaport, or lake shore that, in addition to furnishing water, greatly facilitated commerce with other cities and countries. The problems with land transportation and the need for break-bulk operations encouraged location of industry, commerce, and services in the immediate surroundings, providing an economic base for population growth. The larger cities of most countries are still found on such sites. Cities had to be compact, since slow and expensive horse and human power were the only means of transporting goods away from the rail stations and docks. In many European cities, the majority of the population lived within the cramped areas circumscribed by the city walls.

The waterside location and other topographical features of cities have often been responsible for irregular street patterns. Some medieval cities were also constructed with little regard for geometry (Berman 1982: 177). Nonetheless, with walking as the predominant urban transport mode and the limited range of pedestrian traffic, surveyors, city planners, and others attempted to reduce the distances between all points of the city and maximize the legibility of the street pattern. These efforts were subject to the constraints of topography, preservation of rectangular spaces for buildings, and other factors.

The grid pattern of parallel and perpendicular streets and avenues with fairly short blocks served these purposes well. A straight street minimizes construction problems and provides a convenient route to all adjacent houses and buildings, and to any establishment on the other side of the street. Neighboring streets may be reached either from the back door or by going to the corner. Alleys provide convenient shortcuts, and a large number of alternative paths of equal distance are available for any trip of several blocks, making it possible to do business at a large number of intermediate points with relatively little increase in distance between the end points. The only disadvantage occurs on longer trips, when the traveler covers a distance equivalent to following the sides of a triangle rather than the hypotenuse, an increase of up to 41 percent over the shortest geometrical distance.[1]

Town planners often seek to reduce this extra distance by superimposing diagonal avenues on the grid pattern, forming a cobweb pattern. This technique was formally adopted in parts of Rome and other European cities, and in more recent times in planned cities in the Americas, such as Washington, D.C., Tijuana, La Plata, and Belo Horizonte. It is also seen in the form of diagonal avenues and expressways inserted in cities originally designed on the grid pattern. Winding roads are typically a concession to topography—the only practical way of climbing hills and following the contours of bodies of water. But as soon as distance and space permit, the grid and cobweb patterns have a tendency to reassert themselves.

In previous eras, traffic safety played no important role in this process—a runaway horse was as dangerous on a winding street as a straight one. The need to provide space for troops, carriages, and oxcarts, however, led a number of cities to straighten passageways and to legislate minimum widths, such as 12 to 20 meters for avenues, 6 meters for streets, and 3 meters for alleys.

These were far from universal standards. There were intense pressures to occupy urban space: horsedrawn vehicles were spatially inefficient as a form of urban transportation. Even the automobile required less space than the horse, and was appropriately dubbed "the horseless carriage." Circulation in urban areas continued to be viable through the nineteenth century only because walking provided such high capacity.

The growth of cities increased the distances many citizens had to travel in the course of their daily activities. Demand for a less-tiring alternative grew. Getting a horse harnessed and hooked up to a carriage was a time-consuming process and maintaining horses and a carriage in a city required space, shelter, money, and considerable work. These factors led to the appearance of an expanding market for coaches for hire. The smaller, swifter versions became the first taxis, and the larger, more cumbersome ones, the first buses, or omnibuses.

A technological breakthrough of sorts occurred in the eighteenth century when mine operators discovered that heavy vehicles could be moved more easily when supported by flanged wheels placed on fixed rails. With iron wheels and rails, vehicles could be moved even more smoothly, and by the early nineteenth century, these discoveries gained the streets with the first horse-drawn streetcars.

Steam-powered trains followed the streetcars, but frightened horses, spewed forth sparks and soot, and were rightly regarded as a dangerous nuisance. The tracks of full-fledged trains (as opposed to streetcars) also created spatial and even social divisions in the urban fabric, reflected by the phrase "the wrong side of the tracks." A major technological breakthrough appeared toward the end of the nineteenth century, with the discovery of practical electric traction systems that permitted improved streetcars and subway service. In its several forms, the urban train began to exert a significant influence on urban structure.

Prior to the appearance of the electric streetcar, reliance on walking required a high degree of compactness in cities. Walking more than a kilometer or two from home to downtown made trade and work there difficult, and most cities were circumscribed by such a radius. Living quarters might be euphemistically described as cramped: families were stacked several tiers high in multifamily dwellings with little open space in the immediate surroundings.

In the early nineteenth century, several large American cities had population densities on the order of 30,000 persons per square kilometer or 11,538 per square mile, about twice that of Tokyo's present density and nearly four times that of modern New York (Bottles 1987: 5; Chile 1987). Lille, a leading French textile and manufacturing center, held some 100,000 people within the 3 square kilometers inside the city walls (McKay 1976: 7). The lack of vaccines, potable water supplies, tolerable sewage systems, or even efficient garbage disposal made the city a fetid and unhealthy place. Large numbers of horsedrawn vehicles congested streets and added tons of dung. Even in the early twentieth century, only a few large cities had subways. Electric streetcars, although operating at modest speeds, had become the best option for many cities.

The bicycle saw slow but continuous development throughout

most of the nineteenth century. By the 1880s, tinkerers and manufacturers had developed models that looked like sturdier versions of today's one-speed bicycles (many can still be seen in museums). The "safety bicycle," with two equal-sized spoked wheels, pedals, sprockets and chain finally offered a reliable means of propulsion. Its practical use as a mode of transportation, however, was hampered by the substantial shocks and rolling resistance produced by its hard rubber tires on cobblestones, gravel, dirt and mud, which then constituted most road surfaces. It was not until 1888 that John Boyd Dunlop invented the first usable pneumatic tire (Walter and Conant 1974: 235), and the bicycle took a quantum leap to its one-speed modern version.

Unfortunately, before the bicycle could firmly establish itself as a universal, all-purpose mode of transport, the motorcar was challenging it for the necessary road space. Some cyclists fought against proposals to cede road space in exchange for separate facilities; they held a pessimistic view of their chances of receiving compensating travel space—given the existing street grid and the lack of other space for additional construction—and struggled to maintain the centuries-old right for any citizen to use the public roadway.

But road space cannot be safely shared by motorcars and bicycles without a great deal of sophisticated adaptations, and tradition was not a strong enough physical force to keep the bicycle on public roads. In the United States, the bicycle was largely eliminated from public roads by intense motor traffic early in the twentieth century; in Europe, it hung on until after World War II, aided by the scarcity of fuel and motor vehicles caused by the two world wars and the intervening Depression. Yet, between 1950 and the mid-1970s, bicycle use plummeted from 50 percent to 10 percent of vehicle km in Germany, and from 35 to a mere 1.5 percent in England. British transport authorities considered this to be a beneficial trend, since it relieved them of the responsibility of building cycleways (Downing 1980: 19–41; Hoekwater 1980: 62–74; Mitchell 1980: 5–18; Trevelyan 1980: 47).

The improvement of electrical train systems, however, made streetcars and trains a more reliable form of urban transportation than the automobile well into the twentieth century. In Europe, the same turmoil that preserved substantial use of the bicycle slowed growth in the number and use of cars until the 1950s, although the motorcar began to erode transit ridership seriously by the 1920s (Barker 1987: 3). In the rest of the world, there was limited capacity to produce and purchase motor vehicles before the 1950s, and it was often difficult or impossible to import them in substantial numbers. Although enough automobiles were present to create some serious problems, street-cars, passenger trains, buses, walking, and cycling were the dominant modes of travel into the 1950s.

In virtually all but the poorest countries, nonetheless, the time eventually arrived when substantial numbers of cars invaded the streets. Cars competed for space not only with bicycles and pedestrians, but also with buses and streetcars. Moreover, they offered an alternative—at least for those who could afford them—to the often-deficient public transportation services then available.

In the United States, the private car's challenge came very early, when technological sophistication and reliability of public transportation were limited. As a rule, transit companies were in the hands of private firms, and were regarded by the citizenry as a greedy monopoly. The private car gave the citizen freedom from that monopoly, with its inefficiencies, poor service, and suspected corrupt links to public officials (Bottles 1987: 4–12).

Streetcars rumbled down narrow streets, competing with pedestrians, horses, carts, and early automobiles for use of the very limited street space. Speeds were slow, congestion considerable, accidents frequent, and crowding the rule during rush hours. The streetcar patron had very limited flexibility in choice of boarding spots and destinations outside the central city, or even within it.

In the United States, electrification of streetcars came several years before it occurred in Europe, with little regard for aesthetic values (McKay 1976: 161–65). American streetcar patrons regarded trams as necessary evils (Bottles 1987: 22–121). Citizens felt that transit companies should build subways and provide new and improved services. They thought train and streetcar companies were providing too few cars and services as a way of maximizing their revenues. Traction companies often built lines as an adjunct to their own real-estate speculation schemes rather than for the purpose of improving services on heavily traveled routes. The public in most American cities proved unwilling to approve taxes to fund the massive projects necessary to provide modern subways or elevated trains. New construction was regarded as the traction companies' obligation, even though such investments were something these firms were unwilling and unable to make. The streetcar lines did, however, produce considerable growth in housing on the outskirts of both European and American cities—the suburbs.

In Manchester, the settlement pattern soon took on a nearly perfect star shape, as settlement followed the radial streetcar lines that extended out from the city center (McKay 1976: 218). The "spreading out" of settlement was regarded positively by virtually all town planners and most authorities, since it relieved excessive crowding in the core.

In Europe, the medieval walls around cities were finally torn down, and the considerable open space maintained on either side became available for circular streetcar routes (McKay 1976: 18). Streetcars and automobiles permitted the wealthy and the middle class to move to the suburbs, increasing the demand for paving, lighting, sewers, and schools, and thus eroding the potential supply of funds for publicly supported transit projects.

The increasing automobile traffic—very pronounced in the United States in the first decades of this century—began to interfere with the operation of buses and streetcars, weakening their competitive position. For streetcars in particular, obsolescence became a major problem. Newer systems were very expensive: the diesel bus was a more flexible and less expensive option, and subways could provide superior services. Public regulation added an additional constraint on fares, routes, and policies. Private capital soon lost interest in streetcars, and most municipal governments were unwilling to take over obsolete systems in poor repair. Some streetcars systems were abandoned as early as the 1920s, and the trend continued in the 1930s and 1940s. By the 1950s and 1960s, buses were also becoming a losing proposition for private capital (Lave 1990).

In most other countries, these trends occurred much later and developed with much less intensity. In Europe, transit companies were often publicly owned or subject to very stringent controls with options for municipalization. There was no feeling that the companies were trying to increase fares or bribe public officials to maximize their profits (McKay 1976: 118). A number of municipalities invested tax monies to upgrade and extend rail transit systems, and developed substantial networks of high-quality rail services with exclusive rights-of-way.

In Latin America and some other regions, however, streetcar companies were owned by private foreign interests. They became targets for nationalistic protests, riots, complaints, and governmental fare regulation. Quality maintenance was soon unaffordable, the systems wore out and eventually went bankrupt. Streetcar operations then ceased, either immediately or after a brief period of municipalization.

Buenos Aires built its first subway section in 1913; it developed into the only subway system in Latin America in the first half of this century. By the 1950s and 1960s, the region's relatively few surface commuting trains (linking major cities to their suburbs) also began to show the effects of long periods of neglect (Assmann 1976; Moisés and Martinez-Alier 1977). When narrow downtown streets grid-locked in the 1950s, motorists demanded removal of the "congestion-causing" streetcars; conflicts witnessed in Los Angeles some four decades earlier were relived. There are also plausible but undocumented rumors that private bus companies in Santiago and other cities ordered their drivers to interfere with the circulation of the municipal streetcars and to encircle them at stops to prevent patrons from boarding.

The net result was the eradication of virtually all streetcar systems throughout the Americas. Rail transit fared somewhat better in the few cities with early and relatively extensive subway systems, including New York, a few other North American cities, and Buenos Aires.

Without the added flexibility of the streetcars, rail transit in general suffered a long period of decadence. This was partially inverted in the 1960s and 1970s, when a substantial number of cities in the Americas opted for modern metro systems, with several featuring extensive subway sections. The demise of the streetcars, however, was nearly complete and, apparently, irreversible.

In Europe, Scandinavia, and parts of Asia, rail transit fared much better, but even there the streetcar lost ground, although it made a (largely symbolic) comeback as a policy response to the energy crises of the 1970s.

The demise of the streetcar symbolizes, especially in the Americas, the decadence of public transportation and the Pyrrhic victory of the automobile. Nostalgia is a poor guide to present and future policies, however: it is preferable to develop an understanding of the technical deficiencies of the streetcar system itself.

Perhaps the streetcar's most important drawback was its rather low capacity—superior to the automobile, but far inferior to the pedestrian, which it endangered, inconvenienced, and partially displaced. Many trolleys operated on narrow and discontinuous streets, with sharp curves at corners that limited the units to only one or two small cars. Entrance and egress were hampered by many streetcar designs, and by the use of the street itself rather than platforms for boarding and alighting. Congestion caused by other traffic or problems with any car on the track could reduce a trolley's speed to a crawl or stop it altogether; flexibility was minimal.

Urban and interurban trains offered higher speeds, but even

less flexibility. As open spaces filled in, train tracks were crisscrossed by city streets and roads, causing accidents and protests by irate citizens. Elevated railway sections were installed in some cities, such as New York and Chicago, but were several times more expensive than surface rails. The elevateds were also horrendously noisy and blocked out part of the already scarce sunshine on narrow streets; occasionally, a derailment or other accident occurred, spreading panic.

With the advent of large-scale automobile traffic, the only remaining options for quality rail service were to build subways or redesign the surface rail system. The latter measure called for banning parking of automobiles and restricting their access to areas where streetcars were used; it also called for widening some streets and removing discontinuities from others. Faster urban trains required grade separation at crossings. Few cities were willing to take these steps.

At the turn of the century, a successful subway depended on three factors: (1) high population density, preferably combined with physical barriers to decentralization; (2) an early and ambitious start, so that a fairly extensive network could be built before something more attractive than the streetcar appeared as an alternative means of transport; and (3) an impressive tax base or sufficient political clout to obtain the funds necessary to finance construction and operate the system.

No city has gone far without (3), and most have needed at least one other factor. The importance of the early start is exemplified by New York, Buenos Aires, London, and Paris. The lack of a favorable combination of these factors is seen in the numerous cities where metros are either absent or limited to a line or two, rather than an effective metro system. As Vuchic (1981) shows, this early investment in rail systems in many European cities has maintained high transit usage to the present. Aside from their rail passengers, the bus systems in these cities transport relatively more passengers than buses in counterpart cities that made no such commitment.

It is interesting to note that the main goal cited for building metros—decreasing congestion on city streets—seldom was achieved unless measures were taken to reduce or eliminate parking and car traffic on congested streets. Thus, subway construction does not remove the temptation to try to make traffic flow better by:

widening, straightening, and paving streets and avenues;

removing buildings and other barriers to thoroughfares;

constructing expressways; and

creating one-way streets.

These measures are in turn only successful in reducing congestion in the longer term if vehicle ownership and use is somehow held down; otherwise, the number of trips expands to recreate congestion on a wider scale.

There are only a few ways of holding down private car use in city centers. The most widely used one in North America is the combination of decentralization and the lack of quality public transport systems. This eventually reduces the population density of the core to the extent that central road space becomes adequate. Fewer people want to live in or venture into the downtown area. Over decades, the Yogi Berra principle triumphs.

Another control mechanism is a de facto solution in many of the poorer developing countries: personal incomes are too low for a substantial percentage of residents to own cars.

Discouraging use of passenger cars by rigorous public policy is yet another control mechanism: banning the circulation or parking of cars from certain areas; restricting the number of licenses; charging high fees on use of fuel, streets, and parking space.

Bans are popular in a few areas where traffic is viewed as incompatible with the use of a scarce economic, civic, or recreational resource. Examples include pedestrian malls throughout the world, historic cities in Germany and Italy, and the tourist-oriented islands of Mackinac (United States) and Paquetá (Brazil).

Quotas for car ownership are in force in Singapore (Watson and Holland 1978), where a new car can only be registered by presenting the equivalent of a death certificate for an old one. High parking charges and fuel taxes are standard practice in most countries (although not as high as some economists would like). Road-space user charges are confined to occasional toll booths, often located, for obvious reasons, at bridges.

These differentiated trends have had profound effects on the development of city structures and, in particular, on population densities. Some cities have maintained high population densities due to constrained geographical locations: Manhattan, Caracas, Hong Kong, and Singapore. Others have entered the automobile era somewhat late or in a limited fashion: Manila and many other cities in developing countries fit this category, along with more developed cities in Europe and Asia that have extensive and high-quality public transport systems.

In North American and European cities, some very clear decentralization trends occurred. The suburbs, once the province of those unable to afford housing in the city center, became the haven of the middle and upper classes who wished to flee city centers. In the early twentieth century, there was a lot to flee from: narrow streets that received little sunlight in winter and trapped heat in summer, a lack of open spaces for recreation, horrendous crowding, filth, stench, and the associated facility for communication of disease.

Surface trains and streetcars, however, furnished a limited escape route. They served mainly as spokes that connected central cities to other hubs. These included entirely new suburbs and some neighboring old towns that suddenly began to grow as bedroom communities. Their crucial spatial requirement was that housing and other functions be located close to the rail transit station(s). The geographical space between the population "hubs" and the rail line "spokes" would be filled in by houses and businesses only with the aid of the automobile. In U.S. cities (except New York), auto ownership and urban resettlement soon became so generalized that the central population density declined to very moderate levels. As distance from the center increased, densities fell still further.

The extreme decentralization that resulted is indicated by census data that place New York City as the highest-density American city, with 8,677 persons per square kilometer (22,473/square mile). New York is followed by a small group with intermediate densities close to Chicago's 5,085 persons per square kilometer. Many other large cities have much lower densities: Houston, for example, has only 1,074 persons per square kilometer (U.S. Department of Commerce 1988).

These figures refer to political boundaries and are at times biased by disproportionate sizes in the political units. Often densities are much higher in the downtown area, and some areas attract high volumes of traffic although their residential densities are modest. An extreme case is the center of London (the "City"), with 2.6 square kilometers (1 square mile), 5,000 residents, and a half-million office workers on weekdays (Jones 1988: 433). Another is Manila: the city proper has only 38.3 km^2 of land area and a population density of 41,436 persons/km^2; Metropolitan Manila has 636 km^2 and a population density of 12,314 persons/km^2 (Republic of the Philippines 1990: 1.5).

An alternative approach to calculating population density is to consider the continuous urbanized area. Such a study was undertaken by Peter Gordon, Ajay Kumar, and Harry Richardson, using urban areas measured from LANDSAT imagery, rather than relying on the political boundaries of census publications (1989: 138). Their figures are averages over wider areas (implying even lower population densities) and do not take into account more densely populated subareas. They do, however, show the extent of urban sprawl: Atlanta, with only 688 persons/km^2 (1,783/mi^2), still makes the list of the United States' more densely populated cities; the greater New York area, with Manhattan's influence diluted, still leads, but with an unimpressive 2,144 persons/km^2 (5,553/mi^2). There is at least one surprise: the compact Champaign–Urbana area, corresponding to the University of Illinois student housing near campus, and not too much else, appears on the list as one of the United States' more densely populated urban areas. The proportion of pedestrian travel in a campus area is obviously one factor responsible for such compactness.

Since 1950 there has also been a new wave of decentralization in Europe. Deconcentration of spatial functions has occurred even in the Netherlands, with core cities losing employment and population to suburbs (Jansen and Van Vuren 1989). This is accompanied by significant changes in trip patterns and, in particular, greater reliance on the private car as a transport mode. This phenomenon of "counterurbanization" is widespread, but the predominant trend is a "spreading out" of metropolitan areas rather than ruralization (Champion 1989).

The emergence of the private car as the dominant mode of transportation in North America had profound effects on the finances of core cities, along with their legibility and structure. These cities are no longer largely self-contained units, with channels of outside commerce limited mainly to ports and railroad stations.

The motor truck played a major role in this process, as did electric and internal combustion engines in industry. The use of steam as a source of power for industry favored multistory factories. The steam was generated at the factory site by burning wood or coal and the power could be transferred only a short distance by means of shafts, pulleys and belts. Steam, however, was a very inefficient source of industrial power, and in the early decades of the twentieth century was largely displaced by stationary electric and internal-combustion engines. Simultaneously, the motor truck became a practical and low-cost means of transporting goods from everywhere to everywhere else, with assembly lines and forklifts creating a demand for sprawling, one-story buildings (Bottles 1987: 198). This required large tracts of inexpensive land, available only far from the city core. After decades, these forces have left many core cities in the United States and elsewhere with relatively few manufacturing activities. In the modern central city, the services predominate, along with buildings for governmental offices and entertainment, but the city core no longer has a monopoly on even these functions.

Manufacture of goods and the bulk of commercial functions and services have followed and, at times, led the migration to the suburbs. Long ago business executives, transportation officials, and many other citizens began to perceive the central city, with its congested streets, less as an opportunity to obtain a favorable location and more as a barrier to be crossed or sidestepped by construction of freeways. The freeways in turn separated neighborhoods and imposed a new spatial structure and new visual forms on the city. These same freeways attracted new growth to the lightly populated suburbs, while their noise and proximity to heavily built-up areas imposed negative externalities on the densely populated core cities.

On occasions when the increased roadway capacity was not quickly saturated by a corresponding increase in traffic, the core cities gained increased accessibility in absolute terms. But since it is the relative position that matters, the central cities lost their historic advantage. All areas became more accessible, but the suburbs offered less congestion, and road haulage supplanted the railroad and port.

In many European cities, several countervailing tendencies appeared in the 1950s and later as large-scale motorization progressed:

Influential citizens realized that historic buildings and city centers could not easily accommodate the automobile's appetite for space and that its associated externalities were undesirable. Cars were either excluded from those areas or their numbers were severely restricted by user charges or by requiring permits. This strategy was aided by the compactness of the areas (often within the confines of medieval walls) and the availability of good public transportation facilities.

The citizenry resented the noise, danger, and degradation of the conditions of walking and cycling in the postwar period (Collin 1990; De Wit 1990; Mahler 1990). At heart, this represented the revolutionary idea that road space or alternative facilities should be available for the safe circulation of people, not just motor vehicles. Dutch cyclists staged protests and were probably the most vocal and effective in achieving changes, but the movement spread throughout Germany, Denmark, and Scandinavia, and in a weakened form to most other European countries. It received a major boost from the first "energy crisis" in the early 1970s. Both of these tendencies implied strong support for public subsidies of transit construction, renovation, and operation.

There was a growing popular recognition that neighborhoods should have strict controls over car traffic through modification of street designs, incorporation of traffic humps on surfaces of local streets, parking regulations, and speed restrictions.

These countervailing tendencies should not obscure the predominant one in Europe of a gradual movement toward decentralization and the increased use of the automobile. But they avoided the extreme situation that occurred in the United States, where population densities became so low and automobile use so high that public transportation became almost irrelevant in national terms. Presently, transit use is so low in most American cities that fully one-third of all U.S. commuting by transit occurs in New York City (Pisarski 1987: 53).

In Latin America, there has been no tendency toward loss of population in core areas of large cities (although the 1990 census data may produce some surprises when they become available). Large cities are nonetheless spreading out as they accommodate considerable migration from rural areas and smaller cities, in addition to significant local population growth. The surrounding cities, which were small and somewhat distant centers only a few decades ago, are themselves becoming large, densely populated cities and are merging with the expanding core metropolis. These tendencies imply relatively high population densities spread over increasingly larger areas.

The picture is similar in many Asian and African cities. High birth rates are still common, and rural–urban migration is responsible for considerable urban growth. The small and medium-sized cities in Africa also have moderately high population densities, due to their reliance on walking and cycling as the predominant means of transport. Ouagadougou, the capital of Burkina Faso, grew from 170,000 inhabitants in 1975 to 300,000 in 1983, and Tamale, the largest city in Northern Ghana, grew from 98,000 inhabitants in 1970 to 137,000 in 1984 (Kipke 1988: 11). In the latter years cited, the population densities were 5,000 and 6,122 persons per square kilometer (12,950 and 15,856/mi^2), respectively.

These factors all have profound implications for urban transport planning, and indicate that the problems vary widely across countries and even across cities within a given country. The instinct for preservation of urban forms in Europe contrasts with the rapid change and radically different patterns of legibility in the Americas. It is reasonable to suppose that solutions should be equally varied, but that is getting ahead of our story.

A Tale of Two Cities

The net effect of the interaction of city characteristics with urban transportation modes may be illustrated by a brief description of some salient features of two contrasting city styles. I have chosen for this purpose Brasília and a composite city I will call Urbana.

Brasília, despite its tropical location, represents the low population densities and automobile dependency common in U.S. cities. The lack of regard for pedestrian traffic is present in even more exaggerated form than in the United States. In Brasília, these features are the direct result of planning (Wright 1987a; Wright and Turkienicz 1988).

Construction of Brasília began in 1957 on Brazil's central highplain to serve as the political capital. Its creators, Lúcio Costa and Oscar Niemeyer, adopted Le Corbusier's modernistic principles of total acceptance of the automobile, imposition of a low population density, an overdimensioned road network, and spatial segregation of functions. Other, more noble modernistic principles, such as separation of pedestrians from motor traffic and location of recreational and cultural space close to residences, were followed only in specific locations.

Brasília's low population density was enforced by zoning and a master plan that specified the type of residences that could be built, their number and location, and by providing vast areas of grass, trees, and urban streets and highways in the Pilot Plan (which composes the city of Brasília proper). When more people were attracted to the new capital, they were forced to live at distances of 12 to 40 km (7.5 to 25 miles) from the Pilot Plan, in "satellite cities." Since housing space was also rationed in the satellite cities, many citizens chose locations outside the Federal District where there were no zoning restrictions whatever, and now live even farther away from the Pilot Plan. Jobs are concentrated in the Pilot Plan, however, due to its function as an administrative center and the Federal District's lack of an independent economic base.

The Pilot Plan has by far the highest percentage of trips by car of any major Brazilian city—over 70 percent, compared with 40 percent in São Paulo and much lower in most other urban areas. There is little congestion on most streets and avenues; exceptions include the school sectors on the W-5 Avenue during the brief periods when parents are dropping off or picking up their children, and the South Commercial and Banking Sectors, where parking space is a bottleneck. Since there are no safe crossings, few parents are willing to see their youngsters go to school on foot or by bicycle, although the weather is usually pleasant and distances from apartment buildings are often modest. Few commercial or other activity areas are near residences; the three existing bikeways are designed for recreation and are not usable for transportation.

Virtually all crossings are dangerous for pedestrians, some pathologically so. Cycling outside the residential superblocks is almost suicidal, and cyclists are rarely seen. Daily activities for the Pilot Plan's residents thus depend on use of the private car. Residents of the satellite cities, who generally have much lower incomes and now account for 80 percent of the Federal District's population, face long bus rides to get to work or any other activity in the Pilot Plan.

Despite the low level of congestion in Brasília, motorists spend more on fuel there than anywhere else in Brazil. The Federal District also has by far the highest bus fares, usually nearly double those of other major cities. In the Pilot Plan, neighborhoods are separated by high speed highways and by extra distance introduced in the city plan to provide an unusual amount of "green areas" in the urban setting. Many Brazilians who visit or come to live in Brasília miss the human contact found on the streets and sidewalks of their hometowns. For those accustomed to the bustle of other Brazilian cities, being in Brasília's hotel sector is akin to being abandoned on a lunar outpost.

On the positive side, the city offers an aesthetic quality that is hard to match, an exceptional climate, and little pollution. Children who live in the superblocks enjoy unparalleled opportunity to meet their friends and play in traffic-restricted areas. They just cannot cross streets safely.

Urbana, while imaginary, is real enough. It combines the features of a number of Latin American cities and, indeed, of cities in many other areas of the world. It has evolved over the centuries in response to economic factors and in accord with the cultural characteristics of its people. Occasionally, the mayor and city council have tried to mold its growth by promulgating building codes and development plans. These are soon amended, then amended again, and finally replaced by updated codes and new plans. At times these measures have some positive impact, but in general they have simply produced new layers of bureaucracy and costs for builders. They are thus often ignored, especially by the so-called informal sector of the local economy. Space in the city is a precious commodity and is used intensely. The ecology-conscious citizenry, however, has managed of late to guarantee the preservation of the city's park areas and part of the lowlands. The extensive beaches are open to everyone and serve as the main source of outdoor recreation.

Urbana's traffic is congested most of the day, but somehow people still get around. A substantial number of workers come in from neighboring communities by commuter trains or bus. Most other workers also come in by bus or on Urbana's only metroline. Most of their daily shopping and other chores are accomplished by walking to nearby establishments, a reflection of the mixed pattern of land use. Parking is a major hassle, and car and gasoline prices are high relative to most families' incomes.

A number of downtown streets are so narrow that one stalled car is enough to block traffic. The city successfully "pedestrianized" some of those streets without major protests in the 1960s and 1970s, closing them to motor vehicles. By doing so, it reluctantly abandoned a 1950s' plan for widening some streets that would have required the city's entire tax receipts for two years to raze half the adjacent buildings and compensate the owners for their losses. Over time, the real estate surrounding the pedestrianized areas has doubled in value. Once-decaying businesses have been renovated or have changed hands. The area has become a favorite place for the location of shops, restaurants, and offices. Merchants decorate their storefronts with plants and aid the city in keeping the mall clean and in good repair. This is not done out of any love for city government; merchants take pride in their establishments, and a clean environment is, after all, good for business. The idea of pedestrianizing streets has not spread too rapidly, however. Merchants on wider streets are afraid the elimination of parking spaces and vehicular traffic would hurt business.

The core area is still the city's administrative, financial, and commercial center. Manufacturing long ago moved to outlying areas where real estate is less expensive, and took a great deal of unwelcome filth and noise along. The more modern industrial concerns that have been attracted to the outlying districts have presented relatively few such problems, and the state and local environmental protection agencies, by a combination of legislation and jawboning, have persuaded some of the older concerns to clean up. Most air pollution is now caused by automobiles, buses, and trucks, although the worst problem, leaded gasoline, was phased out over a decade ago.

Mixed land use predominates in Urbana, despite the attempts to introduce more rigid zoning. Apartment buildings mingle with single-family houses, and one is never far from a bakery, café, drugstore, or general store. Schools and churches are within walking distance; crossings vary in their degree of safety. Although congestion reaches moderate to heavy levels in most areas, residents spend less time in traffic than those of congestion-free Brasília, since they can accomplish most errands on foot or shorter motorized trips. Per capita transport energy consumption is much lower in Urbana than in Brasília, and bus fares are half the rate.

Energy-Efficient Cities

The idea that congestion is compatible with lower transportation energy expenditures and bus fares is a revolutionary one. Almost all authors of cost–benefit analyses for urban expressway projects have assumed the opposite and calculated as benefits the lower per kilometer expenditure of time and energy by vehicles resulting from a given increase in road space (see Chapter 10).

P. W. G. Newman and J. R. Kenworthy (1988), however, have shown that the opposite occurs. They have documented a strong negative correlation between congestion and energy use for thirty-two cities around the world. These results hold because congestion occurs in more densely populated areas with intense, mixed land use that supports public transportation and permits people to travel less to obtain their goods and services.

The authors make the valuable distinction between fuel-efficient traffic and fuel-efficient cities. Fuel-efficient traffic is found in Brasília and structurally similar cities that have high ratios of road space to population. Average travel speeds are relatively high, along with the distance a car can travel on a liter of fuel. But each person, traveling much more, ends up using more transport energy than in fuel-efficient cities, such as Urbana. By providing more road space for private cars to achieve fuel-efficient traffic, engineers and planners end up with energy-inefficient cities.

Newman and Kenworthy's data come primarily from cities in developed countries. The distinction between energy-efficient traffic and energy-efficient cities would be even more pronounced if the data included cities in China and other developing countries where walking and cycling are much more significant.

Cost-based bus fares are lower in Urbana than in Brasília because people travel shorter distances on the average. In Urbana, someone is always passing through the turnstiles to help defray the cost of the trip; in Brasília, there are no intermediate stops between the satellite cities and the Pilot Plan. Each passenger has to pay more to finance the long-distance bus trip, even though buses in Brasília have higher average speeds and lower fuel consumption per kilometer.

Automobile-Dominated and Automobile-Threatened Cities

The automobile has become a standard feature in the majority of households in cities with high incomes and low population densities. The resulting dispersed pattern of activities and trips requires large expenditures of time and energy on personal travel. Children and other nondriving family members are dependent on the family driver(s) for most of their travel needs, and there are numerous negative environmental externalities. Nonetheless, the automobile has provided an affordable (though expensive) form of urban transportation for most American and Canadian families throughout much of the current century, and the automobile-dominated landscape has also made inroads in high-income cities in Europe and on other continents since 1950.

In smaller towns far from metropolitan areas, most Americans and Canadians are apparently content with their "automobile culture." They value their individual housing units with large yards and the apparent convenience of their cars. As long as petroleum can be kept readily available and at a low price, they have little incentive for change and little reason to perceive that U.S. involvement in Middle Eastern crises is a consequence of their own lifestyle. (That might change if the cost of the relevant military expenditures took the form of a fuel tax.)

Elsewhere in North America there are fewer reasons for complacency. The near-universal use of cars and trucks to move people and goods, coupled with the requirements for space for these and associated activities, has shifted growth from central cities to the suburbs. In many cases, this growth has been so pronounced that the avenues and expressways that prompted (or at least permitted) such growth have been overwhelmed by it. In the three decades from 1950 to 1980, the number of people living in the suburbs tripled, from 35 to 102 million, reaching a full 45 percent of the U.S. total, while central cities grew only from 50 to 68 million, declining in relative terms to a mere 30 percent of the population (Cervero 1986: 1–10).

From 1970 to 1984, 80 percent of new office space was built in the suburbs, with suburbia accounting for 57 percent of the total in the latter year. As a result, twice as many work trips are now made from suburb to suburb as from suburb to central city. Transit operations, however, continue to focus on the downtown hub or, more accurately, on the old downtown hub. Almost overnight, new "downtowns" have been formed. Developers have rapidly erected some complexes with nearly a square kilometer of floor space (up to 10 million square feet). Many of these complexes offer a range of services rivaling those available in the older centers (Cervero 1986: 31–49). As a result, the expressways and other routes that link the suburbs to everywhere else have often been saturated by sudden increases in traffic that they were not designed to handle. This phenomenon of suburban gridlock has virtually paralyzed parts of California, where it has received the most attention from the media, but it can be found in most American growth corridors, along with several European countries (Jansen and Van Vuren 1989).

The low population densities make it difficult and expensive to provide citizens with public transportation that meets even minimal criteria of flexible and frequent service by using conventional bus and train systems.

The record of train "systems" is singularly disastrous. Planning for San Francisco's Bay Area Rapid Transit (regional) system (BART) began during World War II, intensified in 1947, and plans were formally presented in 1956; revenue service finally began in late 1974 (Grefe and Smart 1975: 1–10). Like most urban train projects in recent decades, BART is a linear system that connects almost nothing to little else, rather than a grid interlinking almost everything to almost everything else. Its location, as typically occurs, was determined more by restrictions on where it could be easily built than by any real urban transport need. As Stone (1971: 72) recognized, BART permits some local downtown use but does not provide convenient access to most of the important points in San Francisco; it is not an integrated metropolitan transportation system, but merely a "high-speed luxurious interurban and commuter service extending well into the country."

Given its linear route, BART has attracted little development near its stations in comparison with that occurring near freeways: development near BART is much lower and apparently unrelated to the proximity of BART stations. For example, only 2 percent of people arriving at the new office towers near the station in Walnut Creek come by BART, since it runs nowhere near their residences or other activities (Cervero 1986: 218). Only about one-fourth of BART's planned service was actually completed a generation after the initial plans were advanced (Grefe and Smart 1975: 1–10).

Construction of the Washington, D.C., metro began in earnest in the 1960s, and that system is also still incomplete. Edwin Mills and Bruce Hamilton show that, even with six metro lines, only 7 percent of residential land area is within a mile (1.6 km) of a metro station (1989: 276–77). Through 1981, the nearly $5-billion capital cost at 10 percent interest, divided by 145,000 weekday riders, yielded an interest and depreciation cost of $13 per round trip. Adding on the $94-million annual operating expense increased the cost to $16 per round trip.

Clearly, projects with price tags of billions of dollars that serve relatively few points and take over a generation to implant partially cannot be promoted as solutions for the urban transport problem, however popular they may be as "status symbols" for the city, mayor, or governor. Better options are needed.

The high rates of car ownership in the United States and some other countries make transit appear unnecessary for most urban adults' transportation needs: there are now more cars than workers in the United States (Pisarski 1987). Yet the Henry Ford paradox implies that many of these workers cannot drive to work in reasonable periods of time. Even in many suburban areas, there is not enough road space to compensate for the private car's low transport capacity. Even worse, much of the current road extension is in bad repair. Many bridges and other structures need to be replaced, and a substantial share of urban and suburban roads needs to be rebuilt.

The estimates of costs of all this vary with the assumptions used to make them, and all need to be taken with the proverbial grain of salt. Yet, since construction costs range up to $40 million per kilometer for a new multilane expressway in an urban area, a billion dollars may provide as little as 25 kilometers of roadway. The repair bill for the U.S. interstate system alone could cost around a trillion 1990 dollars.[2] A study of the California Department of Transportation indicated that a proposed $61-billion road-building program would not solve its traffic problem—nor would any other road-building effort (cited in Lowe 1989: 18). With the U.S. government foundering in debt and state and local governments struggling to maintain minimal services in the educational and health sectors, these fantastic sums are simply not available (Kobran 1990: 38–39). Again, other options are needed.

In Asian and Latin American cities, indices of car ownership are relatively low, with perhaps 20 to 40 percent of urban families owning a car. Most members of car-owning families do not have regular access to the vehicle for their transport needs, yet population densities are sufficiently high to generate enough cars to saturate the limited road space. These cities may be more accurately described as automobile-threatened rather than automobile-dominated, since the automobile's extremely low transport capacity provokes gridlock and other negative externalities long before it becomes a dominant form of travel. Mexico City, for example, faced gridlock in 1983 with only 19 percent of total trips taken by car (Coordenación General de Transporte 1985: 30). Because of their high densities and limited resources for road building, these cities cannot maintain the circulation of people and goods at tolerable levels of time and cost if automobile traffic continues to expand. Subways could provide needed capacity if enough money were available to build and operate a dense network, but that is never the case. There are few sites where quality surface metros can be built, even with elevated sections, so that these usually end up on the drawing board or with a single line and an exceedingly modest percentage of the city's passengers. As in developed countries, better options are badly needed.

In all cases, automobile use should be held in check. Some of my fellow economists have concentrated almost exclusively on this question. They typically recommend high fuel and vehicle sales taxes, parking charges, bridge and expressway tolls, licensing fees, and even electronic road pricing for use of streets and avenues. High fuel and vehicle sales taxes are fairly common in Europe and are one of the reasons car ownership and usage are much lower there than in the United States, even as per capita income differences have faded. In Denmark, for example, there is a 186 percent sales tax on new cars, so that perspective customers pay for three cars to get one (Lowe 1989: 37). In Brazil, the rates set for the country's maze of taxes fluctuate with the whims of each new finance minister, but usually end up doubling the price of a car. The Netherlands has a sales tax of 47 percent, while the U.S. tax is a mere 5 percent.

Fuel taxes rarely if ever approach the levels recommended by economists. Michelle White (1989) calculates that a gasoline tax of about a dollar per liter ($3.75/gallon) would be necessary to compensate for the negative externalities caused by the automobile in U.S. metropolitan areas. In 1989, the U.S. gasoline tax averaged 8 cents per liter, compared with 40 cents in the U.K., 36 cents in West Germany, and 39 cents per liter in Japan (U.S. Department of Transportation 1990: 3.11). Most countries use these taxes as a way of raising revenue rather than for curtailing automobile use; the United States has foregone this source and watched budget deficits soar. Meanwhile, low-interest federal loans in the United States have over generations subsidized the construction of single-family, low density housing. Companies have been encouraged to provide free parking spaces for their employees, since the expenses enter as costs on their income-tax forms and reduce their total tax bills. Employees receive a nontaxable subsidy estimated at $1.20 to $4.00 per day for each parking space (Pikarsky and Johnson 1983: 591). Transit tickets, however, are considered as employee income and thus are subject to tax. By charging far less for car trips than the true costs including externalities, society in effect subsidizes private transportation.

At the risk of understatement, Professor White's suggested dollar-per-liter tax is unlikely to be popular with American voters as a means of restricting car use. Californians did recently pass a fuel tax increase (of a minute fraction of that amount), but they earmarked it for road construction. Some other pricing schemes are even further from being practical tools for restricting car use. With traditional collection schemes, tolls can only be collected on bridges and expressways. Collection costs are high and the toll booths themselves require considerable space and cause delay. Road pricing in a more general sense would require fitting cars and observation points with devices for registering the presence of cars in congested areas and billing the owner for the use of the roadways, much like a telephone company bills its customers for their calls. Although this is now technologically feasible, Sandford Borins questions whether it is possible to approve such measures in a democratic society (1988: 37). In his words, electronic road pricing is "an idea whose time may never come."

Parking restrictions and charges are more effective and somewhat more acceptable politically. If applied in the customary haphazard fashion, however, they may produce some undesirable side effects, like encouraging shoppers to exchange downtown areas for more distant shopping centers.

The problem with such anticar measures is that they do not address the need to provide urbanites with an adequate set of alternatives. A consensus will never form to restrain car use unless the citizens perceive that they can circulate more easily without cars, and this requires a positive perception of other options. The basic characteristic of the automobile-dominated city is that, when one looks for an alternative to the private car, there is little or nothing there. The 1970 energy crises did boost interest in public transportation, even in the United States, and BART extended its hours and number of trains after surviving the 1989 earthquake intact. But in both instances people soon discovered that public transportation could not get them where they wanted to go without a tremendous hassle and much lost time, and little permanent change resulted. Likewise, we saw earlier that parking prohibitions were rejected in Los Angeles and other U.S. cities in the early years of this century because the only alternative was an inadequate streetcar system.

Many European countries, however, have adopted severe restrictions on automobile use in central cities and in residential areas, since public transport is often an acceptable alternative to the private car, as are walking and cycling.

We must therefore address the question of what options are available and affordable for automobile-dominated and automobile-threatened cities. Those that head the list include walking, cycling, buses, carpooling and vanpooling, shared taxis, and jitney services. Each offers some peculiarities that make it more or less appropriate for specific cities and users, and all of them require some modifications in street design and other urban policies. These options are the subject of Chapter 9.

Citizens as Transport Users

With the exception of the home-bound and institutionalized, all citizens are transport users. An equally obvious and overlooked point is that transport users are also citizens. Their role as transport users is only one of the roles they hold as workers, spouses, parents, students, homeowners, and citizens. Both the negative externalities associated with traffic and the public expense of providing transport facilities and services can affect their welfare to an extent equal to or greater than the immediate circumstances they face on their daily journeys. Many characteristics of transport users have been described implicitly in Chapter 6 and other parts of this book. Only a few warrant detailed attention here.

The first and perhaps most important characteristic is the diversity of transport users' needs and preferences. The varied, subtle and qualitative nature of user demand is a persistent barrier to the more successful deployment of mathematical modeling. The recent "behavioral" models (not by coincidence based on the same Lancasterian principles employed herein) represent a first step in the right direction.[3] There are, however, serious limitations in data and statistical techniques, along with the scope of problems that can be effectively modeled in a mathematical sense. Pre-Lancasterian formulations, on the other hand, have proven almost hopeless as guides to policy, as shown by Marvin Manheim (1979) and I. H. Mackinder (1979).

Diversity occurs across societies and among individuals. In the United States, only about one-fifth of motorized travel involves the journey to work and back (Pisarski 1987: 12). In Bogotá such commuting reaches half of all motorized trips; work plus study accounts for more than three-fourths of the total. There is little difference between those who own cars and those who do not (Acevedo 1989: 12). In Mexico City, shopping, social, and recreation trips account for 8 percent of trips, with work, business, schooling, and the trip home accounting for over 90 percent of trips (Coordenación General de Transporte 1985). The data are representative for most Latin American cities and other urban centers in developing countries, since mixed and intense land use eliminates the need for long-distance motorized transportation for most errands.

The variation in trip patterns among individuals in a given city is also great. A low-income person usually has a profile of transport demand radically different from that of a more wealthy individual. But each individual may also exhibit widely varying trip needs and preferences, even within the same day. Frequently, travel patterns are complex. A woman may leave a child at school, go to work, run an errand during the lunch hour, stop after work at three different places for groceries and other supplies, pick up the child at a friend's house, stop at a pizza outlet, return home, and attend a social event in the evening. Her travel the next day takes her on different routes for somewhat different purposes.

Despite the modeling problems this diversity implies, the qualitative message is clear: such patterns require flexible transport. That might be provided by a car in the United States, a bicycle in Copenhagen, or a combination of walking and bus in Copacabana.

Diversity translates into demand for different sets of transport characteristics. The very-low-income rider is out of necessity very concerned with costs. Comfort is appreciated if available without charge, but reasonably low fares are essential. A worker only a notch up on the income scale may be willing to part with a few additional cents to gain access to better, more comfortable service. In Bogotá, for example, many students and workers of quite modest means seek out executive buses with 15- and 25-cent fares, shared taxis at 25 cents, and "superexecutive" buses at 45 cents, although there is no lack of crowded, standard buses and minibuses with 10-cent fares (Acevedo 1989). Many high-income users would not think of getting on a bus with 10 to 12 people per square meter of floor space. If driving and parking are major hassles, however, car owners are willing to use the metro and, if available, quality bus services.

For many users, time is a paramount concern; their schedules or businesses require relatively swift movement from one locale to another. Only the simplest travel patterns do not require a fairly high degree of flexibility. Users, however, abhor both waiting and transfers among modes and vehicles (Ben-Akiva and Morikawa 1990). This represents a challenge to public transport operators: a single metro-line, for example, does not serve very many trip purposes or destinations. Nor do multiple transfers attract many patrons if users have any options.

Consider, for example, one of the more extravagant proposals I have come across. The plan would link two large satellite cities to the tip of Brasília's South Wing by surface rail, where passengers would board an Aeromóvel and travel along W-3 Avenue. This sounds like a reasonable option until one considers the implications for the typical user who does not live at the satellite city's proposed rail station and does not work along the proposed Aeromóvel line. As a colleague and I pointed out (Wright and Sant'Anna 1989: 22), the user would have to walk to a bus stop, take the bus to the rail station, get on the train, transfer to the Aeromóvel, transfer to a bus, and finally alight and walk to the destination. Some users might try that exotic combination once for the same reason a few individuals climb Mount Everest— because it is there. But most would prefer to simply get on a bus near their homes and get off near their work, a much faster and less expensive alternative. Proposals for some U.S. cities are almost as exotic: the user would go by car to a parking lot, walk to a bus, get off the bus at a rail transit station, and, after some additional transfers, walk to the final destination.

The average income level of an urban population is a useful predictor of travel demand only if income is relatively well distributed. This is typically not the case in developing countries, and institutional change is likely to be required to produce more equitable income distributions. Although a few economists still think that income distribution improves automatically over time as countries develop, the evidence points in the opposite direction (Wright 1978). Income distributions are influenced by a variety of factors, including taxation and expenditure policies. Transport policy is one of many instruments that affect income distribution. Transport funds can be acquired through regressive taxation (including inflationary emissions), and then spent on facilities used primarily by high income groups. This is an accurate description of what has occurred in many cities around the world.

Alternatively, neutral or progressive taxation can be used to make modest investments to provide low-cost transport for all. This alternative could have a positive impact on the level and distribution of income. We have seen low public expenditures for bus lanes and facilities for nonmotorized transport in comparison with the astronomic sums allotted for metros and facilities for cars. A savings of as little as $10 per month on transport fares may amount to one-sixth of the income of a poor family in a Third World city, but less than 1 percent of a wealthier family's income in that same city. The traditional assumption of cost–benefit analysis is that the marginal utility of income is constant—a major technical and ethical error.

The citizenry's knowledge of the available options is another important factor in urban transport. This relates to the legibility of the city structure and the degree of orientation provided in conjunction with transport facilities, as we have already noted. But over time a crucial component is the knowledge citizens have of project proposals and possible new directions for transport planning. Too often major financial commitments are made in favor of projects that cannot, by their very nature, provide the services that interested parties are telling politicians and the populace that they will provide. Costly metro projects are inaugurated only to find that they have few users; expressways are built only to create gridlock on a larger scale. Most major changes in a transport system—with their associated effects on urban densities—take place over a generation or more. Neither their full impacts nor the underlying causes are easily identified by the casual observer or the politician ignorant of the principles discussed herein.

These problems have been dealt with in Europe and Scandinavia much more effectively than in the Americas or in most other countries (Collin 1990; Mahler 1990). The virtues of public transit and nonmotorized transport have long been more familiar to citizens in those countries, and a consensus emerged early on for providing them with substantial support. New proposals were not only well researched, but also subject to considerable public scrutiny.

In the United States, the early appearance of large numbers of automobiles and the divisive issue of monopoly in transit services prevented the formation of any meaningful coalition for better public transportation. Transport planning became, by and large, an exercise in expressway and road construction. In Latin America in the 1970s and 1980s, scarce transport resources were also directed to building highways and metros. Neither mode was able to keep up with demand. For low-income users, the subsidized fares and high-quality service of metros made them seem desirable choices, but the possibility of enjoying metro services was ultimately an illusion for the vast majority. The resentment of poor-quality bus services and the illusion of one day having access to a comprehensive metro system made it difficult to form a constituency capable of forcing the changes needed to improve bus services.

Clearly, there is a need to improve the information available to citizens, their representatives, and transport administrators. This is one of the more important aspects of characteristics analysis: it can be understood by a wide public and clarifies choices and their consequences for users and local governments.

From the point of view of public policy, such cultural-specific characteristics as driver behavior are very important in determining the adequacy of traffic-engineering and street-design techniques. Developed countries have in general formed fairly extensive and effective traffic policing and education systems. Their drivers, in the main, demonstrate a considerable degree of self-discipline. In the United States, for example, these factors have lowered death rates in relation to distance traveled even though such factors as street layout often leave much to be desired. In developing countries, traffic law enforcement is often virtually nonexistent, while drivers visibly lack self-discipline. This places an additional burden on traffic engineering and modifications in street design as means of protecting pedestrians and reducing accidents in general.

Users are also diverse in their physical abilities. These differences obviously affect their preferences in more affluent societies where affordable options for those with restricted mobility are likely to be more numerous. In poorer countries, proper strategies are essential if people with limited mobility and other handicaps are to have any usable options at all.

Few topics are as controversial and misunderstood as transport planning for the handicapped. Some of the more common myths include:

> Handicapped people are predominantly those in wheelchairs.

> Measures needed for the handicapped are expensive and are usually not needed by other transport users, since these are distinct groups.

> The best way to deal with the handicapped is to convert the entire city bus fleet to handle wheelchairs.

Some myths of course have a bit of truth in them, and that makes it difficult to banish them from our subconscious and from public policy. Most of the errors in these myths were nonetheless revealed by a survey taken during the implantation of the Vancouver Skytrain (Parkinson 1987: 217). Over seventy-two agencies were identified that represented people with different handicaps. Some of the more numerous handicaps included advancing age, visual deficiencies (30 percent of users, few of them actually blind), and people who could walk but did so with restricted mobility.

Most wheelchair users cannot actively use transit, since they typically suffer from frailty or other problems. They can best be helped by door-to-door services, not by a wheelchair-accessible bus operating on a typical transit line. Skytrain personnel found that even healthy people were often "handicapped" in their movements by the need to carry small children, groceries, books, and the like, having at best only one hand free. The elevators they provided added about 1 percent to project cost and handle only 6 to 20 wheelchair patrons a day (5 percent of elevator use). In fact, the most important function of the elevators is to aid the Skytrain's own staff members in their sundry duties.

The requests from handicapped groups were often incorporated by Skytrain at little expense. Rubber mats were placed at the top of stairs as a tactile warning; a friction marker on the first and last step; ground walnuts were added to the paint on the top and bottom 25 centimeters of each handrail.

A more general observation is that intelligent amenities for the majority of urban travelers are also great aids for the handicapped. Sidewalks should be wide and designed for easy passage rather than as obstacle courses strewn with randomly placed lightposts, signs, newsstands and hawkers' wares. Good drainage should be provided, and curbs should be lowered at crossings with other features designed to ease and protect pedestrian movement. Bus stops and other transit stations should provide easy flow and orientation for users. Motor vehicle traffic should be confined to predictable paths. None of these measures is specifically designed for the handicapped, but those with physical deficiencies benefit by them. Police protection should be available on pedestrian corridors, rather than being usurped by motor traffic and related activities.

The converse is also true. To be able to walk in safety in one's surroundings is an elementary human right that can be independently exercised starting somewhere between nine to fourteen months after birth. The capacity to do so with the aid of a tricycle or bicycle is acquired at about two to five years of age. Neither right requires permission from traffic authorities. Yet our transport systems deny us that basic right in most settings, creating restrictions on our ability to move freely, hampering our movements, and exposing us to danger. The result is that we are all transformed to some degree into handicapped persons, unable to move about efficiently in our urban environments.

Part III

Formulating and Evaluating Transport Strategies and Projects

Chapter 9

Selected Modes and City Types

—————————

ANY SUCCESSFUL solution to an urban transport problem must correctly combine the key elements of three sets of characteristics—those of the transport modes, the city, and its transport users. This corresponds to the second step in our characteristics approach to formulating and evaluating transport strategies and projects. In this chapter we take a closer look at the contributions some modes can make toward a better and financially viable transportation environment.

Walking and Cycling

—————————

> No city can solve its transportation problem if it neglects the greatest self-propelled vehicle of all: the pedestrian.
>
> —Lewis Mumford
> The Highway and the City, 1964

The many positive characteristics of the nonmotorized modes have been largely canceled out in most countries by the danger imposed on them by motor vehicles. They are also harmed by the absence of appropriate infrastructure, causing inconvenience, delays, and the use of unnecessarily long routes. All these problems are a direct result of planning almost exclusively for motorized traffic.

Moreover, the few cities in North America and developing

countries that have shown interest in nonmotorized travel have produced routes with such limited geographical coverage and flawed design that they are incapable of inverting this situation. In some cases the facilities appear to have been designed to prove that nonmotorized transport does not work.

This is best shown by analyzing a variety of examples from the point of view of pedestrians and cyclists, followed by a brief discussion of cycling technology, problems, and possibilities. We then take on the thorny question of the changes needed to make walking and cycling safer and more widely used urban transport options.

Current Problems Facing Nonmotorized Transport

Walking is the universal, basic mode of transportation. Those who cannot walk are also unable to use other transport modes unless some substitute for walking is provided: babies are carried or pushed in strollers, the infirm on stretchers or in wheelchairs. A society can survive with only walking as a form of transport. In fact, until the mid–nineteenth century, most societies depended almost exclusively on foot transport, supplemented occasionally by pack or draught animals. Even today, many African countries and India are heavily dependent on walking for most personal travel and a significant share of the movement of goods (Barth 1988; Barwell et al. 1985).

In Africa, head loading of substantial burdens is common; women in both rural and urban areas spend a good deal of their time and energy fetching water from fairly distant sources (Barwell et al. 1985). Walking is also an important mode in its own right in higher-income cities, particularly where population densities are high. In New York, it accounts for 24 percent to 70 percent of all passenger km of surface travel from 6 A.M. to 9 P.M.; in Brazilian cities, walking is used on one-fourth to three-fourths of all trips of *over* a half kilometer (Baerwald et al. 1976: 63; Wright 1989b). Most of the world's population cannot afford any form of motorized transport and depends on walking or cycling.

Walking is also an indispensable complement to all other modes. Public transport, in particular, requires substantial complementary walking to maintain reasonably high frequencies at an affordable cost. Policies that harm transit usually harm walking, and those that hinder walking harm transit.

Few policies are explicitly designed to suppress walking or to make it a difficult and dangerous pastime. The sins of omission are more serious than those of premeditation. Antiwalking measures result from well-intentioned efforts to provide fast, convenient motorized transportation. The great majority of transportation authorities, engineers, and politicians, not to mention the driving public, tend to think of transportation in terms of motor vehicles; their minds have gridlocked as badly as their urban streets and expressways. For them, road space is *for* cars and trucks, and pedestrians and cyclists should know enough to stay out of the road, following the instructions given to them by their parents when they were children. Sidewalks are an afterthought, installed reluctantly, if at all.

The situation is remarkably similar in both automobile-dominated and automobile-threatened cities, although each country presents its own peculiarities.

Setty Pendakur (1988; 1990) has an intriguing set of slides taken in several Indian cities and Nepal. There, local authorities have taken great pains to fence pedestrians into narrow sidewalks, where they face crowded conditions and inevitable bumping and jostling. This serves to maintain wide streets and avenues free for the unhindered circulation of an occasional motor vehicle; India overall has only 1.5 million automobiles (Lowe 1989: 12). Professor Pendakur draws raucous laughter by asking rhetorically if members of the audience can find any problems in the slides which might be addressed using the concepts in the *Highway Capacity Manual*.

In Africa and China, cars and trucks—though few—speed through towns forcing pedestrians to scatter like chickens. The late Brazilian writer Henfil (1980: 19–20) was enthusiastic about everything he saw in China except its drivers, whom he found to be "impatient, aggressive, arrogant, egotistical: they regard pedestrians and cyclists as someone in their way." In 1987, China produced only 4,045 automobiles, or one per quarter-million people (Lowe 1989: 13).

In São Paulo, where pedestrians account for 70 percent of traffic deaths, Eduardo Daros, founder and president of the Brazilian Pedestrian Association (ABRASPE), leads expeditions along city streets to point out to the press and authorities the dangerous conditions pedestrians face. Since most major national and international firms are entrenched in the motor vehicle camp, ABRASPE is not exactly a rich and powerful organization—but occasionally its voice is heard. Brazil's premier newspaper, the *Folha de São Paulo* (Abrúcio Jr. 1990: C-4) recently dedicated a half-page to one of ABRASPE's carefully documented complaints: traffic signals that do not permit pedestrians to cross intersections safely.

Each of two of the most important intersections in São Paulo give pedestrians only 7 seconds to cross 27.8 meters (30 yds.), requiring a sprint at 14 km/h (9 mph) (a healthy adult's walking speed is only about 4.3 km/h, or 2.7 mph). Some years ago, an elderly mayor, given to theatrical gestures, threatened pedestrians with fines if they crossed streets outside marked pedestrian crosswalks. ABRASPE showed that most São Paulo intersections do not have marked crosswalks, and those that do often have features that make them as dangerous as crossings at "improper" locations. Daros also criticizes sidewalks that are too narrow, collect mud and rain, or are otherwise in need of repair, and the invasion of precious walking spaces by an assortment of light poles, traffic signs and signals, newsstands, hawkers' tables, and the like.

In Ann Arbor, Michigan, where I spent a year working on this book, walking is the mode on which the campus and downtown areas depend. Like most college towns, not much would be left if the university were taken out. Yet walking has apparently never been the subject of a traffic survey and little is done to facilitate or encourage pedestrian movement. The only two exceptions are a pair of overhead walkways: one links a parking garage to the university medical complex, and the second is apparently designed to avoid interrupting motor traffic with a stoplight.

As one leaves the main campus area, sidewalks may be missing from one or both sides of the street. A surface version of the Bermuda Triangle appears at the entrance to North Campus where Fuller Road forms a **Y** with Glazier Way, with apartment buildings on the other side and the Veterans Hospital stranded in the middle. The intersection is located on a hill and a curve that hide pedestrians and cyclists from drivers and vice versa. Walkers and cyclists must cross the intersection unaided by traffic lights in a confusing four-step sequence, and are in danger of being "blindsided" at two points.

The 2.5 km from my apartment to work at the University of Michigan Transportation Research Institute (UMTRI) has several stretches without sidewalks, while other sidewalks connect only buildings and parking lots. In addition to mud and slush on those stretches, there are several points where walkers can be doused by passing cars. Still, my route is better than most. One colleague cannot walk or bike to work since he would have to cross a bridge that has no provision for nonmotorized traffic. Another finds the intervening streets and bike lane excessively dangerous, and goes by car to the gym on a regular basis to pedal a stationary bicycle *(sic)*. Some people test their limits of boredom by purchasing treadmills to get exercise. With decent foot and bike paths, they could get all the exercise they need while going about their daily activities.

Cycling faces even more problems than walking. Most sidewalks end abruptly at the curb with a step of 15 to 30 centimeters (6–12 inches) high; these dropoffs nullify sidewalks as cycle routes and force the cyclist to use the street. The rare bikeways tend to be recreational or token "showcase" projects that are not designed as part of a nonmotorized transport system. Rio de Janeiro has a bikeway that circles Rodrigo de Freitas Lake and another that winds along Flamengo Beach. One has to cross busy avenues to get to them, and they are isolated from the transport system. There are no bikeways along or above city streets where people do business. São Paulo has a bikeway that runs about 250 meters (273 yds.) along the median of busy Juscelino Kubitschek Avenue. It terminates at the first crossing and cyclists are rarely sighted on it. Indeed, it is not clear how they could safely get on or off that "bikeway." Curitiba and a few other cities have paved a path along an abandoned rail line—an easy place to build a bikeway and an unlikely place for cyclists to be. Brasília has three recreational bikeways, none usable for transportation.

The presence of recreational and unusable bikeways often furnishes an argument against providing additional facilities for cycling: "Nobody uses the bikeway we built, so why build more?" I have never seen a cyclist on the São Paulo bikeway and seldom see cyclists anywhere else in the city. Traffic counts reveal almost no bicycles, and they furnish the basic data for the four-stage planning models that "planners" use to project undesirable past trends into the future. Yet a large potential demand for cycling is there. On Sunday, 23 September 1990, the city held its sixteenth Spring Cycling Tour, closing a 10-kilometer stretch of two avenues to motorized traffic. The event attracted an unbelievably large crowd, estimated at 250,000 by the Secretariat of Sports and at 500,000 by the traffic police (Alonso 1990: D-3). The two avenues were so clogged by bicycles that it was difficult to ride them, and many would-be cyclists were forced to dismount and walk their two-wheelers. This occurred from 10 A.M. until 2 P.M., when the avenues were again opened to cars and the bicycles disappeared.

A few Brazilian cities do have at least one nonrecreational bikeway. Most such bikeways were designed to provide a link between a low-income community and an area of employment. Most were built where space was available without regard for any coherent transportation strategy. By providing only an isolated path, such projects have little impact. They neglect, rather than enhance, one of cycling's potential strong points—a degree of flexibility second only to walking.

Two of these bikeways may still be found, with some effort, in two of Brasília's satellite cities. In Guará, a bike path with an extremely rough surface begins mysteriously in the middle of a residential neighborhood and winds back and forth across the nearby streets and busy highways, with no protective signaling or traffic control devices at the intersections; my impression is that the cyclist is better off in the street. The "bikeway" has been torn up and left unrepaired by the light, water, and telephone crews.

In Taguatinga, a bikeway has an equally mysterious beginning, then borders a major avenue lined with stores and warehouses. Cars and trucks park on the poorly marked bikeway and have obliterated it in certain sections.

The situation is somewhat better in Campo Bom, a city of about 35,000 in Brazil's southernmost state, with an urban population density of about 4,200 persons per square kilometer (10,878/square mile). Bicycles, cars and buses each have between 20 and 21 percent of total trips, with walking accounting for 33 percent, and other modes (truck, taxi, motorcycle, animal traction) about 6 percent (Conceição 1985: 8–24). There are some 15,000 bicycles in the city, and about 10,000 are used daily for transportation. Most employment in Campo Bom is concentrated near the city center in shoe factories and in ceramic, paper and metal industries. The factory yards have small but adequate areas reserved for theft-proof parking of bicycles. Up to 800 cyclists may leave a single factory gate at noon and after work.

Four bikeways connect the city center to working-class neighborhoods located several kilometers away. One stretch uses the median of a low-speed residential avenue, while the others run parallel to highways. In the city center, the bikeways either disappear or switch to sidewalks. Unfortunately, the bikeways do not provide a dense enough network to capitalize on the bicycle's potential flexibility, and many areas of the city are far from a bikeway.

In a few other Brazilian cities, there is intense use of bicycles without any visible promotion efforts on behalf of local government. In Timóteo, Minas Gerais (population 41,000 in 1980), the streets are taken over by steelworkers' bicycles within a few minutes after the mill's whistle signals a change of shifts. In Governador Valadares, a larger city in the same region (population 180,000), the sidewalks in front of shops are lined by two wheelers belonging to owners, customers, and employees.

Some special features explain why the bicycle is so important in these cities and foretells coming troubles. First, street paving is very irregular in these cities. Most central streets still have a cobblestone surface. Such surfaces have rough spots between stones and "waves" where rainfall and traffic have combined to form a random set of crests and troughs in the underlying soil. These effects make it extremely uncomfortable for drivers to exceed cyclists' speeds of 10 to 15 km/h (nor are these streets for fragile recreational bikes with narrow wheel rims).

These cities also are characterized by low levels of unemployment; most incomes are low, but not extremely so. This translates into high levels of bicycle ownership and few cars. Since cyclists far outnumber drivers, they tend to take over the entire road, and drivers are forced to tag along behind. These are towns where people have time to stop and talk to their neighbors. People, including drivers, are usually not in a hurry. Most drivers are themselves cyclists and have many relatives and friends who are cyclists; they tend to accord cyclists more than the average respect.

Although these exceptional factors have permitted cycling to endure as a major mode in a few such cities, the trends do not bode well for the bicycle. New cobblestone pavements are now often more expensive than asphalt (depending on the type of stone used). Many residents consider them antiquated, even an embarrassment for a "progressive" city. Bus owners complain that the rough surfaces reduce their vehicles' speed and productivity, while increasing their fuel and maintenance costs. Sooner or later, a mayor decides to "modernize" the city and paves over a few cobblestone streets with asphalt. These new surfaces are rapidly dominated by high-speed cars and trucks, cyclist fatalities soar, and bicycles yield road space to motor vehicles. This process is now complete in Joinville in southern Brazil, a city founded by German immigrants that once stood out for its cycling tradition. The same process was well advanced a few years ago when I visited Governador Valadares and had just started in Timóteo.

Michael Replogle (1989b: 18–19) reports that towns in Indonesia have declared war on pedal rickshaws to "reduce congestion" in city centers. The charge is illogical, since pedicabs occupy less space per person than cars, and it recalls the specious arguments used decades earlier against streetcars in the Americas. Nonetheless, the Indonesian apostles of modernity have ordered the rickshaws thrown into the sea. Literally thousands of small entrepreneurs have lost their main capital investment and are forced to borrow money or rent another rickshaw to get back into business. One of the more depressing aspects of this violence is that motor vehicles cannot effectively replace the services provided by the rickshaws in densely populated urban environments, nor are they a sustainable strategy for the economies involved.

In the United States, the bicycle as a transport mode virtually disappeared from most automobile-dominated cities by the middle decades of this century. A few cities, by and large characterized as college towns, have attempted to bring it back. Ann Arbor is in the forefront, having received an honorable mention among U.S. cities for its bikeway program (*Ann Arbor News,* 10 June 1990: D-12). Unfortunately, the honor does not imply that Ann Arbor has a desirable situation for cycling; it simple means that some cycling is possible there (Von Thurn and Van Eck 1987), in contrast with most American cities. It also reflects the gratefulness cycling enthusiasts show for any crumbs that fall their way from the transport investment table.

Ann Arbor has three types of bicycle facilities:

Sidewalk bikeways. These are by far the most common, but are only narrow sidewalks with a lowered curb at the intersection, meaning they have a small ramp rather than a fifteen- to thirty-centimeter (6–12-in.) drop-off. The investment involved is limited to replacing a piece of curb and sidewalk with a microramp, which can also be used by wheelchairs. Ann Arbor has made a major effort to lower curbs at all intersections, but many corners still feature drop-offs. A number of streets also lack sidewalks on one or both sides, truncating the sidewalk bikeway network.

The cyclist shares all intersections with motorized traffic and is subject to being hit or driven off the sidewalk by parked cars or vehicles entering or leaving the driveways. A typical sidewalk is broken in several spots by tree roots, and is narrow enough to create problems when a cyclist meets other cyclists or pedestrians.

Sidewalk bikeways work best within the central campus area, where they are several meters wide and motor vehicles are not allowed. The high volume of pedestrians, however, slows bicycles to the pedestrians' pace in several locations. Some European cities have a number of sidewalks that are up to 10 meters wide, with different colors or textures built into the surface to separate cyclists from pedestrian traffic.

On-road bike lanes. I refuse to use any such lane in any circumstance. Bicycles are "separated" from motor vehicles by a white line painted on the roadway itself. In addition to facing all the dangers presented by sidewalk bikeways, the cyclist can now be sideswiped or run over from behind. This is an especially likely event when visibility is poor: One study found that cyclists were hit from the rear in 90 percent of nighttime fatalities (Hoque 1990: 10). Some especially pathological versions of these facilities allow parking between the bike lane and the curb: the cyclist may then be maimed by someone opening a car door or reentering the traffic flow.

Class I Rights-of-way. These are bikeways that offer exclusive rights-of-way or ROWs shared only with pedestrians. These are rare, since the typical American urban layout provides for intersections at about every 50 or 100 meters, with driveways in between. Bikeways with exclusive ROWs are thus limited to parks or sites along highways where a river, a wooded area, or some other barrier has precluded random building of residences and businesses. Most cities have precious few such locales, and they are unlikely to connect major pedestrian and bicycle routes. Ann Arbor, the "City of Trees," is somewhat more fortunate, with an exceptionally high number of parks in relation to its population and area.

Nonetheless, there are few Class I bikeways in Ann Arbor that lend themselves to any significant transportation use. The newest facility is squeezed between the Huron River and the railroad tracks, and is complete with a long, expensive wooden bridge. The bikeway links the Bermuda Triangle to a downstream reservoir, and is designed exclusively for recreation. It is probably symptomatic that cycling facilities were transferred a few years ago from the city's transportation division to parks and recreation.

Extending outward from the Bermuda Triangle, however, are two bike paths that can be used for transportation. To appreciate the advantages and disadvantages of each, the reader is invited to accompany me on two of many trips I made during my year at the university as a visiting scholar.

My journey to Main Campus starts from home in an apartment complex just off the Bermuda Triangle. The first problem is to get to the bike path, since the buildings' entrances and exits are designed exclusively for cars. There are no sidewalks. I solve the problem by heading the wrong way out the entrance, leaving space to "bail out" should a car come roaring in. There is also no sidewalk on the south side of Fuller Road, so I await a chance to cross Fuller to get onto what remains of a sidewalk on the other side. The Bermuda Triangle lies just ahead and I meet a number of people who have just crossed it after leaving their cars in the parking lot below and are now nearing work at the Veterans Hospital. No one was run over today.

Getting across the Triangle during rush hour is risky and also virtually impossible without getting off one's bike. On the other side, there is a choice of following the narrow and broken shoulder of Fuller Road, or facing a steep climb on the bikeway through the edge of a wooded area. For safety, I take the latter. Below, the "bikeway" gets progressively nearer the road, and actually becomes the shoulder of the roadway near the bridge. The presence of an open field and Fuller Park on the right produces only two intersections over the next half-kilometer. From Maiden Lane on, the path degenerates into a side-walk bikeway with frequent intersections and heavily trafficked streets through to the core area of Main Campus.

My second trip, from home to UMTRI, lies in the opposite direction and offers several uninspiring options. The first goes through North Campus, via the Bermuda Triangle. Most of this is sidewalk bikeway, the climbs are quite steep, and the sidewalks disappear far-ther up. There is also a point where the cyclist will be hard-pressed to cross an intersection and make the turn without going off the sidewalk or hitting a stop sign that has been artfully placed at the wrong spot.

The two shortest routes have even more extensive sections without sidewalks. In December's snow and cold, I walked these routes, winding through parking lots and tramping across fields. For biking, I choose the longest route, since it offers the least interference from motor vehicles. Again, there is the problem of getting on the bikeway. I use the driveway exit, wait for an open space in the traffic flow, speed across the road, dip into the ditch, and pedal up a 3-meter hill diagonally. Not exactly a route for the aged, and even I cannot fol-low it in winter. Right ahead is a dangerous intersection, followed by a long stretch interrupted only by three entrance/exits from Huron High School. The first few meters are an obstacle course of tree roots and protruding slabs of broken asphalt. Shortly thereafter one reaches the lowlands.

Here I am reminded of the three principles of highway con-struction: drainage, drainage, and drainage. Well known to the Romans and the Incas, these principles were ignored on the next 2 kilometers of Ann Arbor bikeway. Most stretches are built below the level of the surrounding terrain, with no drainage tiles or even a respectful acquiescence to the effects of gravity on water: this is a cowpath with an asphalt covering. Ponds form after rains, and freez-ing turns the whole mess into a vast sheet of ice. On some days, the bikeway offers the only spots in the area where water collects; at some points, freezing and thawing have destroyed the asphalt surface altogether. Near my destination at UMTRI, some 30 meters of bike-way were torn up in October 1989 during unrelated construction work, leaving me the choice of using a busy highway with a high curb or plowing through a challenging stretch of mud and rubble (I tried both and opted for the latter). This stretch was well marked with a green and white bikeway sign, to which someone with a sense of humor once added a helpful handwritten paper sign, "Walk Bikes." The sign disappeared after the first rain, and the stretch was not repaired until July 1990.

From there on, I face only two dangerous crossings. A 20-centimeter drop off a curb and the use of a short stretch of the roadway get me to UMTRI, where, for lack of a bike rack, I chain my bike to a small tree, occasionally shared with a colleague's bike.

Climate and Bicycle Technology

Ann Arbor makes a serious attempt to keep a number of sidewalks and bikeways open during the winter, using tractors with snowplows, rotary brushes, and salt spreaders. If the bikeways were built according to the three principles of highway construction, they would be usable on virtually all winter days. As the mathematicians say, if and only if.

It is said that the Eskimos have a large number of words to describe different forms of snow and ice. I began to appreciate this in my "field research" conducted while trying to get around Ann Arbor by bicycle in the winter. I discovered that most types of ice are punctuated with enough snow or rough spots that it is possible to cycle at moderate speeds, at least if the tires have good tread. Three-wheelers can go through anything but heavy drifts (a few models are commercially available as minor adaptations of regular bicycle models, including the narrow-tire, multispeed, lightweight variety). Light, remarkably warm, insulated clothing is now available at moderate prices and permits cycling in cold weather. In severe cold, such as $-15°$ Celsius (5° F), or at somewhat higher temperatures with strong winds, some precautions are necessary, such as a ski mask or scarf to protect the face, earmuffs, and well-insulated gloves and footwear. (All this is in vain if bikeways are not swept clear of snow or if they are designed with "cowpath technology.")

Few heavily populated areas of the world present such extreme cold. In other areas, the cyclist adjusts the pace to the weather. In chilly weather, a brisk pace and a sweater keep one warm. When it is hot, a slower pace avoids exertion and still creates a refreshing breeze: the cyclist keeps cooler than the pedestrian or occupants of motor vehicles without air conditioning (an energy-wasting device absent from much of the world's vehicle fleet). For those who ride long distances in hot weather to get to their workplaces, showers can be installed at low cost. Rain can either be ignored or fended off with lightweight rain suits that cost about $20 and can be folded compactly to fit into a briefcase, purse, or backpack.

Topography can be an important limitation for bicycle use, but its negative effect should not be exaggerated. Hilly areas make cycling more difficult and, other things constant, decrease bicycle use. However, modern, multispeed bicycles have reduced this disadvantage considerably. The reasonably fit cyclist now dismounts only on severe slopes, and gravity presents a partial compensation on the way down. Moreover, most cities are located on reasonably flat areas or ones that present fairly extensive level areas for roadway construction. The mountainous city of Itabirito in the Brazilian interior, for example, had considerable bicycle use even when most two-wheelers were of the one-speed variety. Most important roadways lay in the valley, and one of the main destinations was a steel mill located outside the city. Cyclists are harder to find in recent decades as the roadway has become excessively dangerous, due to the increase in speed and volume of motorized traffic.

There is a wide variety of bicycle and tricycle technologies and accessories currently available. A lack of information about them has been an implicit barrier for appropriate planning of facilities for non-motorized transport, and for that reason they are mentioned below.

For personal transport and carrying the attendant small burdens, a bicycle of the one- or multispeed variety provides good service. Ideally, it should be equipped with fenders, a chain guard, a basket (or other carrier with elastic cables), a chain and padlock, a bell, reflective tape or lights, a helmet, and a rain suit. In most countries, this corresponds to an outlay of about $200 if the bike and all other items are purchased new. A serviceable used bicycle can frequently be purchased for as little as $30, and, at the upper end, several thousand dollars can be spent on sophisticated models. The fenders keep the cyclist clean if minimal attention is given to drainage in bikeway construction. Nothing on the bike should be oiled—the oil only serves to collect dirt and soil clothes. Without it, any dirt on clothes or hands (even from repositioning a slipped chain) comes off with soap and water. Those using slacks with wide cuffs should narrow them with a band or clip to avoid tangling with pedals or chain. Special fasteners are sold in bike shops, but a paper clip or woman's hair clip works equally well.

The most trouble-free bicycle is the one-speed model with standard tires and rear-hub brake. The lighter-weight, multispeed models are also reliable if made of good material and of the type with gears changed by sliding the chain from one sprocket to another (those with in-hub gears seldom hold up for long). The chain occasionally slips off during shifting, especially if the gears are poorly adjusted, and the hand brakes need occasional adjusting and maintenance to perform properly (special pads should be used to provide adequate braking in wet conditions). Other things constant, the more speeds a bike has, the more slip-offs and adjustment problems it will give the rider, but 3-, 4-, and 5-speed models can also be practically maintenance-free. Models with 10 speeds or more are a decided advantage where there are appreciable grades or the cyclist wants to pedal at high speeds. Many sport models have excessively thin wheels that are easily damaged by potholes and curbs; fenderless, they throw dirt on the cyclist's clothing and parcels. (Fenders may be added at bike shops.)

For cargo transport, there are many types of human-powered utility vehicles (HPUVs). J. Vander Tuin (1986: 1) defines a HPUV as a human-powered vehicle (or vehicle-trailer combination) designed specifically for carrying cargo or passengers weighing more than 40 kg (88 lb.) in addition to the rider. HPUVs vary from cycle rickshaws to small trucks and trailers, including one capable of carrying a washing machine, considerable furniture, or a complete set of camping equipment. The Swiss post office owns 3,700 utility bikes and more than 4,000 heavy-duty cycle-trailers, finding them the least expensive way of delivering mail. Brazil's postal service also has a number of utility bikes in cities where traffic permits their use. In Bogotá, a major bakery reduced its distribution costs from 27 percent to 8 percent of overhead by setting up a fleet of 800 HPUVs. In Europe, Asia, and the Americas, HPUVs are also used for urban and farm-to-market food delivery; milk, bottled gas, and newspaper delivery; street vending; laundry pickup and delivery; refuse collection; child transport; carrying pumps, lawnmowers, and other machines; and many other uses.

Vander Tuin reviews an incredible array of special HPUV designs, including 2-, 3-, and 4-wheeled vehicles and 1- to 4-wheeled sidecars and trailers. Except for the 2-wheelers, these vehicles present problems associated with turning and use on nonlevel surfaces. He recommends the use of smaller, stronger wheels, with interlocking tires and wheels to avoid slippage of tire on rim, along with multispeed hubs and reliable brakes. Improved, lighter-weight, multispeed models are being designed, tested, and in some cases marketed by both commercial firms and appropriate-technology groups (Balen 1987; CESTA 1986; Replogle 1988b; 1989b; Stallings 1981).

In 1987, 99 million bicycles were manufactured worldwide, compared with 33 million automobiles (Lowe 1989: 13). Bicycle production is concentrated in Asia, with 41 million in China alone. In most countries, they are used primarily for transportation. Yet we have seen that bicycles and HPUVs receive little support—and at times outright hostility—from local governments. In most cases they are threatened by an increasing amount of high-speed motor vehicle traffic.

An Appropriate Environment for Nonmotorized Transport

We have seen the inadequacy of strategies that seek to accommodate pedestrians and cyclists without making significant changes in urban layouts and facilities for motorized transportation. Sidewalks and sidewalk bicycle routes are often reduced to obstacle courses. An occasional trail along a forest, river, abandoned rail line, or highway does not a network make.

The numerous plans that present such projects are based on the implicit assumptions that motorized traffic must predominate and that space and expense for nonmotorized modes should come out of what is left over (if anything) after the motorized modes have been taken care of; road space is for motor vehicles, not people (Wright 1989b).

A direct consequence of this type of thinking is the lack of quality options for nonmotorized transport in high-income cities and a deterioration of conditions of transport in low-income cities where most people cannot afford cars or, in many cases, any other form of motorized transportation.

Street layouts and traffic facilities should be designed on the opposite assumption: the safety and ease of walking and cycling are the first priority. Motorized transportation can then be accommodated in whatever areas are left, with priority given to buses and other high-capacity modes that complement the nonmotorized modes on medium- and longer-distance trips.

These principles are so far removed from practice in most cities around the world that they sound like science fiction. In high-income, sparsely populated cities, there is some question whether it is possible to implement them at reasonable costs or, indeed, if there is any significant demand for facilities so designed. Nonetheless, there are enough examples of such strategies in medium- and high-density cities to show that they are an economical and successful solution. The first illustrations are drawn from Brazilian experience, followed by references to some recent European examples.

Case 1. Belo Horizonte is perhaps the most spectacular demonstration of the positive effects of pedestrian–bus-oriented strategies on the quality of life in a Brazilian city. In reality, the Belo Horizonte example represents an experiment with its own control groups, since the changes made within the original city limits were not extended to the contiguous areas.

The original city was built as the new state capital of Minas Gerais in the 1890s following the general lines used in Washington, D.C., La Plata (Argentina), and Tijuana. The basic idea was to increase the accessibility of all points in the city for pedestrians and horse-drawn vehicles by superimposing diagonal avenues onto the conventional grid pattern of parallel and perpendicular streets and avenues. This cobweb design resulted in the convergence of traffic from a large number of ways at gigantic rotundas or circles, as shown in Figure 1. At the center of each rotunda was a monument of questionable taste surrounded by a few square meters of grass. The unit was an oversized forerunner of the roundabout or traffic circle, with all traffic movements imaginable permitted within the shaded area. With the advent of large numbers of cars in the 1950s, the rotunda areas became extremely dangerous for pedestrians who, for lack of alternative paths, were forced to use them. The residential streets leading to the rotundas also became high-speed ways, even during the rush hours when the rotundas gridlocked. Belo Horizonte had the highest per-vehicle pedestrian death rate in Brazil and was challenging São Paulo, a center several times larger, for the absolute leadership (GEIPOT 1987: 37–40).

In the late 1970s, a group of young professionals with training in architecture, city planning, and traffic engineering came up with a plan for altering the basic structure of those intersections to recreate the environment the preautomobile planner had in mind—making life more practical for the pedestrian. The problem areas were transformed by eliminating the central rotundas, extending the sidewalks and other traffic-dividing spaces forward to the new intersection, and installing traffic lights with phases for pedestrians. The convergences from residential streets were eliminated, and the parts of those streets nearest the intersections were converted into small parking lots. Through traffic was physically barred by making the parking lots cul-de-sacs; each entrance and exit was narrowed into a single lane with a sharp curve to ensure very slow speeds, and a safety island was placed between them. An additional benefit was the reclamation of up to 0.5 hectare (1.2 acres) of urban space for small parks, benches, cultural events, and so forth at each of the former rotundas.

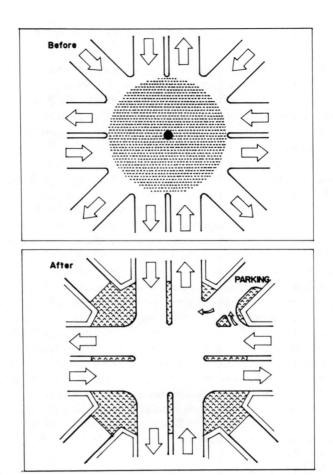

Figure 1   Before modification in 1980 (top,) *a typical intersection in Belo Horizonte funneled traffic from perpendicular and diagonal avenues and streets into a giant rotunda (shaded area). All right-bound maneuvers occurred as drivers went around the central island (dot) and onto any of the other streets and avenues. The original design shortened walking distances and facilitated flows of horse-drawn vehicles; by the 1970s, heavy motor traffic transformed the rotunda into a death trap for pedestrians and an inferno for drivers. The modified design* (bottom) *replaced about an acre of asphalt with miniature malls, sidewalks, and safety islands. Sidewalks and medians were extended forward to force drivers to follow one of a few well-defined paths. Traffic lights were used to control flows, with phases for pedestrian crossing, and the local diagonal streets were closed to through traffic, with the first block used for parking. Citywide accident rates fell by three-fourths with these modifications in core-area intersections.*
Source: *Wright 1990: 7, based on GEIPOT (1987: 37–40).*

In 1976, the traffic death rate in Belo Horizonte stood at 45 per 10,000 vehicles. In 1981, just after these design changes had been implemented, it fell dramatically to 12. Since the statistics are aggregate for the city while the improvements were limited to the central area planned in the 1890s, the real reduction within the modified area itself was even more spectacular than the already impressive statistics indicate. Bus lines were also simultaneously redrawn to reduce the number of transfers for a user to get from the original bus stop to a given destination.

I was in Belo Horizonte on two occasions before the modifications were made and found it to be one of the most unpleasant urban areas it had been my misfortune to visit. Many shopkeepers were preparing to move out of the decaying core area to planned shopping centers in the suburbs. Upon returning in the mid- and late 1980s, I found within the "experimental" area one of the most pleasant urban environs in Brazil, and one that would also rate quite highly in Europe. Traffic noise has ceased to be a problem in many areas. Police officers can do something besides direct traffic: the feeling of physical safety in the Savassi area is substantial enough that the sidewalks are crowded at night with people pausing to buy newspapers and magazines, ice cream cones, and the like, and conversing at the outdoor tables of the numerous cafés. Shopkeepers are thriving, and the suburban shopping centers have gotten a delayed and rather modest start. Untreated areas of the city regretfully continue to be, for the most part, dangerous and unattractive for the pedestrian and thus places those with a choice in the matter prefer to avoid.

Case 2. Curitiba, at around 1.5 million population, is perhaps half the size of Belo Horizonte, and has the reputation for being Brazil's model city. In 1970, however, it was in danger of becoming a Brazilian version of some of Detroit's more negative examples of car culture. One street, XV de Novembro, was particularly depressing. It had gridlocked with the associated noise and chemical pollution invading the neighboring shops, schools, and offices.

During the ensuing decade, a former head of the municipal planning commission became mayor and was able to put his ideas into practice. A number of streets in the downtown were closed to all motor vehicles, and only buses were allowed on others. Bus speeds and noise in the central area were reduced by confining them to narrow channels built 15 centimeters below the adjoining pedestrian mall surface. In other areas, cars could enter and leave buildings on similar channels at pedestrianlike speeds, but no through traffic was allowed. Still other innovations included:

"advancing" the sidewalks toward the center of the roadway at pedestrian crossings. This confined cars to narrower, more predictable paths and reduced the crossing distances over which pedestrians were exposed to accidents;

closing some residential streets to through traffic;

modifying the geometry and surfaces of other residential streets to hold vehicular traffic to a crawl and make it safe for children to play outside;

providing a large number of amenities, such as shelters and telephones at the bus stops and a limited number of vendors providing newspapers, magazines, coffee, and other refreshments;

creating avenues with improved boarding–alighting facilities and semi-express bus service;

providing the best bus service and lowest fares of any large Brazilian city (Fares have often been in the 15- to 20-cent range and provide enough profit to keep unsubsidized private operators in business.)

Presently, the XV de Novembro street is a pedestrian mall from end to end, although punctuated by a few intersections. The local population has embraced the aesthetic improvements, the tasteful landscaping, and the presence of some flowerstands by renaming it "The Street of the Flowers." Not incidentally, Curitiba also has the lowest per vehicle accident rate in Brazil. Again, in the areas affected by the walk–bus strategy, both pedestrian and other fatalities are lower in relation to the traffic volume than in untreated areas of the city.

Case 3. Campina Grande is a medium-sized city in the interior of the Brazilian northeast. It stands out as a relatively prosperous community in a geographical region characterized by considerable poverty. Some years ago a colleague, José Alex Sant'Anna, headed a group responsible for both physical infrastructure and the bus service (Urbema 1985). Within a few years the group had redesigned much of the downtown area, created pedestrian malls and safety islands, and implanted unconventional geometry at a number of intersections to force cars to go slowly. Bus services received priority and routes were redesigned to ensure that virtually all trips could be made on one bus rather than two or more. Buses and bus stops were color-coded and given improved numerical identification. The colors and large route numbers on all four sides of the bus provide clear visual information for users regarding which buses serve each stop and their respective destinations. The city's outdoor public telephone booths enable users to register their complaints and thus inform the bus transit agency staff of any problems with the bus services. The same phone system enables users to receive information on routes, stops, and schedules. Only the São Paulo metro and Campina Grande buses offer such service in all of Brazil. In its class of cities, Campina Grande also has the best and least expensive bus service (with fares of 10 to 15 cents a ride) and the best environment for pedestrians.

Case 4. São Paulo, with relatively high car-ownership figures and high population density, suffers from monumental gridlock. Nonetheless, there are some positive examples that stand out in the sea of mediocrity that characterizes the city's transportation system.

Some years ago the city's historic central area was so congested it was impossible to get a taxi there. Taxi drivers also refused to take passengers there if they boarded elsewhere. Average bus speeds fell to less than 5 km/h. Noise and pollution reached intolerable levels. The area was finally closed to cars, with some streets pedestrianized and others reserved for taxis and buses. The malls are now rather pleasant areas, and noise is no longer a major problem in the immediate environs. Taxis can now be obtained in the central area and buses move reasonably well. Pollution continues to be a problem, as the majority of it floats in from nearby sources where traffic continues to be intense.

The historic center and the Santo Amaro–9 de Julho busway mentioned earlier are the only central locations where traffic speeds have increased in recent years. Due to the "Henry Ford paradox," the rest of the city has watched gridlock extend to cover most daylight hours and most of the municipality.

Case 5. For some good examples of bicycle and pedestrian planning, we turn to Europe, where the Dutch, Danes, Scandinavians, and Germans have taken the lead in improving conditions for nonmotorized traffic.

One concept involves an integral new city design with roadways separated from ways for cyclists and pedestrians, exemplified by Lelystad in the Netherlands. A relatively small town, Lelystad has a commercial and public-services sector placed at the center, surrounded by residential neighborhoods. Each neighborhood is linked to the downtown area by a highway and a bikeway, and the two ways are separated from each other by a fairly wide strip of land covered with grass and trees. Each neighborhood is connected to its counterparts on either side by a pedestrian–cyclist bridge over a roadway, with the road built slightly below the surrounding terrain. The bridges and roadways are built into the landscape in such a way that the cyclist is only required to go up a slight ramp rather than to "climb a mountain" in order to get over the bridge. Housing is of the townhouse variety: the design employs parking lots rather than individual driveways and entrances to avoid high speeds and danger to nonmotorized transport. The main negative factor of this layout is the excessive spatial separation of functions. The neighborhoods have few if any services, making them unduly dull and requiring relatively more trips to the center.

England offers an example of a half-hearted effort to retrofit a bikeway network to a "new town" (Milton Keynes) after it was already under development. The bikeways have been criticized by British cyclists for excessive grades, poor visibility and lighting, unprotected obstructions, inadequate posting of crossing, and poor maintenance (McClintock 1987: 271). Dense plantings along the roadsides decrease social surveillance and increase danger of assault, encouraging cyclists to use the roadways rather than the separate facilities. As a result, the city has a higher than average cycle accident rate.

In traditional neighborhoods, the Dutch have attempted to tame the automobile through a variety of measures designed to create a "woonerf," or "living backyard" in residential areas (C.R.O.W. 1989). Before the idea had a legal basis or even a standard definition, it had spread beyond residential areas to include shopping districts, downtown areas, and historical sites. Subsequently, the term was shortened to "erf" or "backyard" and given legal and engineering definitions.

The basic idea subverts the grid pattern of straight streets and avenues. Areas of the city are conceptualized as a backyard (erf), a place for families and pets to roam in without being run over by speeding cars. The entrances are marked by traffic humps to slow vehicles to a crawl. The ensuing street winds inward, lined by stakes, trees, and even bollards connected by chains to guide drivers to parking areas and to remind them constantly that they are not on a street or highway. In general, through traffic is not permitted; the erf is a cul-de-sac. The car is conceived as a guest, welcome only in certain areas and on the condition of good behavior. There is an effort to avoid overly obvious separations of road space from pedestrian space; motorists would increase speed if they identified their path as a roadway rather than as a backyard. Trees and benches, however, are used to keep cars off strictly pedestrian areas, such as playgrounds and miniparks. Speed-reducing devices are omnipresent and include off-center lines, poles, booths, height differences, "sleeping policemen" (traffic humps), and anything else that, psychologically or physically, slows drivers down. Entrances have clear markings and speed-reducing changes at least 20 meters from the erf itself. Heavy traffic is not allowed, and even buses and heavy through bicycle traffic are discouraged. Areas for loading and unloading of trucks are marked, reserved, and properly dimensioned.

In Germany, a similar but more modest idea has been adopted. There it is considered that creating prohibitions for automobile traffic would negatively affect welfare if widely adopted. Instead, whole residential zones, rather than individual streets, are marked for maximum speeds of 30 km/h (Collin 1990). Near these areas authorities attempt to provide faster roadways (50 km/h) for transit, goods vehicles, and the private car. Traffic lights, lane markings, and pedestrian crossing marks are removed from these zones to avoid distinctions between the roadway and other uses in the hope that this will decrease speeds.

The evaluators are optimistic about the results: "Tempo 30 has shown its effectiveness; with limited resources it is possible to increase the quality of life in neighborhoods" (Collin 1990: 13). There has been a measurable reduction in emissions, accidents, and speed. The data, however, also reveal that the improvement is small, and the results would have been much more substantial had physical modifications in the street structure been employed, following the erf model.

In Scandinavia, town planning and residential living and parking environments have also been modified to tame the automobile and to provide a less dangerous and more pleasant environment for walking, cycling and other activities (Plowden and Hillman 1984: 189–98). On the European continent, the Dutch have been very active in producing engineering solutions to improve safety of cyclists and pedestrians, with specially designed traffic lights, turn lanes, and the like.

Some similar modifications have been introduced in Brazilian cities. "Sleeping policemen" have become very popular in residential zones everywhere. In Curitiba, residential streets have been blocked off at one end. Children can then play near the barrier with relatively little danger, and problems with noise and vibration virtually disappear. The only requirement is that the neighboring streets be equipped to handle the increased traffic. In some areas, erflike environments have been created. And one neighborhood finally got rid of drag racing by implanting the winding "island roadway" described in Chapter 4.

Two conclusions are clear: (1) physical barriers and structural modifications are much more effective in producing the desired changes than speed limits and policing—they are the only measures likely to work at all in countries where drivers have a low degree of training and self-discipline; (2) the measures are still woefully incomplete in all countries. There are only a few areas in Amsterdam or Hamburg where I would feel reasonably safe as a cyclist, and nowhere in Latin America except on a few recreational bikeways.

Pedestrians benefit relatively more from an erf environment than cyclists, simply because bicycles are used for longer distances. Bicycles require a network of bikeways with exclusive rights-of-way or, alternatively, a series of interconnected erven (plural of erf). Lelystad is the only city I am familiar with that has a comprehensive network of bikeways and erven. Other cities have, at best, an incomplete mixture of (semi-)exclusive bikeways and sidewalk bikeways, interspersed with avenues and highways that constitute formidable barriers to the use of bicycles. The "bikeways," as our examples have shown, rarely offer exclusive rights-of-way for any significant distance. Sidewalk bikeways are tolerable only for a short distance or where they offer long stretches (say, 300 to 1,000 meters) between intersections. If there is considerable pedestrian or cycle traffic, they also need to be wide (preferably 5 to 10 meters), with color or texture distinctions on the surface to separate cyclists from pedestrians. These conditions are occasionally found in European cities, but are still the exception rather than the rule. Bike lanes—that is, stripes painted on the street— are at best a waste of paint. At worst they convey a false sense of security for the cyclist; they offer no real protection from motorized traffic.

The above situation explains an apparent paradox: although a number of cities, from Hamburg to Ann Arbor, publish maps of bikeways that appear impressive on paper, they actually present only a few routes where biking is convenient and safe. Even by summing all the Class I bikeways and high-standard sidewalk bikeways, the resulting "network" is a very small subset of the street network available to cars. The North American street pattern results in a particularly truncated set of possibilities, due to the prominence of the short city block and the ubiquitous driveway.

A similar situation exists for pedestrians. A few city centers, such as Curitiba, Belo Horizonte, and Hamburg, offer pedestrian malls and integrated transit services. But these environments are not found throughout the city. Curitiba's urban network is severed by two major highways, where a large percentage of fatal accidents occur (Pereira and Ribeiro 1988). The *pedestrianization* of the core area has not been extended to other heavily trafficked streets and avenues. On the outskirts of the city, communities spring up along streets and roads where no sidewalks exist. There, pedestrians are often killed while walking at the edge of the roadway, especially in rainy weather when they try to avoid wet grass and mud by walking in or near the roadway.

At the beginning of this chapter we raised the question of the changes needed to make the nonmotorized modes safer and more widely used as transport options. For the medium- to high-population-density cities we have been discussing (in Europe, Latin America, Asia, and parts of Africa), the answer is clear.

First, cycling needs a basic network of bikeways with exclusive rights-of-way that act as expressways or avenues for the exclusive use of nonmotorized transport. This network should take the cyclist to within some 300 meters of the most frequent destinations, within 500 meters of most others, and in no case more than 1 kilometer from a destination. The final stretch of a bike trip would then be made on a high-quality sidewalk bikeway. The sidewalk bikeway should normally be at least 5 meters wide (even if that means reducing a residential street to one lane and one-way traffic), with a minimum distance of something like 300 meters between intersections. All intersections should provide for safe crossing without excessive delays, by adequate signaling, safety islands, traffic humps, or vertical separation. When vertical separation is used, the cycle bridge should be built with a modest incline and height and on a natural path.

Next, walking needs safe and convenient paths throughout the city, preferably with easy access to public transportation.

In most cities, the initial requirement implies major changes in the layout and rules for use of streets, avenues, parking lots, and other facilities. These include:

closing many less-trafficked streets to through traffic, converting them to malls or (after widening sidewalks) parking lots: each dead end removes an intersection from a sidewalk, a bikeway, or sidewalk bikeway;

widening sidewalks at most corners to confine cars to more predictable paths and to reduce crossing distances and exposure of pedestrians and cyclists to accidents;

replacing a number of parking spaces with widened sidewalks equipped with bike racks; ten bicycles can be parked in the space needed by a parked car, and widening sidewalks reduces the distances pedestrians are exposed to accidents at crossings;

modifying or eliminating driveways at entrances and exits of buildings and parking lots for the convenience of pedestrian and cycle traffic;

using all the erf planning techniques to discipline motor vehicle movements and parking;

reserving spaces for delivery vehicles, to avoid double parking and difficulties with provision of essential services (this may be done, for example, by placing rounded cement slabs on strategic parking spaces as barriers for private cars, which larger vehicles can traverse);

installing elevated walkways and bikeways where required to cross over major highways and expressways; both bridges and elevated longitudinal sections must be installed when necessary to complete the network and guarantee easy and rapid movement of pedestrians and cyclists over busy thoroughfares.

The above list is a technical specification of the measures necessary to provide nonmotorized traffic with a comprehensive network of exclusive and semi-exclusive paths like those motor vehicles now use. All of these measures have been used in cities around the world, but (excepting a Lelystad or two) no municipality has adopted all of them throughout its urban area. This raises the issues of appropriateness, cost, and political acceptability.

Such solutions are appropriate to urban areas with mixed land use and reasonably high population densities, precisely those situations where most daily activities can be performed on foot or by bicycle. They may appear somewhat exotic in low-density areas, particularly where land use is highly segregated by zoning or monofunction development projects. Even in these cases, however, some piecemeal application may be appropriate.

The cost varies basically with the type of materials used. A lot of money can be spent to make malls and sidewalks attractive if brick, special stones, or tiles are employed. A low-income city can be creative and economical—some well-placed dirt, local plants, and a bit of cement may be equally attractive at a fraction of the cost. The money can come directly out of municipal funds, or shopkeepers and residents can pay directly for the improvements and upkeep along their properties. In national terms, the projects are potential money-makers; they reduce domestic use of petroleum fuels and other transportation-related expenditures, including costs of accidents. Since pedestrian areas increase in value, city property assessments and tax receipts also increase. Residents and most other users benefit by decreased transportation expenses, and the business community will enjoy a larger clientele.

The political acceptability of such measures is questionable. The underlying principles are the opposite of those implicitly adopted in most cities around the world. Inertia is a powerful force, especially when helped along by the highway lobby. Yet, piecemeal, a number of European cities are adopting these principles. The measures would be a major boon to the vast majority of citizens of developing countries who do not own cars, as well as an important step in alleviating the considerable poverty and social inequalities in such societies. Where such measures have been employed, the elites have frequently approved—they too are pedestrians. In Buenos Aires, the Calle Florida and other pedestrian malls are favorite spots for car-owning families to go on Saturday nights (or any other time). There is more valuable real estate, windowshopping, and entertainment to be found there than anywhere else in the city.

Improved Bus Services

For cities in China, India, Africa, and other regions where car ownership is very low, the above measures may well suffice. Almost everyone depends on nonmotorized transport for virtually all trips, and the best policy is to make walking and cycling as safe and easy as possible.

These measures are also essential in medium- and high-density cities that depend heavily on motorized transport, but they are no longer sufficient. Transit must also be improved. The excessively high cost of metros and the inability to insert a significant number of surface rail lines into the urban tissue imply an important role for buses. Yet this role cannot be adequately performed by overcrowded buses operating in mixed, stop-and-go traffic.

As seen earlier, there is a trade-off between frequency and flexibility of bus services. Geographical coverage must be reduced somewhat to maintain high frequencies at reasonable costs. Complementary walking or cycling is required to reach a large percentage of streets. For healthy citizens, this can be a pleasant, easy, and regular way of meeting minimal exercise requirements if erf environments are provided throughout the city. This should be an important and explicit selling point in marketing transit services and erf projects.

One specific task of planning and operating bus services is the provision of rapid, high-frequency service to all major travel points in the city, with a minimum of transfers. In low-density, automobile-dominated cities, this is a very difficult task; a greater burden will be placed on complementary walking and bicycling precisely in cities where people are accustomed to driving within a few meters of their destinations and parking in garages attached to their houses.

In congested areas typical of medium- and high-population-density cities, the task is potentially much easier, but requires a network of busways and semi-exclusive bus lanes. It also requires creating a "user-friendly" system of routes. To use another computer industry analogy, transit authorities have to create and to market better hardware and better software.

The basic idea of a semi-exclusive bus lane or a busway is simple enough: a curb or some other lateral barrier must be implanted in the roadway to physically reserve lengthy longitudinal sections for buses only. Where bus traffic is not particularly heavy, other high-occupancy vehicles can share these ways. "Lengthy" sections, however, are seldom available in a typical urban grid of streets and avenues, so a number of perpendicular streets must be transformed into cul-de-sacs to reduce the number of intersections (geometrical change at the other end should be used to control entrance and exit speed). Each cul-de-sac is a step toward an erf environment. Elevated sections can be used at some major crossings, enhancing the bus lane's advantage at a considerable increase in costs and aesthetic problems introduced by such structures.

Almost any street or avenue can be transformed into a semi-exclusive bus lane or busway if other traffic and parking are removed. This is a good solution, as shown by the downtown Curitiba busways. There is a danger, however, that the absence of other vehicles will lull the pedestrian into being unprepared for the sudden approach of a high-speed bus. Some solutions include slowing buses down a bit, and using landscaping and physical barriers to keep pedestrians off the busway. In Curitiba, bus speeds are moderate to low, and the vehicles are noisy enough to announce their presence without creating a major acoustic problem. High-speed buses require physical separation in such an environment, and moderate-speed, silent trolleybuses should be fitted with an identifying noisemaker to avoid running over unsuspecting pedestrians. The use of a band of rough surfacing on the malls about 2 meters from the bus path is a useful way of warning the pedestrian that danger is ahead; this precaution is essential for the deaf.

Traffic authorities may insert a bus-only lane in a multilane avenue. This avoids the need to close other streets to car traffic and parking, and offers the possibility of achieving reasonably high bus speeds. Private-car drivers are partially compensated for the reduced space at their disposal by the removal of the buses from the remaining lanes. Unfortunately, the heavy traffic on these avenues sacrifices the benefits of placing buses on their own exclusive streets as a step toward creating an bus–erf environment.

Other problems also appear. The continuation of car and truck traffic in one or two lanes in each direction requires that drivers enter and exit from the right side of the avenue, constantly invading the right lane (in non-British systems). The bus lane must then be moved to the center of the avenue and additional space created for pedestrians to stand, board, and alight, either from a safety island or a station environment. This problem has largely been overlooked or inadequately treated in many bus corridor projects, including the Santo Amaro–9 de Julho example cited earlier.

The correct approach is to provide adequate pedestrian space at stops. When 15,000 or more passengers are being transported per hour in one direction, considerable space is needed for waiting and walking. This space requirement is minimized if boarding–alighting facilities are placed on the median and used by passengers headed in either direction. Unfortunately, that solution requires accident-prone counterflow bus lanes or buses with doors on the left side, which in turn requires: (1) manufacturing buses with doors on both sides; (2) redoing all bus stops in the city for left-side boarding–alighting; or (3) manufacturing left-door buses for such corridors, with right-door buses unable to use them. Only manufacturing buses with doors on both sides appears to be a workable solution, and it implies an increase in cost and either a bus retrofitting problem or a couple of decades to replace existing buses with the newer models.

To my knowledge, practical experience with such options for buses is rare to nonexistent, although most passenger trains have doors on both sides as standard equipment. Traffic authorities have either left insufficient boarding space on the medians or taken space from car lanes, sidewalks or neighboring buildings. A better solution would be the conversion of an avenue with three lanes in each direction to a bus lane plus a car lane in each direction. Bus "convoys" (with buses traveling in a fixed order) work well only in highly disciplined environments. Otherwise, the buses require passing space, particularly in the vicinity of stops.

Boarding at the median encourages pedestrians to take short

cuts when crossing half of the avenue to catch their buses, a dangerous situation requiring fences and other unpleasant devices to funnel bus users to less dangerous crossings. The Santo Amaro corridor, along with ones in Porto Alegre and other Brazilian cities, are dangerous for pedestrians—although probably no more so that the usual traffic schemes they replaced. Such schemes should be accompanied by speed-reduction devices in the car lanes near pedestrian crossings, unless grade separation is provided.

Grade separation should not require the pedestrian to walk an extra 200 meters or climb up 6 meters of stairs or ramp. Some of the pedestrian bridges inserted into the street networks in São Paulo and Rio de Janeiro look more like training courses for mountain climbers than pedestrian facilities usable by the elderly, handicapped, and infirm. Well-designed pedestrian bridges, such as the one near Hamburg's Congress Center or the one along the Flamengo beach in Rio, blend so well into the landscape and the pedestrian's path that no one would think of not using them. Those are the only type that should be built. If a pedestrian–cyclist bridge looks like an obstacle course, another solution is needed.

Avenues and expressways with three or more lanes in each direction are often better places for buses to travel on than to pick up and drop off passengers. By themselves, they cannot provide a sufficiently complete network to permit high-level transit services, nor do they promote erf environments in the vicinity. The formation of a suitable bus network should include conversion of other streets and avenues to exclusive bus use.

Robert Cervero rightly criticizes the "spoke and hub" pattern of bus routes found in most American cities (1986: 109). These routes take everyone to the downtown bus station and require a transfer to go anywhere else. For most destinations, this yields time-consuming, indirect routes. Cervero recommends a "cobweb" network of bus routes with timed transfers, so that the user can go from anywhere to anywhere else by a much more direct, faster route. Such innovations increased transit ridership in Portland, Denver, and Vancouver by 50 to 200 percent at a time when ridership was declining elsewhere, and Cervero believes they are viable when residential densities are about 1,150 persons per square kilometer or more.

The concept also applies to busway and bus-lane networks, and is even more important in automobile-threatened cities with much higher population densities (say, 5,000 persons per square kilometer or more). A high-quality transit system combines ubiquitous erven with a reasonably dense cobweb of busways and semi-exclusive bus lanes. The bus-lane cobweb is still a subset of the street network, but it begins to resemble a street network. Again, no city has implanted such a complete system of bus facilities to date, but piecemeal steps in this direction have proven highly successful. A synergistic effect is present, that is, the more good bus and pedestrian facilities there are, the easier it is to use them regularly between a greater variety of origins and destinations. This is an argument for expanding the busway-erf solution until it provides comprehensive coverage of the entire urban area.

Again using our computer analogy, providing this basic hardware for the transit user is a giant step in the right direction, but peripherals and software are often just as important. The peripherals and software are the complementary goods, services, and information bus riders and pedestrians need to make their trips pleasant and productive, accomplishing more than just getting from point A to point B.

Shelters should be provided at stops for protection from inclement weather; they should either have independent lighting or be located by a public lamppost. Proper design and location of the shelters are essential. Rest rooms should be available at more heavily traveled stations or at the edges of pedestrian malls. Public telephones should be easily available with tokens sold nearby, especially in developing countries where few people have telephones in their homes. A limited number of stands and shops is needed to provide access to coffee, other refreshments, newspapers, and sundries. These places of business must conform to minimal aesthetic criteria and be properly positioned to avoid interference with pedestrian flows. These stands or stalls can be authorized to sell bus tokens or printed passes at a slight discount in lots of, say five or more to make boarding much simpler and eliminate the problem of providing change within the vehicle or congestion at the turnstiles. If complemented by an enclosed area on the boarding platform, the turnstile and in-vehicle fare collection can be eliminated entirely, reducing labor costs and speeding service. The bus may then be equipped with three wide doors rather than the two narrow ones normally required for fare control, further reducing boarding–alighting times.

The cobweb of busways and lanes, if properly coded by a combination of names, numbers, and colors, can confer a greater degree of legibility to the network of routes and even to the city itself. As a simplified example, the northwest side of the city is the destination of five bus routes, numbered from NW1 to NW5 against an orange background. All bus routes starting or continuing from a given bus stop are outlined on a simplified map within the shelter or beside it, with mate-

rials chosen to maximize legibility, discourage vandalism, and facilitate replacement if damage should occur. There is also an easily
readable map of the immediate environs of each stop or station for
alighting passengers to consult, along with another map showing the
relative position of the stop in a broader context, and a complete city
map with a street index. The maps are extremely helpful even in cities
in developing countries with low levels of literacy: most people demonstrate remarkable good will in trying to provide information to
other travelers. That good will is of little avail, however, when even lit-
erate persons have no information available. Conversely, the availability of such maps and street signs is the incentive that many adults need
to enroll in literacy classes. A public phone should be available at or
near the shelter; a toll-free, three-digit phone number permits the user
to obtain additional information and also to inform the transit managers of any problems observed with the service, eliminating the need for
a lot of highly paid and ineffective inspectors on the transit authority's
payroll.

The buses themselves should be coded for the user's convenience, not to satisfy the vanity of the bus owner or the bureaucratic
whims of the transit manager. Frequently, color is used by a bus company to distinguish its vehicles from those of other firms; only by
chance do colors correspond to routes. At times the color schemes,
while not necessarily attractive, become complicated enough to make
repainting a time-consuming and expensive task when the bus incurs
some minor damage—a fairly frequent occurrence in most developing
countries.

At the other extreme, Brasília's transit managers recently
imposed a face-lift on the local bus fleet; all companies suddenly
appeared with the same, rather attractive, functionally useless color
combination. Each bus has a huge number stamped on it in several
locations—for identification by the transit inspectors. Neither the colors nor the visible numbers help the user get on the correct bus. That
information is available only on a black-and-white sign in the small
display panel at the top front of the bus; the panel is not easily read
from a distance, or even from close up by people with poor eyesight or
limited reading abilities. To further complicate things, bus owners
often resist painting route numbers on their buses, since this intro-
duces considerable inflexibility in the company's scheduling and
increases its costs.

Alex Sant'Anna solved this problem in Campina Grande by
color coding the buses by the neighborhoods they served. These neighborhoods are wide enough to permit the companies to substitute buses

among the neighborhood routes, avoiding scheduling inefficiencies. Large route numbers are affixed to all four sides of the bus by inserting steel plates in special slots; these route identification plates can be manually inserted or removed from their holders in a few seconds. The fleet manager can have all four route identification plates on a bus switched in three minutes or less; the user can identify the general destination of a bus by its color the minute it comes into view, and the specific route shortly thereafter. Even from behind the bus, the information is useful—it is possible to see if you have just missed your bus.

At present, routes in most cities are formed by tradition and regulatory jostling rather than users' travel needs. Although we defer discussion of regulation and privatization to Chapter 11, an example of the possible benefits of reorganization is given here.

On 21 February 1984, Campina Grande had a traditional "spoke and hub" system of 52 bus routes, each with a round trip of 6 to 10 kilometers (Urbema 1985: 7–30). The index of passengers per kilometer (IPK), that is, the distance in kilometers divided by the number of fare-paying passengers, varied among lines from 1.8 to 6.9 passengers/km. Each bus company had its own route(s), and each transfer required the users to pay an additional fare.

On 22 February 1984, the 52 routes were collapsed into 6 new urban routes and 14 interdistrict routes. All became neighborhood-to-neighborhood routes, although they still passed through the downtown area. The length of the lines more than doubled, ranging from 18 to 22 km. The range of the IPK narrowed to only 3.8 to 4.6 passengers/km. Most destinations became accessible by using a single bus, so that the total number of fares paid declined substantially, from 100,000 to 68,000 per day. The accounting cost used to establish the fare fell to 75 percent of the former value, as did the distance covered by the fleet, and 2,500 liters (660 gallons) of diesel fuel were saved daily. Average speed went up from about 6 km/h to more than 16 km/h.

Informal and Contracted High-Occupancy Vehicles (HOVs)

This category includes a wide range of vehicle types and operating policies. In the United States, Robert Cervero (1986; 1990) and W. K. Talley (1990) view contracted paratransit services as a way of reducing deficits of transit agencies. A. A. Odutola and A. C. Taylor (1990) see them as economic ways of providing transport for the elderly and the handicapped and divide them into demand-responsive paratransit (dial-a-ride, shared-ride taxi, short-term rental cars, rental cars, and jitneys) and prearranged ride-sharing (carpool, vanpool, and subscription buses). Most of these vehicles are car-size or van-sized. Standard-size buses are seldom used.

Some of the more interesting experiences with HOVs in the United States started with employers who, for the first time in American history, accepted some responsibility for getting their employees to work. This now occurs in gridlocked environments in California and other states, and during emergencies. Cervero finds many "transportation management associations" within large companies, but they are short lived or of limited effectiveness unless accompanied by some form of public incentive or regulation (1986: 95–147). This is understandable, since the benefits of HOV usage by a firm's employees are external to the firm. The reduced congestion and pollution are not noted by either the firm or its employees unless a large number of other firms are involved. Each firm is tempted to be a "free rider" and is reluctant to pay much to improve everyone else's welfare.

Ride-sharing is effective only when employers are involved in the provision of vans, the modification of working hours, and the exchange of information on companions for rides. Municipal governments at times encourage firms to take these steps by taxing or charging high fees for parking spaces or levying other burdens on firms that do not encourage ride-sharing. At some companies, carpools and vanpools account for as much as 20 percent of commuting (Cervero 1986: 87).

This is not a definitive tendency, however. Many of the traffic-reducing measures are being challenged in court, while employers often compensate employees for parking charges designed to reduce traffic. Shared rides are the exception rather than the rule for an additional reason: almost all workers use their cars one or more times a week for other errands and drop out of carpools on those days. As Cervero indicates, the new building developments themselves are one underlying problem, since developers do not provide for housing or other services within walking or cycling distance. He recommends more mixed land-use patterns and states that at least one center, in Denver, has land values two or three times higher than its competitors because of that mix (1986: 87).

Another needed feature in developments is a "campus" environment, where one can walk or cycle among the buildings within the development. It would obviously be even more desirable to walk or cycle to and from the development, but we have already seen that American road infrastructure has to be modified to permit this benefit.

In developing countries, informal HOV services usually take the form of jitneys that provide private, unsubsidized competition for regular bus services. Isaac Takyi defines a jitney as a car, station wagon, van, or minibus operated along a fixed or semi-fixed route (1990: 164). Passengers are picked up and dropped off at any point along the route, subject to vehicle capacity. Such vehicles normally have room for 5 to 12 passengers (up to 15 in Caracas and Manila) and account for 5 percent of trips in Taipei and Tel-Aviv, 40 percent in Caracas, and 65 percent or more in Manila and some other Asian cities.

In Manila the first jitneys were made by converting jeeps left behind by the American army at the end of World War II; they were appropriately dubbed "jeepneys." Currently, the jeepneys are produced locally and are usually equipped with secondhand diesel motors imported from Japan. They are exceptionally resistant vehicles; many have stainless-steel hoods and fenders to ward off corrosion from sea mist and exhaust fumes, and the suspension system is sturdy. Access and egress is from the rear; the low roof requires passengers to stoop while getting on or off, but everyone has a seat on one of the two benches placed at the sides facing each other. The window area is large and open for ventilation; a short canvas is rolled down when it rains. The jeeplike front end and windshield have been carefully preserved, and the jeepneys are the Philippines' most visible form of popular art, embellished by gaudy decorations, mirrors, and inscriptions; a few have a music-box tapes that are activated by the turn signals. The jeepneys are remarkably inexpensive: a large, high quality model can be purchased for under $9,000. The fare is currently set at 5.4 cents for a ride of up to 4 kilometers plus 2 cents for each additional 4 kilometers. This fare is down from 7 cents per ride a couple of years ago and, as I indicated earlier, may not cover full costs, but the operators would still probably make good money by local standards at 8 or 9 cents a ride. They are covering their short-term operating costs; buses charge the same rate for the first 4 kilometers, and something below the jeepney rate for each additional 4 kilometers.

In Caracas, the van and jitney services accounted for 74 percent of all public transport in 1983, compared with a mere 6 percent for the metro and 20 percent for buses (ECLA 1985: 31). They charged fares averaging about twice those of buses. In San Juan, jitney fares are generally between 25 and 35 cents, much more expensive than in Manila, but San Juan routes run up to four times longer.

Jitneys are illegal in most of Brazil, but there may be 6,000 10-passenger "Kombis" (an inexpensive van manufactured by Volkswagen) in the city of São Paulo alone; the Kombis generally link contiguous neighborhoods where good bus connections are lacking (Wright 1982). These vehicles offer "extra" services, for example, taking housewives to open air markets and dropping them off near their homes with their purchases on the return trip. In Brasília, these Kombis pick up riders at bus stops who would otherwise be condemned to a long wait and charge about twice as much as buses. Often the Kombis are not regular passenger operations; the Kombi owner may be a construction foreman or a repairman on his own way to and from work, making a little extra money on the side.

Jitney services usually improve the geographical coverage of transit and improve frequencies where transit lines already exist. They provide faster and more flexible service; some charge the same rates as buses, others up to twice bus rates. Vans and jeepneys usually offer more comfort than buses and travel with seated passengers only; the Kombis are often exceptions, however. Their disadvantages include considerable danger from overcrowded and often frail vehicles and the chaos introduced by sudden stops at any point to drop off or pick up passengers. Venezuela, the Philippines, and some other countries have sought to regulate jitney services, forcing them to approximate regular bus services. Brazil and other countries declare jitneys illegal, but in practice tolerate them in areas without good bus services.

If any generalization is possible, jitney services prosper where they dominated motorized transport before organized bus services appeared. Public and private bus companies that fail to provide users with frequent and comprehensive services suffer intense competition from jitneys even on the main bus routes. A few countries, such as Brazil, organized bus services to replace them, and these jitneys are now condemned to a clandestine existence. Manila has tolerated jeepneys, but has done little to actively promote them.

To my knowledge, no country has seriously tried to promote buses and jitneys as alternatives to the private car. Caracas, for example, attempted to deal with its traffic problem by concentrating all its efforts on road building in the 1950s and 1960s. This merely increased congestion and pollution, given the high population density and the surrounding mountains that act as physical barriers to both decentralization of population and dispersion of pollutants. Authorities then decided to build a metro, without making any effort to provide improved bus services. Jitneys continue to transport the majority of the population; they offer faster, more frequent service than buses, cover the vast areas not reached by the metro, and free the car owner from the battle for parking space. Jitneys and buses in Caracas, however, offer a much lower level of service than they could provide with exclusive road space.

Bus and jitney services can be complementary means of improving urban transit options; minibus services are a key to keeping Buenos Aires transport at tolerable levels, for example (Vincente and Brennan 1989). Good bus services, however, require unfettered access to stops and stations along their routes. They also need a substantial amount of exclusive and semi-exclusive road space to lower their overall travel times. Jitneys have a place in urban public transport, but routes and stops must be defined to avoid interference with buses, and the safety issue has to be more effectively addressed than it is now.

Political Aspects of Bus–Erf Environments

Bus–erf environments are designed to tame the automobile's appetite for urban space and to reduce its speed in many areas of the city. They are not, however, an anti-automobile strategy. The individuals and groups who promote bus–erf programs should emphasize the positive aspects of bus–erf programs for car owners. Of equal importance, they should avoid measures that, inadvertently perhaps, irritate car owners or place them in an adversarial position. Some selling points are the following.

First of all, in densely populated cities, congestion will get worse if bus–erf strategies are not implemented, because the car uses urban space so inefficiently. The goal of bus–erf programs is not to eliminate the option of the automobile, but to provide other options, to relieve congestion, and to reduce the automobile's other negative impacts. The typical car-owning couple receives the following benefits from bus–erf programs: slower traffic on their residential street, with less noise and danger to their children and grandchildren; elimination of the cost of a second or third car; safety in journeys by transit-walking, transit-cycling, and walking or cycling, consequent improvement in physical fitness and mental and emotional well-being; less air polluted by petroleum and a world less dependent on it.

Second, facilities should be designed with simplicity, tact, and care. Entrances to most streets should reduce vehicle speeds and place cars in a narrow, predictable, clearly defined path, without requiring the driver to slam on the brakes or make a 90-degree turn. The design should create the impression of entering one's own driveway: care and slow speeds are required, but it is good to be home. Traffic humps should not catch the driver by surprise or damage vehicles. They should be well posted, painted with bright colors rather than camouflaged, and preceded by strips built into the pavement that increase surface roughness to a noticeable, yet nonaggressive level. City engineers should design large, smooth humps that allow cars to pass without jolts, provided the design speed is not exceeded, and that speed should be clearly posted. They should use similar schemes throughout the city to maximize driver recognition of the erf environments.

Third, the community should always receive some visible advantage from the project; it may be little more than signs indicating that Easy Street is participating in the city's program to protect children from traffic accidents or thanking the driver for cooperating with the Easy Street Walkers' Association. In other areas, creativity can enhance the project at little cost. For example, in an area devoid of green areas and recreational space in Makati (metropolitan Manila), some streets have an irregular design with an "asphalt sea" at one end. The pedestrian has a long hike to get across the street, without any advantage for motorists. Proper design would convert the asphalt seas to playgrounds and basketball courts (basketball is the Philippines' national sport), with fencing to keep basketballs and children from dangerous areas. Cars would enter the streets at 10 kilometers per hour, parallel to the recreational areas and on one side only; drivers would be treated to an enjoyable neighborhood scene with no loss in accessibility or parking space.

Finally, simple engineering is usually aesthetically sufficient. On occasion, a bit of tasteful landscaping or playground facilities may be added; it is not good practice to invite the city's mad artist to decorate the facilities.

Chapter 10

Project Formulation and Evaluation

W E NOW DEVELOP a formal method for generating and evaluating urban transport policies and projects. The key concept is the technically appropriate set of transport options, defined by the intersection of the characteristic sets of modes, cities, and users.

The Characteristics Approach to Project Choice

Our use of the term *project* includes both modifications in physical infrastructure, and policies, plans, and strategies used as complements to or substitutes for physical modifications. *Project analysis* and *policy analysis* are synonyms for the process of formulation and evaluation.

This process is based on the Lancasterian postulates discussed in Chapter 2. The relevant points are:

The characteristics of transport modes affect transport users and other urban residents either positively or negatively.

Modes and the ways of operating them are our means of producing sets of characteristics.

A given characteristic can be obtained from more than one mode: for example, high personal-transport capacity per area occupied may be obtained from buses, other high-occupancy road vehicles, walking, cycling, or rail systems.

An appropriate combination of modes may furnish a better set of
characteristics than if modes are considered separately or are
poorly integrated; for example, bus corridors plus an erf environment can provide high capacity, reduce pollution, relieve
congestion, promote exercise, and improve residential and shopping environments.

Modal characteristics are objectively measurable, but users value them
differently; there is need to make a variety of transport options
available for travelers.

Our simple, iterative method for formulating and evaluating
urban transport projects has a distinct similarity to systems engineering principles and consists of the following steps:

1. *Define the problem*. Specify the transport-related characteristics
   considered inadequate and whom they affect. The relevant context of the city (and, if pertinent, nation), should be considered.
2. *Search systemically for all general alternative strategies for dealing
   with the defined problem*.
3. *Make a cost–financial check*. Get some ballpark figures on the
   costs of alternatives and determine whether the local government agency has a realistic possibility of financing them; check
   monetary values for significant distortions, such as excessive
   taxes, subsidies, or unrealistic exchange rates, and verify
   whether the entity in question can remove the distortions or
   has to live with them.
4. *Do a coherency check*. Check the strategies and financing schemes
   for coherency with the original problem definition. Verify
   whether the problem itself has been adequately defined or
   needs redefining and whether other alternatives might provide
   the same or similar characteristics at lower cost. If there is any
   incoherence, go back to the first step and begin again.

   If the results are coherent, the set of technically appropriate
   projects has been defined in a preliminary fashion. These are
   the projects that will improve the performance of transport-
   related characteristics to an adequate level and at a cost bear-
   able by the city and its transport users. The "technically appropriate options" are those the mayor, city commissioners, and
   citizen groups should choose from; other options are either
   too expensive or do not improve the deficient characteristics
   sufficiently.

   The role of the technical staff is to produce this set of options
   and explain in clear language the cost and other characteristics

that led to the inclusion of those options in the technically appropriate set. The staff should also explain why other options were excluded and may recommend a specific option within the technically appropriate set (for example, "we recommend 'B' since it has characteristics similar to 'A' at half the cost"). The choice, however, is clearly in the political sphere.

5. *If pertinent, proceed with more detailed iterations.* Repeat steps (1) through (4), replacing the original, somewhat vague, strategies of (2) and the ballpark figures in (3) with a progressively more detailed set of alternative projects and more precise cost and financing data. This requires a systemic search for modifications that lower costs or enhance positive characteristics at little or no additional cost.

The process terminates when the problem is satisfactorily defined, the solution (or set of solutions) is coherent with the problem definition, and no other solutions can be generated that offer roughly similar characteristics at equal or lower cost.

Decisionmakers receive the following information:

a description of the characteristics of the problem and those affected by it;

an analysis of the performance of the alternative solutions across the characteristics examined;

the reasons for excluding options that do not appear in the technically appropriate set but may be of interest to citizen groups or decisionmakers;

the advantages and disadvantages of the recommended solutions(s) in relation to others, with their respective costs and alternative financing schemes;

any relevant tax, subsidy, or other distortions, with the alternatives for correcting them.

Comparison of Characteristics Approach with Other Methods

The five steps of the characteristics approach are in accord with systems engineering, a hybrid methodology that aims to ensure that a project or system, "selected from the range of options on offer, is the one most likely to satisfy the owner's objective in the context of long-term future operational or market environments" (M'Pherson 1986: 330). More specifically, the first four steps correspond to the policy-analysis phase of systems engineering: defining objectives and likely future environments, the range of options capable of achieving those objectives, and evaluating the options by examining their consequences and impacts on the objectives and value criteria. The last step corresponds to the design phase of systems engineering, where a cost-effective design specifies the detailed design, engineering, and production phases.

The characteristics approach presents some significant differences from cost–benefit analysis. Cost–benefit analysis begins with a project that is assumed "ready" to be evaluated (on occasion, a very few alternative projects are considered). The monetary costs and benefits are estimated for each year of the expected life of the project. If taxes, subsidies, or exchange rate distortions are judged significant, these monetary values are "corrected" to reflect the underlying "economic" costs and benefits and then discounted by the social-discount rate (Chapter 2). The discount rate is an abstract interest rate assumed to represent the cost of capital to society.

In cost–benefit analysis, the social-discount rate plays a key role in the calculations, yet there is seldom agreement on what its numerical value should be. I have seen annual real discount rates ranging from 5 percent to 18 percent in transport projects. A high discount rate weighs heavily against projects whose benefits lie far in the future relative to costs. In particular, the long-term sustainability of a project does not matter: with a 10 percent discount rate, the present value of one dollar received thirty years hence is less than six cents (the difference is not due to inflation; we are talking about real values).

The key features of cost–benefit analysis are analyzed below, including comparisons with characteristics analysis and systems engineering.

Project Formulation

Cost–benefit analysis is not a method for formulating projects. This is a fatal and irreparable flaw, since no meaningful evaluation can be conducted separately from project formulation. The typical one-stage, product-oriented cost–benefit evaluation is one conducted after the important decisions have been made. It occurs without the use of any explicit formulation method and with no effort to educate the population or decisionmakers regarding the advantages and disadvantages of the available alternatives. From my observation, by that time key political figures are committed to going ahead with the project.

The tendency to form commitments in the project-definition stage is very strong. For example, Grefe and Smart (1975: 11) point out that BART's linear, fixed-rail design was virtually chosen politically before technical consultants appeared on the scene, and all other decisions followed along the same path, including the selection of the engineering firm to design the system. Cost–benefit analysis is not to blame for this tendency, but neither does it counteract that tendency. The characteristics approach, by starting at the beginning of the process, offers more promise than cost–benefit analysis which, in philosophy and practice, starts when it is too late.

Nonmonetary Impacts

Cost–benefit analysis requires that nonmonetary impacts, such as accidents, noise, pollution, and aesthetics, be translated into monetary units, excluded from consideration, or analyzed outside the cost–benefit paradigm.

The first alternative, monetarizing the nonmonetary impacts, leads to placing a monetary value on such things as pollution, aesthetic values, capacity, time, noise, pain, grief, suffering, and human life. As noted in previous chapters, such exercises are often ludicrous.

The second alternative, excluding nonmonetary impacts, is, as E. J. Mishan (1988) reminds us, equivalent to ignoring the horse in a horse and rabbit stew (see Chapter 2). Under this alternative, cost–benefit analysts must avoid the problem rather than dealing with it. Those who take this path analyze the rabbit because their techniques apply only to rabbits; their academic training has done them permanent harm, depriving them of their olfactory sense.

The third alternative has been recommended by Mishan (1988: 154–55); he suggests that the analyst calculate the benefit–cost ratio without the nonmonetary impacts, plus some description of them. Unfortunately, Mishan does not present a method for providing this description nor indicate what is to be done with it. The process yields a decision rule only when the externalities are all positive and B/C>1 (accept the project), or when the externalities are all negative and B/C<1 (reject the project). There is no decision rule when: some externalities are negative and others positive; all externalities are positive and B/C<1; or when all externalities are negative and B/C>1. More important, the third alternative does not address the question of how to improve externalities and decrease costs.

On occasion, the characteristics analyst may be unable to generate a project that provides the desired performance across characteristics and is still within the financial constraints of the governmental agency. The analyst must inform the decisionmakers that one or more standards must be lowered and list the alternatives for bringing the project within budget—much like an architect who has designed a couple's dream house and must then discuss the modifications necessary for them to afford it.

If the analyst generates more than one affordable project with the desired performance across characteristics, the decisionmakers choose among them. This is a political choice, based on the characteristics sets of the projects; this choice is fundamentally different from the assumption in cost–benefit analysis that the decision is given "technically" by the value of the cost–benefit ratio (in turn the result of the analyst's arbitration of monetary weights to each of the separate characteristics).

Cost–benefit's inability to deal with qualitative questions has been espoused as a virtue by some of its proponents. Herman Leonard and Richard Zeckhauser, for example, ardently defend cost–benefit as a method of quantification (1986: 43–44). Arnold Harberger reinforces their point of view by adding that economists have no professional qualifications for evaluating such things as aesthetics; he comes close to saying that the standard for judging the validity of the evaluation process is that economists agree on it (1971: 785). Appropriately, Harberger explicitly forfeits any claims of scientific validity for his paper, considering it a tract, an open letter to the profession. (Some statements should be taken at face value.)

Leonard and Zeckhauser reason that cost–benefit analysis is quantitative, ergo superior to alternatives (1986: 43–44). Although they do not say so, by "quantitative" they mean monetary quantification, since without a monetary yardstick the analyst cannot add up decibels, minutes, and lives to calculate the benefit–cost ratio. As we have seen, such quantification is inappropriate; moreover, characteristics analysis and systems engineering are also quantitative and have the advantage of using physical units of measure where monetary quantification is inappropriate.

Neither the characteristics approach nor systems engineering attempts to assign monetary weights to physical units that do not have market prices. Instead, both of these systemic approaches provide quantitative information on deficient characteristics, formulate the options for improving them, and calculate the costs of each option.

The characteristic and systems approaches are similar in nature

to linear programming, with its restrictions and quantitative characteristics. An example is the diet problem: choices are to be made
among available foods with differing nutrient contents. The nutrients
are analogous to characteristics and must be kept within certain limits:
the linear program looks for the combination of foods that satisfies the
restrictions at least cost. Also by analogy with linear programming, if
any "prices" emerge for characteristics, they are "shadow prices," a
result of the analysis rather than an input.

For example, the characteristics analyst may examine the options for reducing traffic deaths and inform policymakers that $1,500
invested in traffic humps at three locales is expected to save three lives
per year, and all other options save fewer lives and have a greater cost.
The $1,500 is the shadow price (that is, it indicates the resource cost)
for three human lives and poses the relevant question for decisionmakers, "Are you able and willing to invest $1,500 to save three lives per
year?"

In contrast, the cost–benefit analyst is divorced from the question of project generation and must examine whatever project is
placed on the table. The hapless analyst must either ignore safety considerations or attempt to incorporate them into the cost–benefit ratio
by placing a monetary value on human life. The cost–benefit analyst is
more than happy to calculate the shadow price of foreign exchange,
but has no experience in providing the relevant resource cost of
achieving specific goals like saving lives.

I am not suggesting that the characteristics approach be transformed into a mathematical technique such as linear programming.
The analogy, however, illustrates a qualitative difference in two approaches: cost–benefit analysis commits a basic error by assigning
monetary weights to physical characteristics; the characteristics approach proceeds correctly by examining the restrictions on performance across characteristics and searching for the least-cost alternatives to satisfy those restrictions.

Systems Features

Cost–benefit's only "systems feature" is the social-discount
rate. This rate links a specific project to the national economy rather
than to the immediate urban environment: projects with a rate of economic return superior to the social-discount rate are thought to
improve the overall performance of the national economy and should
be approved; the others represent an inferior use of resources and
should be avoided. Again, the calculations can only be done if the

impacts can be quantified unambiguously in monetary terms—an unlikely hypothesis for urban transport projects.

In contrast, the characteristics approach looks at the citywide transport problem, user and city finances, and, when pertinent, the interactions of policy and resource demand at the national level. The characteristics approach conducts a systemic analysis of the relationship of the project to the larger picture of the overall quality of the local transport system and the urban environment. Local, regional, or even national issues are analyzed when they are appropriate to the scope of the project.

Cost–benefit analysts have on occasion questioned the benefit–cost ratio as an exclusive base for a positive or negative recommendation. Hans Adler (1971) suggests that a financial viability study accompany every cost–benefit analysis.

The term *financial viability* means different things to different people. One interpretation of such a financial analysis is a cost–benefit analysis without its attempt to compensate for taxes, subsidies, and other distortions. Such financial analysis is a purposeless exercise: it relinquishes a potential advantage of cost–benefit analysis (locating distortions), while failing to verify whether the local authorities can finance the project.

Under Adler's rule, a project is viable only if both cost–benefit and financial analyses are satisfactory. This rule, however, also undermines the cost–benefit paradigm by questioning the adequacy of the discount rate as the system link. A cost–benefit analyst might attempt to incorporate financial limitations by increasing the discount rate (to infinity?); this is a strange and unwieldy manner in which to deal with city hall's budget restrictions.

Characteristics analysis interprets financial viability as city council might: some combination of government revenue and user charges must be available to finance the project.

Information for Decisonmakers and the Public

Despite the basic simplicity of the cost–benefit approach, the jargon and estimating techniques are often too arcane for the decisionmaker to understand much more than the final recommendation. The more obscure parts of cost–benefit analysis include the mathematical techniques for estimating the monetary value of nonmonetary characteristics, discussions of tax, subsidy, and exchange rate distortions, and references to Pareto improvements. Decisionmakers find the first unintelligible because the underlying idea is nonsense, however clever the analyst may be in hiding that fact; they do not grasp the relevance of the second because it has none (city council does not fix the country's exchange rate); and they do not understand Pareto improvements because no such thing exists in real-world transportation projects.

The last item requires a word of explanation. A Pareto improvement makes someone better off without leaving anyone worse off and so allows the economist to escape from making interpersonal value judgments. Since real-world transport projects tax some to benefit others, they involve value judgments and are not candidates for Pareto-improvement status (even inertia benefits some people and hinders others). Economists have attempted to circumvent this inconvenience by inventing the "hypothetical compensation" test: a project represents a Pareto improvement if those who benefit from the project could compensate the losers and have some benefit left over. The problem is that these compensations cannot be paid in a real-world urban transport project—the costs of making the transfers would be astronomical. So the hypothetical compensations are truly hypothetical, and city council does not understand why the analyst brought Pareto improvements up in the first place.

Few city council members, citizen groups, or journalists have the time, inclination, or competence to wade through the average cost–benefit study and discover the size of the boondoggle that is literally being papered over. In most cases, few copies are made of the study and those are not likely to be available for examination outside the proposing and funding agencies. Often the size of the documents and the difficulty of reproducing them are natural reasons for restricting circulation; confidentiality may also be invoked.

The characteristics approach, in contrast, provides a description of the characteristics of the problem, the alternatives for dealing with it, and the costs of each alternative. At the strategy level, these are expected to be clear and short documents. Only when a final engineering project is needed—after successive iterations by the technical staff and final selection of a specific project by the decisionmakers—is the level of technical detail likely to outstrip the layperson's understanding.

Table 7 resumes the main features of the characteristics approach, systems engineering, cost–benefit analysis, and three additional methods. The additional methods are:

Multicriterial analysis. This approach assigns grades to the performance of each of several alternative projects across a number of characteristics, weights the characteristics, and selects the project with

Table 7
Characteristics of Project Methodologies

Characteristics	Method	Comment
Basis in economic theory	*Characteristics analysis*	*Lancaster's 4 postulates*
	Cost–benefit	*Traditional consumer theory, Pareto optimality*
	Financial analysis	*Profitability*
	Multicriterial analysis, systems engineering, and analysis of consequences	*Only indirectly related to economic theory*
Characteristics considered	*Characteristics analysis, multicriterial analysis, and analysis of consequences*	*Those relevant to problem*
	Systems engineering	*Those specified by client*
	Cost–benefit and financial analysis	*Those measurable in monetary units*
Starting point	*Characteristics analysis and systems engineering*	*Definition of problem*
	Cost–benefit, financial analysis multicriterial analysis, and analysis of characteristics	*A solution or small number of existing solutions*
Searches for better solutions	*Characteristics analysis and systems engineering*	*Yes*
	Analysis of consequences and multicriterial analysis	*Implicitly, perhaps*
	Cost–benefit and financial analysis	*No*
Units of measure used	*Characteristics analysis, systems engineering, multicriterial analysis, and analysis of consequences*	*Physical or monetary units, grades, or rankings, as appropriate to characteristics analyzed*
	Cost–benefit and financial analysis	*Characteristics can only enter criterion if weighted with a monetary numeraire*
Weighting of characteristics	*Characteristics analysis, systems engineering, and analysis of consequences*	*Quantitative weighting not necessary; some performance levels may be considered as restrictions*
	Cost–benefit and financial analysis	*With a monetary numeraire*
Treatment of transfers among individuals	*Characteristics analysis*	*Explicit from problem definition onward*
	Systems engineering, multicriterial analysis, and analysis of consequences	*Considered if requested*
	Cost–benefit and financial analysis	*Ad hoc, outside paradigm and in conflict with the theory they are based on*

Table 7 *(continued)*

Characteristics	Method	Comment
Externalities and distortions	Characteristics analysis	Directly incorporated as part of characteristics; distortions considered as constraints if relevant governmental unit cannot remove them
	Systems engineering, multicriterial analysis, and analysis of consequences	Can be considered if requested; no specific grounding in economic theory
	Cost–benefit	Distortions incorporated, even if relevant governmental unit cannot change them; externalities treated if expressed in $; otherwise ignored
	Financial analysis	Both externalities and distortions ignored
Information provided to decisionmakers	Characteristics analysis	Problem definition, characteristics and alternatives, costs, financing schemes
	Systems engineering	Least-cost alternative for providing specified performance level
	Analysis of consequences	Consequences of proposed solution
	Cost–benefit, financial analysis, and multicriterial analysis	Within paradigms, a number
Treatment of controversy	Characteristics analysis	Mitigation measures in project formulation, choice among technically appropriate solutions by political decisionmaking body
	All others	No explicit consideration in paradigm; implicit in analysis of consequences
Nature of final decision and criteria	Characteristics analysis and analysis of consequences	Political, but with information on technical adequacy provided by analyst
	All others	Thought to be the result of analyst's calculations, given the project proposal or initial characteristics specifications

the highest overall grade. Marvin Manheim has criticized the method's doubtful grades and arbitrary weights (1979: 363–65). In fact, the explicit weighting comes close to the cost–benefit technique of translating the physical impacts of a project into a monetary yardstick. Nonetheless, some project teams have taken the idea back into the project formulation stage and attempted to see if a given project could be redesigned to improve its performance on one or more characteristics—a step in the right direction.

Financial analysis. As defined by Kirk Harlow and Duane Windsor (1988), financial analysis examines the profitability of a public project as though it were a private endeavor (a fundamental difference from both our definition of the financial viability of a project and that of cost–benefit analysis). Financial analysis considers a project acceptable if and only if the city's receipts from the project will exceed its expenditures. Harlow and Windsor consider financial analysis appropriate for projects such as a parking garage: the city should not invest in it unless it will pay for itself, since no ethical issues are involved in excluding those unwilling or unable to pay.

Analysis of consequences. Developed by Veli Himanen (1985) of the Finnish Technical Research Center, this approach examines the consequences (performance with regard to characteristics) of a project. Analysis of consequences conveys the idea that modification or substitution is in order when performance on key characteristics is found deficient. Although the systemic aspects of this method are not formalized, it is implicitly coherent with many aspects of the characteristics approach and systems engineering.

The characteristics approach is consistent with systems engineering and Lancasterian microeconomic theory. It has some points in common with analysis of consequences and, to a lesser extent, multicriterial analysis. It incorporates both financial viability and cost-effectiveness considerations (thus the latter are not included in Table 7).

The characteristics method is similar to cost–benefit analysis in the treatment of tax–subsidy and other distortions, if the entity responsible for the project can remove the distortion. Otherwise, characteristics analysis considers it as a restriction, while cost–benefit alters the monetary impacts to "compensate" (in the abstract) for the distortion. By pretending that the local agency does not have to live with the distortion, the cost–benefit approach may transform a second-best solution into a third-best solution.

These considerations establish the conceptual superiority of characteristics analysis (and other systemic approaches) to cost–benefit analysis. We will now see how the characteristics approach may be applied to generating and evaluating solutions to real-world urban transport problems.

Case Studies

The following case studies apply characteristics analysis to a variety of urban transport problems, ranging from a very general conceptual strategy to specific technical options. Although I will not illustrate final engineering details here, the method may be used at any level of detail, such as selecting the width, materials, and landscaping for a sidewalk. In each case study, I point out the differences between the characteristics approach and cost–benefit analysis.

Case 1. Aesthetics and Streetcars

Since aesthetic qualities are not conducive to monetary quantification, cost–benefit analysts tend to ignore them (Harberger 1971: 785). Although this example predates the formalization of both the characteristics approach and cost–benefit analysis, it illustrates how aesthetic values can be incorporated into project formulation and evaluation, following the steps of characteristics analysis.

The first commercially successful electric streetcar system using overhead wires was implanted in Richmond, Virginia in 1888 (McKay 1976). This and most subsequent early trolleys were lucrative for private operators, and their speed and capacity were far superior to horse-drawn streetcars. The overhead cables were more efficient than batteries; they were also more reliable than ground-level conduits and less likely to electrocute pedestrians and horses.

The trolleys, however, presented the disadvantage of unsightly supporting posts and wiring. In the United States, this factor was largely ignored; municipalities gave traction companies free rein to implant the trolleys, and by 1903, 98 percent of U.S. streetcars were using the system. The early systems were profitable and, except for aesthetics, the externalities were positive. Had cost–benefit analysis been available, it would undoubtedly have endorsed the trolleys.

European municipalities implicitly adopted an approach remarkably similar to our characteristics analysis. Europeans considered the catenaries unsightly and objected to the trolleys for that reason;

the trams made little initial headway. Municipalities searched for alternatives; some experimented with underground conduits, others tried batteries, and many more continued using horses. The catenaries were superior on all technical and economic grounds, but the American design was unacceptable.

At this stage, some technical people sought to redesign the catenaries to make them as unobtrusive as possible. They placed the heavy feeder cables underground, leaving visible only the lighter and more delicate wires actually needed to supply power to the trolleys. While U.S. systems supported the catenaries with large wooden posts—often painted with horrendous colors—European technicians used handsomely decorated steel poles. Many of these well-designed poles were placed on medians and pedestrian islands and used simultaneously for street lighting. McKay (1976: 106–8) writes that the municipalities' zeal regarding aesthetic qualities led them to maintain careful control over contracts with private operators and to retain options to buy out the system if improved technologies became available, in contrast to the U.S. experience, where contracts were often perpetual. European municipalities also had to evaluate the trade-offs with cultural, social, and utilitarian goals, winning substantial improvements in all areas. On the decisionmaking process, McKay remarks, "Having established the facts, the technical people could present their material, as well as their recommendations, for public discussion and policy formulation. The public and its representatives could then weigh and debate the alternatives intelligently in light of their preferences and aspirations. They could choose their alternative as they sought to design a transport future they could be proud of."

As a result, American cities adopted the electric trolley a decade before their European counterparts, but Europe received a more attractive, second-generation system that the population supported and one that improved the urban environment. Thus, many European cities developed an effective transit system, along with vigorous, attractive city core areas. European cities still present a relatively high fuel efficiency, in contrast with the typical American city (Chapter 8).

Case 2. Urban Roadways

Many urban roadway projects throughout the world have been evaluated using cost–benefit analysis. These studies tend to ignore both the alternatives to the private car and the long-term feedback effects of such projects—a logical omission since cost–benefit analysis begins with a solution rather than an analysis of the problem. In a typical case, the cost–benefit analysts estimate the costs of constructing and maintaining a new avenue or expressway; these costs are compared with the benefits, using the social-discount rate for both. Estimated savings in travel time, fuel, and vehicle-operating costs are the principal benefits included in calculating the benefit–cost ratio, although other items may be included, such as a monetary value for accident reduction.

In the typical cost–benefit calculation, a substantial part of the estimated benefits come from additional traffic generated by the new roadway(s), in strict accord with cost–benefit manuals such as E. J. Mishan's (1988: chap. 1–5). The analyst's key assumption is that greater road space will reduce congestion, increase travel speed, and reduce fuel consumption per vehicle kilometer of travel.

P. W. G. Newman and J. R. Kenworthy (1984; 1988), however, show that the alleged fuel efficiency increase is actually a loss when the feedback effects are taken into account. As seen in Chapter 8, high-density, mixed land use enables more people to use transit and reduces the amount of motorized travel needed for other activities. Residents use less fuel per capita, although their cars use more fuel per kilometer.

Newman and Kenworthy recommend omitting fuel-savings calculations from cost–benefit studies; although they do not mention it, by extension, the estimated vehicle-operating-cost savings should also be excluded, along with the value of travel time and lives saved. In other words, all the alleged benefits of such highway projects should be excluded, or, even more appropriately, reestimated as part of the cost column.

The characteristics approach is systemic in nature and requires consideration of interrelationships and feedback effects. Projects are not seen in isolation but as part of a general strategy. Characteristics analysis does not analyze individual roadway projects without first asking what the problem is and devising a general strategy to deal with it. So we begin by developing an urban transport strategy for a major city in Case 3).

Case 3. A General Mobility Strategy for São Paulo

The failures of urban transport systems do not come from lack of attention to detail in specific projects, but from the lack of a coherent overall strategy; they derive from neglect of major parameters, such as the overall capacity of the transport system, the income per capita of travelers, and the population density of the city.

We implicitly used the characteristics approach in our discussion of major cities and modal choices in Chapters 8 and 9. A brief recapitulation of São Paulo's transport problems and alternatives follows.

Step 1: Problem definition. Virtually all citizens face excessive travel time, congestion, noise, pollution, accident potential, and the like. Buses and trains are crowded, and most buses move slowly in mixed traffic. The problems are found throughout the city, rather than on a specific corridor. About half the city's families have a car, but it is used primarily by the head of household and is not regularly available to most family members. Many of these families have great difficulty maintaining a car, and only do so because of the poor quality of most transit options; half of São Paulo's families depend exclusively on transit and walking. Their family incomes are often less than the costs of maintaining a car. The city's population density is nearly 10,000 persons per square kilometer.

From 1977 to 1987, São Paulo's regional population increased by 56 percent, car use by 21 percent, public modes by a mere 0.2 percent, and walking by a full 82 percent (São Paulo Metrô 1987). As a result of poor transit conditions, per capita motorized trips fell by a third, to only 1.07 per day. In 1987, 43 percent of motorized trips were by car, 8 percent by metro, 6 percent by suburban train, and 43 percent by bus; walking accounted for 9.5 million daily trips, cars for 7.4 million, and transit for 9.7 million.

Steps 2 and 3: Generation of solutions and financial viability check. São Paulo's high population density requires promotion of public transport and nonmotorized transport, and restrictions on private-car use if congestion and other problems are to be alleviated. The only modes capable of providing the required capacity are trains, busways, and bus lanes plus pedestrianized (erf) environments (the creation of erf environments may eventually permit the addition of bicycling to the list of alternatives). The bus-priority schemes are much more cost-effective than trains; no unused rail lines permit significant addition of surface rail lines. The city has never been able to afford railways; they are operated by state and federal entities and are heavily subsidized. The state-owned metro cost $85 million per kilometer ($137 million/mile) to build and depends on a 60-cent operating subsidy for each 40 cents of fare-box receipts, yet accounts for only 8 percent of trips.

The city has a "soft" budget constraint—funds can be found for priority projects, and it currently wastes enough money subsidizing its public bus company to finance bus–erf programs. Bus–erf projects are the only ones capable of providing the needed increases in transport capacity within the city's budget. Moreover, both bus lanes and erf environments have worked well where implanted in São Paulo; they are not pipe dreams. The busways and bus lanes can be implemented to enhance safety and decrease pollution and noise by using environmental control techniques, switching from diesel to natural gas as a bus fuel or, at an increase in cost, using trolleybuses on the busways.

Step 4: Coherency check. The bus–erf strategy is coherent with the problem definition. The resources required are within the city's soft budget restriction, and may be obtained, say, by switching transit subsidies from the public bus company (CMTC) and other roadway investments to bus and erf projects. CMTC's subsidy is $25 million a month (see Chapter 11 for ideas on how to transform this waste into productive investment); bus–erf projects can eventually be money winners for the city by increasing property values and tax receipts along the erven.

Since we have found the only coherent general strategy, the characteristics analysis terminates at this point. Note that our strategy is a significant departure from most municipal and state actions during the last forty years. The city and state have funneled the vast majority of their transport investments into the creation of new road space destined primarily for private cars, along with sizable investments in the metro and suburban trains.

Our strategy also contrasts with the recommendations of the numerous cost–benefit analyses conducted for individual urban roadway and rail projects during previous decades. The conceptual problems with the roadway projects were covered in our discussion of Case 2. In São Paulo, however, the feedback mechanisms were not strong enough to produce low population densities; thus fuel consumption and travel time for a given distance have increased over time for most travelers, as gridlock has expanded to more areas and hours of the day (the results for São Paulo have been worse than for cities in developed countries with lower population densities).

This is a predictable, depressing picture of expanding car-induced gridlock in a densely populated city. Bus service has been degraded by congestion, and many citizens must walk long and dangerous distances on foot, if they travel at all. Yet cost–benefit studies routinely justified the individual road projects that added up to gridlock.

Case 4. Computerized Traffic Lights

One interesting cost–benefit study among the São Paulo roadway projects is SEMCO, a project to increase the efficiency of car circulation in São Paulo through computerized traffic control (Germani and Szasz 1985: 50). The economic benefits that justified SEMCO were the monetary values imputed to the time and fuel that would be saved through SEMCO—two minutes and one-tenth liter per car per day, enough to cover the cost of the project in five months.

Neither of these savings occurred. A system of coordinated traffic lights improves traffic flows only in light-to-moderate traffic; in gridlocked São Paulo, SEMCO is no better than simpler, less expensive systems. SEMCO is demanding of human and financial resources and has seldom had enough of either to work properly (*Folha de São Paulo,* 12 October 1990: C-4). All this would have been obvious from a simple, yet systemic analysis of the city's burgeoning car traffic, such as that in step 1 of Case 3, above.

Finally, there is no opportunity cost for two minutes saved (in this case, not saved) in traffic. The "value" of time saved in most cost–benefit studies of urban road projects is another example of a number that is not a number, but numerical silly putty. The mathematical models used to generate this figure typically include savings of a few seconds; when multiplied by millions of users and a given wage rate, these seconds produce large monetary "benefits" and an "economic justification" for almost anything.

Case 5. The São Paulo Monorail Proposal

Some years ago, an elderly mayor of São Paulo, given to theatrical gestures, proposed building a monorail between the districts of Freguesia do Ó and Santo Amaro. His office eventually produced a formal proposal that was sent to state and federal governments in an unsuccessful search for funds (Prefeitura do Município de São Paulo, 1988). To my knowledge, no cost–benefit analysis was done for the ex-mayor's monorail proposal, but let us consider the following hypothetical scenario under the cost–benefit paradigm before doing a characteristics analysis.

An analyst from the mayor's office, employing numerical silly putty, produces sufficient value of travel time and human life saved by the monorail to generate a benefit–cost ratio of 1.3. This cost–benefit analysis is sent to a federal government office as support for a request for funds; a staff member redoes the benefit–cost calculations by changing the assumptions, and produces a benefit–cost ratio of 0.1. Whom is the decisionmaker to believe, and why?

The characteristics approach produces a more definitive result and avoids a sterile discussion over the "realism" of the assumptions. For example, the mayor's office assumed a construction cost of $300 million for the first 15 kilometers, or $20 million a kilometer, only a third of what monorails cost in Japan; the mayor's office also expected the São Paulo monorail to transport about four times as many people as the Japanese version. Both assumptions are pure fantasy, but the project can be shown to be inferior to the alternatives without questioning them.

The monorail proposal illustrates the fundamental error of most urban transport projects and their cost–benefit analyses—starting with a solution rather than a definition of a problem. Characteristics analysis, however, corrects for everything but lost time, even though we start at step (3) or (4) rather than with step (1). The algorithm asks if the solution is coherent with the problem definition and if there is a less expensive way to furnish the same characteristics. In other words, we return to step (1), the problem definition phase, and begin anew.

In Case 3 we examined transport-related characteristics in São Paulo and found them deficient throughout the entire region. The proposed monorail route is in no greater need of improvement than most other routes in the city. In fact, the proposal's "priority" section from the Freguesia do Ó to the core area features a long stretch parallel to the Tietê River, a multilane expressway, and the river's floodplain. The route is more suited to implanting the monorail than to responding to transport demand: the Tietê floodplain is one of the few places in São Paulo that does not generate many trips—monorail users would have to take a bus to get to the stations.

A monorail is actually a very expensive, elevated trolleybus (Chapter 7); it might carry about 0.5 percent to 1 percent of São Paulo's current motorized passenger trips and 1 to 2 percent of its current bus passengers. Not much for a third of a billion dollars (or maybe a billion dollars) in construction costs.

One obvious alternative is the bus–erf strategy outlined in Chapter 9. If the $300 million proposed for the first 15 kilometers of the monorail were spent on busways, bus lanes, and pedestrianization, most bus riders would enjoy vastly improved transit performance and lower cost-based fares, and there would be fewer serious accidents (the monorail is safe enough, but quantitatively irrelevant). Better bus circulation would reduce fuel use and pollution, even if diesel buses were chosen over electric. Bus–erf projects can be implanted piecemeal, starting immediately with whatever funds are available; the monorail would sop up $300 million and five to ten years' time before producing any benefits.

Once the urban transport problem is adequately defined in municipal terms and the impacts on the total transport picture are considered instead of a single corridor, the bus–erf strategy is easily seen to be superior to the monorail with regard to all characteristics, and we may terminate the characteristics algorithm. It is not clear that a cost–benefit study of the monorail could add any useful information to our results.

Case 6. Rail Transit Projects

Don Pickrell (1990) finds evaluations of nine out of ten U.S. rail transit projects wide of the mark, with ridership at about one-third of predicted levels. J. S. Gutman and R. G. Scurfield (1990) find only two of thirteen systems in other countries that came close to achieving predicted ridership levels. In Brazil, the new Recife and Porto Alegre rail lines carry about as many passengers each as a priority bus lane; the third, in Belo Horizonte, is still incomplete after more than a decade of planning and construction, and carries even fewer passengers (Brazil 1987: chap. 5). Even those rail systems with a surfeit of passengers are not success stories: Manila's overhead light rail line can seldom keep all its trains running and transports an insignificant percentage of the metropolitan area's seven million inhabitants. The availability of operating funds for Brazil's rail systems is now in question, as they recover only 10 to 40 percent of their costs from the fare box (Lima 1989). The Rio metro at one point had dismantled eleven of its original twenty-four trains to obtain spare parts, and has tottered on the verge of collapse on several occasions.

Most of these projects were accompanied by favorable cost–benefit analysis. Ian Thomson (1983) reviewed several of the Latin American studies and found costs underestimated and benefits exaggerated.[1] Gutman and Scurfield of the World Bank, along with Pickrell, are skeptical of the methodologies and estimates; in light of such experience, the World Bank has become reluctant to make loans for urban rail transit projects.

Again, within the cost–benefit paradigm, there can be a methodological stalemate. Proponents can produce estimates of passenger flows and time savings that result in favorable benefit–cost ratios. Funding agencies sympathetic to rail projects may finance them, more alert lenders may question the assumptions. The characteristics approach takes a different path, asking if available funds are adequate for building and maintaining enough rail transit lines to provide comprehensive, flexible service. The response is almost always negative. Wright and José Alex Sant'Anna (1989), for example, show that a doubling of Brazilian urban train passengers during the 1990 decade—a wildly optimistic idea—would absorb only one-third of the expected *increase* in transit passenger trips.

At this point, the characteristics approach asks if affordable alternatives are available to provide flexibility and other desirable characteristics. Depending on the city characteristics, these alternatives range from improving nonmotorized transport to bus–erf projects. Rail transit may be an important element for a few high-income cities, but it is always incapable of solving the mobility problem by itself.

A caveat: rail enthusiasts often insist that trains provide an extra "something"—benefits that are hard to quantify and that buses are incapable of offering. Gutman and Scurfield's paper indicates that the World Bank, after having financed a number of disappointing rail projects, is inclined to ignore such "benefits."

In order to be included in the characteristics approach, the "extra something" must be specified as a measurable characteristic, and it must be shown that other modes (for example, good bus service) could not provide the same characteristic. Moshe Ben-Akiva and T. Morikawa (1990) conducted an analysis of passengers' preferences with respect to choice of modes in Washington, D.C. They found that passengers are as receptive to good bus service as to good train service and that travelers prefer good bus service to poor commuter train environments, just as they do in Rio de Janeiro. Not surprisingly, the researchers found waiting at transfer points the most negative feature of the transit services. The train, with its limited flexibility, is the mode most likely to impose that nuisance on the traveler.

This is not to deny that, under certain conditions, some people prefer trains. The English, for example, are famous for that attitude. But they are comparing quality train service with buses trapped in congested vehicular traffic. The Australians chose the O-Bahn bus because it offered better overall service at less cost than alternative rail systems (Araújo 1989; Wayte 1989).

Case 7. A Solution to a Nonexistent Problem

The cities of São Paulo and Rio de Janeiro are about 400 kilometers (249 miles) apart: the smaller, but dynamic center of Campinas is about 100 kilometers from São Paulo. Railway enthusiasts lobbied to build a high-speed train (HST) of the Japanese or French variety to link these cities, at a cost of $4.2 billion. In the 1970s, Brazil's minister of transportation took a trip to Japan and became infatuated with the bullet train; other cabinet members and the president were less impressed—the same minister had foisted the "Steel Railway" on them, and it was already a classical boondoggle. As a polite way of stalling, they requested a cost–benefit study of the matter, accomplished in 1978 using what are still state-of-the-art behavioristic techniques to estimate the demand for such a service (GEIPOT 1979). (The study has a happy ending—before it was concluded, the minister of transportation was enjoying his retirement.)

The GEIPOT study concluded that the HST had a positive net present value on the stretch lying within the state of São Paulo, but that the section in the state of Rio and the project considered as a whole had negative net present values.

The next minister of transportation went to France and saw a second-generation HST. The fallout from that trip was a second document (SNCF 1981) stating that, if the earlier HST study were redone, the net present value would be positive for the entire line. The authors reasoned that improvements in technology since the earlier study had lowered construction costs, while population and income increases had augmented the benefits, and these effects would be enough to tip the balance in the HST's favor.

These studies are classic examples of decisionmaking processes that start with a solution and tack cost–benefit analysis on at the end. The characteristics approach, in contrast, begins by attempting to define the problem as follows.

São Paulo and Rio are connected by a four-lane divided highway (the Via Dutra) and by an unspectacular rail line that provides some cargo service and a few passenger trains each week. There are two modern four-lane divided highways and an electrified rail line connecting São Paulo to Campinas. All three cities have international airports; São Paulo and Rio also have in-city airports with a shuttle service using ancient Electra prop airplanes. The trip by air costs $45 one way and takes about 50 minutes; this will fall to 30–40 minutes when Rio's city airport runways are lengthened a bit and modern jets replace the retiring Electras. Proven versions of the HST would make the trip in about 90 minutes. Modern, comfortable São Paulo–Rio buses leave stations in each direction every five minutes or less, take about 5½ hours and cost a mere $8 one way ($16 for a luxury sleeper). Three independent bus companies compete on this route; competition is based on service quality since the price is regulated. Bus service on the Rio–São Paulo route is the best in the country—perhaps the world (Wright 1989a). Luxury buses also connect Campinas to São Paulo, the ride takes 80 minutes and costs $2.

The populations of Rio and São Paulo have never shown any major concern about getting from one city to the other. Riots do occur at times in both cities due to urban transport problems *within* each city, but these are hardly curable by an intercity HST.

We thus have a curious situation: a $4.2-billion project would be considered economically sound by an updated cost–benefit analysis, even though there is no identifiable problem. The two cost–benefit studies cited may have identified the only transport flow in Brazil that does not present any major problems. Moreover, the proposed $4.2 billion would be enough to rebuild virtually all Brazil's important federal transport facilities and provide considerable badly needed new capacity on some of them, (see Brazil 1987 and Wright et al. 1989).

Case 8. Duplicating the Via Dutra

This is an illustrative sequel to Case 7. When it became clear that funds were not available for the HST, proposals were made for constructing another four-lane divided highway parallel to the Dutra. A 54-kilometer stretch was built (the *Trabalhadores*), based on the argument that the Dutra would soon be saturated by increasing traffic (it turned out to be lightly used). Other proposals included upgrading the existing parallel rail line to divert heavy freight traffic from road to rail.

Nilson Martins (1984), an inquisitive engineer in the São Paulo branch of the National Highway Department (DNER), used an eclectic method similar to the characteristics approach to redefine the problem and to provide a novel, low-cost solution.

Martins separated traffic counts on the Dutra into rural and urban sections; he observed that congestion on the Dutra was actually an urban problem, that is, it occurred only on the urban interfaces of the highway. The predominant intraurban and other short-distance traffic could not be diverted to rail, and duplication of the Dutra would not provide enough capacity in the urban sections where additional capacity was needed. Martins then took into account DNER's limited budget and its 80-meter right-of-way in designing a solution. Both had been ignored by previous proposals that featured conventional duplication and cloverleaf intersections.

Martin's solution featured sets of closely spaced parallel roads that separated local, metropolitan, and long-distance traffic. These roads are interconnected with simple crossovers for merging, and entrances and exits occur from local streets with connecting arcs and simple overpasses.[2] On my last visit to São Paulo, Martin's project was complete at two priority locations; it provided high levels of service (levels B and C; see Chapter 3 for definitions), carried about 150,000 vehicles per day, and had reduced once-frequent accidents to minimal levels (DNER 1989). Municipal authorities were co-opted to pay for the local lanes, making the project financially viable despite DNER's nearly empty coffers.

Case 9. Bus–Erf Projects

As noted earlier, both European trolley planners and Martins implicitly used methods similar to the characteristics approach. The same occurred with bus–erf strategies in Brazil. A few key staff members in different transit agencies had been exposed to traffic engineering, urban design, and multicriterial analysis. Their practices reflected this multidisciplinary training, and most of them benefited from an intimate knowledge of their cities as long-time residents. In Curitiba, the head of the planning agency (IPPUC) became mayor and was able to put his group's plans into practice. In Belo Horizonte, a similar group (METROBEL) had the only coherent plan when the mayor and governor decided to do something about the expanding chaos in the city's urban transport. The story is similar in Campina Grande. The characteristics of these projects and their success were described in Chapter 9. Here we add a similar case, that of Maceió, a medium-sized city in the Brazilian northeast.

The mayor of Maceió called on urban transport specialists at GEIPOT soon after taking office in the late 1970s. As he described it, the previous administration had formulated projects for seven overpasses in the downtown area (complete with favorable benefit–cost ratios), and he was being pressured to implement them. He was worried about two things: there was no money to build them, and if built they would ruin the tourist-oriented city's visual appeal.

GEIPOT technicians spent a lot of time studying the city's characteristics, developing plans, and discussing them with the mayor. They also ended up, at times reluctantly, discussing traffic engineering concepts with other influential citizens. The group was verbally attacked by a radio announcer for widening some narrow (0.6 m) sidewalks instead of widening the adjoining avenue; he felt a "modern" city should have wide avenues. The group leader explained to the announcer and listeners that the existing traffic lanes had irregular widths in some areas, such as two and a half lanes. The extra half-lane created confusion and accidents, reducing rather than increasing traffic flow; both drivers and pedestrians would be better off with the half-lane used to widen sidewalks.

The GEIPOT (1981) solution used simple traffic engineering measures and a bus-erf strategy. A pedestrian mall complemented the widened sidewalks, and parking fees were instituted to discourage long-term parking and provide free space for short-term parking. Some simple measures were instituted to improve bus service. The only physical infrastructure projects of note were the mall, the sidewalks, and an underground drainage system to avoid flooding during heavy rains. The transport and traffic problem improved substantially, and the once-decaying downtown commercial district took on new life.

Case 10. Brazil's Ethanol Program (Proálcool)

This project was introduced in the 1970s to sustain sugarcane plantations through a period of declining prices on the world sugar market. Subsequently, Proálcool was expanded to reduce dependence on foreign oil. Opinions vary regarding the economics of the program, many of them pessimistic. F. Joseph Demetrius (1990: 45–48), however, shows that some of the more negative cost–benefit evaluations of Proálcool are based on the use of an excessively high price for sugar (the mills' alternative to alcohol production). Demetrius argues that Brazil would have depressed world sugar prices by expanding its production and foreign sales of sugar instead of switching much of the cane-processing capacity to ethanol production. By correcting for this error, Demetrius estimates that ethanol replaces 125 to 140 thousand barrels of gasoline per day and saved Brazil a billion dollars in foreign exchange in 1985.

The conclusions of cost–benefit studies of Proálcool, however, depend heavily on the price assumed for a barrel of crude. At $15 a barrel, Proálcool is considered uneconomic; at some point between $30 and $40 a barrel, it becomes a good investment (Franco 1989: 198; Motta 1985). During the recent hostilities in the Mideast, Proálcool's star rose again.

The inconclusive results of cost–benefit analysis contrast with the results of the characteristics approach. As in the HST case, the systemic nature of characteristics analysis reveals a crucial point in the problem definition phase (step 1). Ethanol is used only in cars (Brazil has the technology to run either Otto-cycle or diesel bus and truck engines on alcohol, but this has never been employed on a significant scale). Ethanol production thus permitted and even encouraged the emergence of automobile-threatened cities. A direct consequence of this strategy is that trucks and buses operate in extremely congested conditions in mixed traffic. Proálcool-induced congestion thus implies substantial waste of diesel fuel in urban areas. Furthermore, diesel fuel, rather than gasoline, determines the level of crude imports, since Brazil's refining technology still yields a rather low 36 percent of diesel from each barrel of crude, an improvement over previous levels but far less than that obtained in Europe (Franco 1989: 197).

The systemic nature of characteristics analysis accounts for the negative effect on diesel vehicles' fuel efficiency caused by private cars. Given that diesel fuel use determines the level of imports, if automobile-induced congestion wastes 20 percent of urban bus and truck fuel, and 50 percent of diesel fuel is used in urban areas, then congestion causes an increase of some 8 percent in petroleum imports. This is equivalent to importing an extra 33 million barrels a year;[3] at $15 a barrel, this is about half the foreign exchange Demetrius estimates that Brazil saves through Proálcool; at $30 a barrel, the entire savings disappears.

Paradoxically: the high oil prices benefit–cost analysts think necessary to make Proálcool competitive with petroleum eliminate the alleged benefit of Proálcool's alleged foreign exchange savings. This occurs since the use of ethanol in private cars augments congestion and use of diesel fuel, increasing imports of crude oil.

Characteristics analysis, having identified the incoherence of Proálcool, moves on to the search for alternatives. One obvious alternative is to eliminate Proálcool. In retrospect, this is an easy recommendation, but in the 1970s and early 1980s, Brazil risked being unable to import oil, and that threat reappeared with the recent war in the Gulf. Methanol may be a less expensive alternative, but that was not known when Proálcool was launched. And Proálcool made Brazil the first country in the world to completely eliminate lead from its gasoline by adding 10 to 20 percent of ethanol in the resulting mixture. But Brazil could have done much better by giving priority on street space to buses and shared taxis, powering them with alcohol and gasoline. Fuel imports would have decreased, public transportation would have improved vastly, and traffic accidents and smog would have diminished.

Discussion

In the case studies cited above, the implicit and explicit uses of the characteristics approach provided a means of generating appropriate projects and convincingly rejecting boondoggles such as the high-speed train and the monorail. The characteristics approach proved useful in generating appropriate general strategies (for example, bus–erf), along with conceptual design and final engineering projects (Maceió, Curitiba, Belo Horizonte, Campina Grande, Dutra). The basic tools needed for the characteristics approach are elementary problem definitions and easily accessible hard data obtained from traffic engineering manuals, maps, per capita income figures, and an intimate knowledge of each city and its transport users.

The true believer in cost–benefit analysis may allege that I have not proven anything. A sampling of such objections is given below, culled from seminars and papers I have presented in several countries, with my replies in parentheses. (Lest the reader think these are strawman arguments, I have documental evidence in some cases and witnesses in others—true believers really do say these things.)

> *My examples are limited to urban transport.*
> Granted, this book is on urban transport; I have run across similar examples in other areas, a theme for future work.
>
> *My examples are not from a random sample.*
> Granted, but I have included a large number of road and rail transit projects around the world, and virtually all important urban transport decisions since 1960 in Brazil, one of the world's largest and most populous countries.
>
> *I have not proven that the characteristics approach will always produce good results.*
> Granted, but it has never failed me, and hit 1.000 in the case studies while the others struck out.
>
> *The characteristics approach does not guarantee that the optimal solution will be chosen.*
> There is no optimal solution—remember Lancaster's fourth principle. But the method promises decisionmakers the

technically appropriate set of alternatives and considerable complementary information to base their decision on. In the real world, you cannot do much more than that.

I have presented a straw-man case, choosing examples of poorly done cost–benefit studies. As one true believer put it, "People who do bad cost–benefit analysis should be shot."
I fear that if his advice were taken, more blood would be shed than in the average revolution, even though cost–benefit is used sparing in most countries.

My attacks are a criticism of the way cost–benefit is often used, rather than of the technique itself.
Something must be wrong with a method that does not routinely reduce good results when used by highly trained people.

Cost–benefit analysis would also approve good projects, like the bus–erf examples.
Granted, the analyst deals with numerical silly putty and can produce favorable benefit–cost ratios for good and bad projects; hence the problem. A farmer wants a dog that is hostile to chicken thieves and foxes, in addition to being docile with chickens; why should an economist want an evaluation technique that cannot distinguish boondoggles from good urban transport projects?

If the "missing chapter" on project formulation was provided in the cost–benefit manuals, cost–benefit would come out much better.
Granted, if you start with a good solution, all you have to do is approve it; the present chapter is a candidate for the missing chapter, but may not fit the cost–benefit paradigm very well.

Cost–benefit can still be used if all relevant characteristics can be quantified in monetary units, all relevant projects are analyzed and distributional effects are unimportant.
Granted. If and only if. I have never seen such a project, but it may exist; early U.S. hydroelectric projects may have fit this case.

One of the defects cited in cost–benefit studies—neglect of income distribution considerations—can be dealt with by weighting effects.

This is a variant of the previous theme. As E. J. Mishan shows in his 1988 book, distributional weights can produce favorable cost–benefit ratios for project with poor distributional impacts. More important, cost–benefit analysis does not address the need to generate projects that provide for the transport needs of low-income travelers. In the case studies, the characteristics approach provided almost automatically for the needs of low-income pedestrians and bus users.

The iterative characteristics approach is time-consuming, and the informational requirements are enormous.
Actually, the initial iterations take very little time and are the most important ones. A number of highly qualified experts from several countries spent over six months to come up with the wrong answer in the cost–benefit studies of the Brazilian HST proposal, while I did the characteristics analysis in an afternoon, working alone. A team with local and foreign consultants ran around for over a year trying to find a place where they could insert a monorail in São Paulo and a plausible argument for it—cost–benefit analysis would have taken even longer. It took me about ten days of individual effort to dissect the São Paulo monorail proposal and do a complete characteristics analysis of the monorail and alternatives, including several pages of quantitative simulation of key aspects. The authors of the Maceió, Curitiba, and Dutra projects took much longer than I did to complete their studies, but they produced final engineering projects. It would have taken them longer to produce equally detailed bad projects and to "justify" them with cost–benefit studies. There is nothing in characteristics analysis that requires more data or time than conventional methodologies; it does, however, show the user how to put the pieces together and what is actually relevant to the case at hand.

Although valuation of effects may vary from analyst to analyst, welfare economics [the true believer means "cost–benefit analysis" here] provides a framework for consistent valuation of effects.
Cost–benefit analysis provides a consistent framework only if characteristics can be unambiguously quantified in monetary terms, a rare and possibly nonexistent phenomenon in urban

transport projects. The true believer is right about one thing, however, when analysts attempt to monetarize nonmonetary characteristics, they get different answers.

Characteristics analysis may not prevent decisionmakers from choosing a bad project.
Granted. Nonetheless, in many instances what really counts is the ability to produce reliable guidelines and critiques quickly, to fend off a bad idea, to get on the right track at an early stage in project analysis. On this point, cost–benefit analysis has nothing whatever to present, and the characteristics approach does quite well.

I agree with you, but our agency is applying for a loan from an agency that requires cost–benefit analysis.
Your problem is not so serious as it seems. Use characteristics analysis to generate the best project for your city's needs and financial capabilities. Then do the cost–benefit exercise.

Chapter 11

Viable and Sustainable Transport Strategies

THE IMPACTS OF transportation systems on the environment and on public finance are an increasingly important aspect of urban transport choices.

Marginal improvements in the efficiency of petroleum-powered vehicles will not, by themselves, reduce the demands on our global resource base enough to guarantee sustainability at reasonable costs for more than a generation or two. An effective Mideast cartel or a major disruption in production and distribution could provoke a major crisis even in the short run; global warming and related environmental problems may require a reduction in the use of hydrocarbons within ten or twenty years.

Alternative fuels have a potentially important role to play, but they too present supply and environmental problems. The nonmotorized modes, independently and as complements to public transportation, are effective solutions in some very-low-income nations; they should be nurtured and encouraged to maintain their predominant role in urban transport. In countries at a higher level of motorization, walking and cycling are generally losing ground and, in the extreme case of North America, transit and cycling constitute a negligible percentage of trips. Most current conditions of street design, traffic, and urban layouts make these modes unattractive to users.

Walking needs to be actively promoted as an integral part of urban planning and transport planning in all countries, both as an independent mode and as a complement to motorized modes. Nonetheless, the limited speed, range, and burden-carrying capacity of walking leave a gap that can only be effectively filled by the bicycle and its cousins, the human-powered utility vehicles.

In societies with significant levels of motorization, these human-powered vehicles cannot fill the gap under current unfavorable street-design patterns and traffic rules. This situation cannot be transformed by incantation, pilot projects, or recreational bikeways; such measures solidify the image of the bicycle as a recreational toy rather than a viable form of urban transportation. The future of the bicycle as a transport mode in motorized societies requires major changes in street design and traffic laws.

There is a similar need to implant transit–erf environments throughout the city, not just at a downtown mall or in a pilot residential area.

Erf environments require cyclists to travel at rather slow speeds and to follow indirect paths. A complementary network of express bikeways is thus needed for the bicycle to become the fastest, most practical middle-distance mode in the urban setting.

A network of express bikeways is one dense enough for the cyclist to travel to within a few hundred meters of any point in the urbanized area; this network must be complemented by omnipresent erven in the areas between the express bikeways and any point in the city. The express bikeways should include as many pedestrian–cyclist bridges and elevated longitudinal bikeway sections as necessary. The bridges should be blended into the landscape as natural, privileged paths rather than as obstacle courses designed to avoid causing any inconvenience to automobile traffic. These measures have been taken successfully in parts of a few European and Japanese cities, and throughout the Dutch city of Lelystad. They are hardest to implement exactly where they are most needed to diminish harmful demands on our global resource base—high-income cities with low population densities built on the North American model. There, a useful complementary strategy may be to begin with a carpool–erf strategy, plus a series of bikeways to transit stations (Replogle 1988a). A caveat: the scarcity of public transport in many North American towns and cities may reduce the impact of these measures to insignificant levels, making a network of bikeways the only real alternative.

Technological discoveries may push back the petroleum and other resource constraints for additional generations. Cold fusion or perpetual motion may work after all. Or we may not want to worry about these problems—we may be too egocentric to act on behalf of future generations.

There is, however, an issue that must be dealt with in the short run in all countries; in some, it is already part of a day-to-day struggle. This issue is the fiscal and administrative crisis of government and its effects on the urban transport sector.

Extreme views abound; for some, the market does not work in urban transportation, and the state should take over. Well into this line of thinking, the current administration of the City of São Paulo proposed free bus services for the entire municipality of 10 million persons, a measure to be financed by increasing the urban property tax several fold (*Folha de São Paulo* 5 October 1990: D-1).

Realism at times prevails, and the city council rejected the administration's zero bus fare policy. The populist administration itself backed off from its campaign promise to "municipalize" bus ownership, and most bus service continues in private hands. One reason for this change of mind is the city bus company: it absorbs most of the $25 million a month that the municipality funnels into transit subsidies. An ex-president of that company was recently indicted for corruption, and the city plans to fire 4,110 employees (*Folha de São Paulo*, 21 November 1990: D-1; 24 January 1991: C-5). The city bus company is such a headache that the administration's zero-tariff proposal was based on contracting the bus services from the private sector.

At the other extreme are the ideologues of privatization who want the government out of urban transport entirely. They advocate the end of subsidies to transit, but conveniently forget to advocate Professor White's $3.75 a gallon gasoline tax to compensate for the externalities caused by private motor cars (White 1989). They also overlook laws that implicitly subsidize parking and construction of low-density, individual housing units.

In this debate at least, I will follow Myrdal's counsel (1969) to be objective by stating my bias. I have a Lincolnesque position: in urban transport, the government should do what the private sector cannot do or cannot do as efficiently as government; other tasks should stay in the private sector.

The private sector can operate buses more efficiently than government. This is not an ideological position on my part: if a public bus company enjoys the private sector's rules and has honest, dedicated, and efficient personnel at all levels, it can operate with equal efficiency. The outcome usually depends on the rules of the game and the competence of the players.

The basic problem is that public companies seldom operate

under the same rules as private companies. In developed countries, citizens' groups, the mayor, council members, and many others demand that the public company provide bus services that cannot pay for themselves. The Japanese work ethic seems restricted to Japan; elsewhere, employees form unions, and the city bus company soon finds it impossible to fire even the most complacent and incompetent employees. Since only the city offers transit services, the union can shut them down, and it uses this power to elevate wages and benefits well above the average for similar professions. Charles Lave (1990) concludes that U.S. public ownership and governmental subsidies transformed public transit into a "sugar daddy"; early on, municipalities became unable to pick up the tab by themselves, and state and federal subsidies were required to keep transit afloat.

Regulations often made it difficult to provide transport services efficiently, as a case of "regulatory overkill" in Kalamazoo, Michigan, illustrates: legal specifications required, in effect, tailor-made vehicles for its minuscule taxi market (Ross 1981).

In developing counties, public companies typically face a few more problems. A mayor may put most of his relatives and a number of political cronies on the bus company's payroll. The government may not increase fares to cover inflation for fear of touching off a wave of rioting. Private businesses may refuse to sell supplies to the city; the city's accounting procedures do not allow payment in cash and the city cannot be counted on to pay its bills. Attempts to combat corruption may make things worse; they entangle the company in regulations, reporting, and paperwork, and add an army of accountants, lawyers, and inspectors to the payroll, when funds and personnel are not available to keep the buses running. Similarly, the failure of regulatory agencies to authorize increases in tariffs to cover inflation can lead to the collapse of private services. Unwise regulations can be adopted overnight; regulatory reform in transport may require years of effort (Heggie 1989).

There are some extreme examples. In Maputo, Mozambique, a fleet of modern buses has been taken out of circulation for lack of funds for maintenance and repair (*Horizontes Urbanos* 1990: 3). In Trindad, the public bus corporation received $5.5 million in fares in a year, spent $8.4 million to collecting those fares, and had a total operating cost of $67.7 million (*Mass Transit* 1985: 10, 50).

Even efficient public transit companies tend to decline over time. The Brazilian Federal District's public bus company, TCB, ran in the black for a number of years; it had a good staff, a monopoly on the best routes in the Pilot Plan, and charged the same fares as private companies (Wright and Ferreira Netto 1985). Eventually, however, the District's government began to hold fare increases below inflation; this endangered private companies and, to compensate for the price squeeze, the district made the TCB give some of its profitable routes to private companies and absorb high-cost routes, including lightly traveled rural lines. TCB soon became a reliable money loser.

Unfortunately, privatization and deregulation are not by themselves satisfactory solutions unless antitrust protection is available and some effort is made to provide buses with improved bus lanes or with semi-exclusive busways.

Between 1980 to 1983, Chile canceled all public regulation of urban bus transport except traffic laws and vehicle inspection (Chile 1985). The bus owners had long worked together in an employers' association to pressure the government to increase fares and maintain monopolies on individual routes. When the government ended all fare and route regulation, the companies decided to cooperate rather than to compete with each other; their freedom to fix their own fares produced fares higher than in other Latin American countries.

The Chilean price increases dampened enthusiasm for completely deregulated urban transport in Latin America. They apparently improved service, however. A subsequent survey found that over half of the users surveyed in Santiago felt that service was good, only 11 percent judged it poor, only 30 percent found fares to be "expensive," and still fewer (20 percent) said their choice of mode was determined mainly by price (Lopez 1989).

A mixed public–private model is also a common ownership pattern in some larger Latin American cities. The public bus company may provide 10 to 30 percent of bus services (with or without subsidies); private companies provide the rest at fixed fares without subsidies. This ownership pattern gives the city some leverage in countering the private companies' threats to shut down services if the fares they demand are not granted. The city learns how to operate a bus company and can take over the private companies' operations temporarily if faced with a lockout. (A disadvantage: the increased competence means the city may actually intervene and make a mess of things, as occasionally happens in large Brazilian cities.) The city bus company can hold its employees' wage demands at reasonable levels by mentioning the lower wages paid by the private companies and threatening to shut down operations; private companies may have to pay their employees a bit better, due to comparisons with the public company's wages and working conditions.

These advantages, however, seldom compensate for the money

lost by the public company, or the increase in fares required to keep it afloat—the private companies are normally content with a fare high enough to cover the public company's deficit.

Robert Cervero (1990) recommends measures such as allowing private commercial services and contracted bus services to reduce transit budget deficits in U.S. cities. Competitive supply conditions can result in lower bids by private firms for provision of certain bus services than the cost of supplying them through a public company.

Results have been mixed in Britain, however, the only developed country with a national policy favoring contracts (Mackett 1990). The benefits of reductions in subsidies have been largely canceled out by fare increases and reductions in ridership.

Qualitative problems in less developed countries often undermine governmental interventions in bus operations. A case in point is Brasília's "caixa único" (literally, "single teller," or unified fare-receipt system). In 1985, proponents argued that the single-teller system would provide lower and more uniform fares by permitting the government to inject subsidies into the system and to compensate the private companies for their costs, based on the distance traveled by their buses.[1] Nay-sayers like me were ignored.

Shortly after the single-teller system was inaugurated in June 1986, problems began to appear. It suddenly became profitable to run empty buses: companies had to turn over all turnstile-registered fares to the single teller, and were paid for the distance their buses traveled. Since passengers were an inconvenience, bus drivers started bypassing many stops; at other stops drivers would skid to a halt, rev their motors, and roar away before all passengers could board. (These brusque maneuvers frequently caused minor injuries to passengers: on one rapid pullaway, I saw a woman fall backward, her foot caught in the door; she was pulled along for about 10 meters before the passengers got the driver to stop.) On more lightly traveled routes and at night, buses seldom stopped. Fare collectors and agile riders entered into tacit agreements—riders paid half fare and either jumped over the turnstiles or entered and exited from the same doors. Informed guesses placed the increase in fare evasion—formerly insignificant— at 30 percent of riders and climbing. Bus owners discovered that money-losing routes were suddenly profitable for them: they were paid for miles driven, not passengers. These conservative business-people dropped their longstanding objections to local residents and politicians' lobbying for new money-losing routes. Taxpayers and honest riders paid for the inefficiency and corruption. The subsidies failed to decrease fares since the government could not find enough funds to fill the single teller's bottomless sack; subsidized fares out-stripped the increases in fuel prices, wages and inflation.[2]

The periodic wage disputes no longer took place on the prem-ises of the bus companies—they began to be conducted in the gover-nor's office. Bus company owners, once known for their stinginess in wage negotiations, became passive and indifferent spectators as wages escalated and were automatically covered by increases in tariffs and subsidies. Bus drivers gained a six-hour workday and a guarantee that these hours would be continuous, rather than split over two peaks. Since many buses are idle in off-peak hours, some drivers now work as little as two hours per day. Other legislation passed the cost of many work-related trips to employers, further relieving the pressure to keep fares down.

Unfortunately, the result of all these factors has been to almost double bus fares. As this book went to press, fares in Brasília stood at 70 cents. As usually happens, these fares are paid by those least able to afford them—the unemployed, the underemployed, and those who are self-employed in low-paying activities.

Rail transit projects nearly always run large deficits. The pri-vate sector will only accept them if the government guarantees high prices and ridership levels, plus gifts of adjacent properties and other additional revenue. I suspect such schemes work only in Japan.

The rails remain an important part of the transport environ-ment in cities wealthy enough to afford them. Most cities are unable to build and operate enough rail lines to make a dent in their urban mobility problems, and these projects siphon off funds and enthusiasm that could be used on more cost-effective bus–erf strategies. In less-developed countries, bus and paratransit services can be provided by the private sector without subsidies, with lower fares than for subsi-dized bus services in developed countries. Bus fares are not necessarily "low" in relation to the income of the poorest residents, yet large num-bers of transit users are willing to pay for improved service (Acevedo 1989; Wright 1982). Subsidies seldom result in substantially lower fares and are often associated with degradation of service quality.

This does not mean that government should abandon transit; rather, the public sector should invest in measures that lower costs and improve the performance of bus services. This means redesigning bus routes and operations and providing an extensive network of bus lanes, busways, and erf environments for complementary pedestrian trips. Such projects doubled bus speeds in Campina Grande, reducing fares and transfers (Urbema 1985); they also worked well in São Paulo (Szasz and Germani 1985: 31–32).

The $25 million per month that São Paulo wastes in subsidizing inefficient bus operations in mixed traffic could finance ten kilometers of semi-exclusive bus lanes or several kilometers of O-Bahn each month, each with a surrounding erf environment. In a single four-year government term, a mayor could implant unparalleled improvements in bus transportation and create extensive erf environments. Considerably less fuel would be used, and pollution could be diminished by switching motors to natural gas, ethanol, or, in a longer time frame, electricity. Decreases in operating costs for buses could be passed on to users in the form of lower fares (recently, fares have increased despite subsidies, as buses in stop-and-go traffic have high costs). Within a decade, the whole city could be covered with a web of closely knit bus lanes and erf environments; the oppressive noise and pollution that mark life in São Paulo would become a thing of the past.

Cities in developing countries with low levels of motorization have the option of limiting motor traffic early on. This can be done by funneling motorized traffic into specific channels and reserving most streets for nonmotorized traffic. Where motor vehicles are permitted, their speeds should be kept down by street design and traffic humps, guaranteeing safe and efficient use of nonmotorized transport. A proper investment strategy in these circumstances can provide much of the population with virtually free transport by implanting an adequate infrastructure for walking and cycling.

Many European cities and their more wealthy Asian counterparts can extend their transit–erf environments. The erven have proved popular, and funds from some transit subsidy programs could be used to expand them.

Such measures have a strong tendency to improve the performance of urban transport systems across almost all characteristics. This runs counter to the interpretation of urban transport as a conflictive process, one in which a desirable characteristic can be had only by sacrificing some other desirable characteristic. The conflictive interpretation may be valid for the poor solutions often recommended for urban transit problems, particularly those favoring low-capacity private cars in densely populated urban centers. Better solutions are available, and they are often synergistic in nature: doing one thing right often makes other good things happen.

Each city has characteristics that define the technically appropriate choices for improving the transport environment at an affordable cost. The characteristics approach is a valuable aid in understanding the nature of these choices and their consequences for the well-being of travelers and their cities.

Chapter 12

Summary and Conclusions

---

*I*N THIS BOOK we have taken a problem-solving, characteristics approach to urban transportation planning. The characteristics paradigm combines extreme simplicity with a systemic view of the problem. From Lancaster's four postulates on the nature and importance of characteristics, we follow the commonsense path of asking what the problem is and what means are available for dealing with it. The means are transport modes and the myriad ways of operating them to produce a more desirable set of transport-related characteristics. The modes are subject to technical, political, and financial constraints on their operation, and appropriate modal choices must match the characteristics of the city and its transport users.

This matching process allows us to generate the technically appropriate set of solutions, that is, the solutions that provide the desired levels of characteristics and meet the constraints, taking into account that, in the real world, the desired levels of characteristics and the budget constraints are both of the "soft" variety. The technically appropriate set normally consists of projects that present somewhat different sets of characteristics and have varying price tags. Since individuals value characteristics differently, decisionmakers have the task of choosing the characteristics set that best fits their preferences and their agency's or city's budget.

An "optimal" solution exists only in two degenerate cases when only one project is technically appropriate, or the desired levels of characteristics and the budget constraint are rigidly preset and the

251

problem is reduced to a simple mathematical exercise in cost minimization.

In the second case, it is probable that a slight alteration in the prespecified characteristics levels would result in considerable savings in cost. Mathematical optimality results from imposing rigid and arbitrary constraints on a problem; given those constraints, one solution offers the lowest cost.

In urban transport planning, some or all of the restrictions are "soft," and different solutions can qualify as "satisfactory" and "affordable." Some academics may object that these are weasel-words, too imprecise to be admissible in a discussion of methods. But the evidence is on the other side, as city council members deal with such concepts all the time, and lucid academics have taken the forefront of their professions by learning to apply them. Herbert Simon, for example, won the Nobel Prize for economics on the basis of his demonstrations that businesspersons, faced with the real-world limitations of less-than-perfect information, exhibited "sufficing" behavior— suboptimal, but good enough under the circumstances (1978; 1979). Computer experts, for similar reasons, now recognize the value of imprecise terms and have invented "fuzzy programming" to enable computers to work with concepts like "almost," as humans do.

Decisionmakers can relax constraints, enabling the characteristics analyst to product similar or better solutions at a cost below that of the least-cost solution with rigid, preset requirements. In effect, city council can find a better solution than the mathematically optimal, however semantically awkward that may be.

The technical people's task is to help decisionmakers define and understand the technically appropriate options. The decisionmakers then debate the advantages and disadvantages of each option and choose among them.

Aside from its commonsense, intuitive appeal, the characteristics approach is supported by Lancaster's new consumer theory and its coherence with the principles of systems engineering. The combination of practicality and theoretical rigor recommends the approach as an effective way of informing interested parties about the nature of urban transport and transport-relevant city characteristics, and the choices available to them. Its usefulness in defining cost-effective options for dealing with the city's transport problems is expected to improve political deliberation and decisionmaking.

Now that we have seen how the characteristics approach works in a variety of settings, we can ask how the principles of transport planning change in relation to the traditional paradigm.

The methodological and other qualitative changes are extremely important. The traditional approach initiates the process of public evaluation and debate when the project has already been developed; often there may be a political commitment to go ahead with it. The evaluation is normally confined to a specific proposal, with limited reference to the rest of the system or an overall transport strategy. Little is done to inform interested parties about transport characteristics, even less to generate a project that is coherent with the city's characteristics and the needs of its residents.

Under the characteristics approach, interested parties are given a view of the larger picture of transportation in their urban area. Project teams are *teams* rather than a collection of individuals with narrow technical knowledge. Specialists are not banned; rather, they develop a knowledge of how things fit together and what their colleagues are doing. This intellectual broadening of the specialists increases the opportunities for effective interaction and exchange of ideas. The economist, who formerly appeared toward the conclusion of the process with cost–benefit analysis, now participates from the beginning, helping the engineers discover ways of producing the same or similar characteristics at lower costs, and evaluating potential user reactions to different strategies and specific projects. The engineer is not assigned the task of building a rail link from A to B, but helps to define the technically possible ways of producing desirable transport characteristics sets between A, B, and other points.

Decisionmakers assist the technical staff in defining and redefining the problem; they accompany the process of systematically generating and evaluating the options for dealing with the problem. The decisionmakers are asked to check the preliminary list of technically appropriate solutions for coherence with the problem statements, and are informed of ways of reducing costs while maintaining or enhancing the positive attributes of the projects. Decisionmakers participate directly in the search for viable financing strategies. During this process, they learn a great deal about the characteristics of transport modes, their city, and its transport users.

There are also political implications. In more democratic societies, the process of characteristics analysis reaches well outside narrow administrative circles to involve the press and citizen groups. Knowledge is power, and characteristics analysis provides easily understood technical information. Better-informed local citizens, journalists, bureaucrats, and politicians should make better choices; furthermore, as people begin to understand the nature of characteristics and costs, it becomes harder to hoodwink anyone with expensive projects that deliver few desired transport characteristics or serve few people; better and less expensive alternatives are studied, debated, and evaluated. This contrasts with cost–benefit analysis, which presents the decisionmakers with a number (B/C, B – C, or r) and a recommendation to accept or reject a given project. Under the cost–benefit paradigm, few decisionmakers or journalists are able to penetrate the analyst's assumptions and estimation techniques and discover that there are few hard data to back up the conclusions; even if the analyst has the best of intentions, such analysis is unreliable; without such intentions. . . .

In contrast, the characteristics approach presents data that are predominantly of the "hard," but intelligible, variety. This makes it easier to catch errors and attempts at falsification. (The attentive reader of this book may qualify as an expert witness with respect to a number of characteristics.) The greater transparency of characteristics analysis does not eliminate the occurrence of errors or misstatements of the absolute value of costs. It does build in some checks, however: (1) the data on characteristics are easily verified; (2) several alternatives are formulated and compared with the status quo, rather than one project, considered in isolation, as is normally the case with cost–benefit analysis; (3) modal choices have to match the characteristics of the city and its residents; and (4) errors in pricing a barrel of oil or a rail system are less likely to lead to the wrong decision, as demonstrated in the case studies.

This last feature allows the analyst to take income-distribution effects into account. In developed countries, some projects are targeted specifically to low-income groups or handicapped citizens. Low-cost, low-fare options are found for the poor; the disabled receive the personalized services they really need rather than a fleet of buses most of them can never use. In low-income cities, characteristics analysis provides good solutions for poor residents more or less automatically: the solutions that are affordable and suitable for solving the general mobility problem are also the best solutions for low-income citizens, since they comprise the bulk of the population.

In the examples from Brazilian cities in Chapter 10, the strategies and projects provided improved bus services at lower cost, while improving conditions for walking and cycling. These benefits are enjoyed by all citizens, but the poor depend more on those modes and receive the largest proportional benefit. The financing strategy can be explicitly tailored to favor low-income citizens (a gas tax to finance busways and erf environments, rather than more highways).

The politics of zoning, city planning, and environmental and international transport-related problems are influenced positively by a better knowledge of transport characteristics and options. With few tanneries and smokestacks in modern cities, it is no longer necessary to rigidly separate residential and other urban functions through zoning ordinances. Businesses can be required to be clean and quiet wherever they are, rather than forced to take their noise and filth elsewhere. Mixed land use makes a variety of activities available near residences and workplaces, reducing the need for motorized travel. With safe walking and cycling paths, parents can spend less time as taxi drivers; relieved of that burden, parents' travel patterns are greatly simplified and they can also walk, cycle, or take the bus.

The oil problem is basically a transportation problem, and personal transport is a major contributor to environmental damage. The systemic characteristics approach makes progress on both accounts easier, since it is more likely to provide cost-effective solutions than alternatives that start with preconceived solutions. Non-OPEC countries will not find themselves so easily placed over a barrel (pun intended) by events in the Middle East.

Under the characteristics approach, city planning and traffic engineering are intimately related. The people involved work together in planning measures that influence population distribution and density, street layout, traffic engineering, and transit services. Transport modes are not chosen in a vacuum but by matching their characteristics to those of the city and its transport users.

One obvious implication: each city adopts some measures that are uniquely tailored to its peculiar characteristics. Walking and cycling, however, have such vast potential in their own right and as complements to other modes that their roles are enhanced over time in all cities. Also, since flexibility is always important for a significant number of trips, there is an enhanced role for shared taxis, carpools, vanpools, and minibuses in relation to rail and conventional bus services. The social desirability of increasing occupancy rates encourages the promotion of high-occupancy vehicles and charging car owners the full costs of parking spaces.

The characteristics approach recognizes that traditional mass transit strategies do not work well in high-income cities with low population densities (on the U.S. and Canadian models). Walking and cycling strategies require hard choices—incantation is not enough, as we saw in the analysis of Ann Arbor bike facilities in Chapter 9. Although the infrastructure costs of quality walkways and cycleways are lower than facilities for any motorized mode of transport, the traditional paradigm leaves them with the part of the budget allocated in the process of rounding the decimals. This is not enough to retrofit safe and convenient walkways and bikeways in cities where decades have been dedicated to closing out those options to make way for the automobile. For a time, as many human and financial resources should be dedicated to walkways and bikeways as to road programs. Under the characteristics paradigm, tokenism is not enough for these modes.

Relatively wealthy cities with intermediate and high population densities (common in Western Europe) are expected to continue to provide a wide variety of options for motorized transport, including expansion of urban rail services where a significant network already exists. But in all cases the options include more exclusive and semi-exclusive right-of-way for buses and better complementary facilities for passenger information and comfort. Buses can offer performance equal to trains on most characteristics, and surpass trains on flexibility and frequency—all this with much lower costs.

The characteristics paradigm provokes the greatest change in developing countries; there, the current paradigm produces automobile-threatened cities, along with decisionmakers and technicians who can think of nothing better than importing expensive mistakes from other countries. The characteristics paradigm literally and figuratively returns precious urban space to the people, through the creation of bus and erf zones throughout the city. The car is restricted to a fairly limited number of streets and a few avenues and held to fairly low speeds by road geometry and traffic humps. Car owners are charged the full social costs for the use of parking space.

This last measure is not be to confused with proposals that begin and end with increases in fuel taxes, road use charges, and parking fees. Such charges in theory can reduce congestion and increase average vehicle speed and are useful parts of a coherent transport strategy. They cannot by themselves, however, create exclusive space for buses, pedestrians, and cyclists, and without quality bus service and proper facilities for walking and cycling, there are no decent alternatives to the private car in either rich or poor cities.

Characteristics analysis reveals that walking, cycling, and buses are necessary parts of an efficient and sustainable urban transport system and shows what is needed for these modes to perform their proper roles. It also demonstrates that isolated measures—the mainstay of previous methods—are insufficient or counterproductive. Wider avenues and new expressways fail to revive urban centers because they remove the conveniences associated with walking that make people want to go there in the first place. The frequent and dangerous intersections that characterize most downtown areas drive people to suburban shopping centers (pun intended), where, once inside, shoppers are free from motor vehicle traffic. Subsidies fail to build transit ridership because they leave buses mired in mixed traffic and trains as inflexible as ever, and both without attractive facilities for the complementary walks involved. Cycling projects fail because they involve nothing beyond isolated bikeways and lack the flexibility needed to make cycling an attractive option.

Characteristics analysis enables people to understand urban transport as a rather simple, organic whole. Its ultimate contribution is to show how each city—whether rich or poor—can develop an improved transport environment, uniquely suited to its characteristics and to the needs and financial capacities of its citizens.

Notes

Chapter 2. On Method and Madness

1. This means that, with other things constant, a rise in the price of a good causes consumers to buy relatively less expensive substitutes. Most consumers deal rather well with this reality without learning how to derive the underlying Slutsky equation or, for that matter, ever having heard of it.

2. For example, I recently examined the indexes of fourteen introductory economics and microeconomics textbooks in the University of Michigan's Sumner Library and found only one (Hyman 1986: 93n, 99, 360n) that contained a brief description of Lancaster's new consumer theory. A second (Browning and Browning 1983) listed Lancaster's (1966a) article as an uncommented reference, and the remainder either did not list Lancaster's name at all or did so with reference to his other contributions, such as the "theory of the second best." The new consumer theory forms the basis of mathematical models of demand for urban transport (for example, Ben-Akiva and Morikawa 1990; Domenchic and McFadden 1975) and for automobiles (Feenstra and Levinsohn 1989b). It has also been used in explaining product differentiation and industrial organization (Feenstra and Levinsohn 1989a; Lancaster 1979), but the work in this area has been scant, possibly due to the difficulty of the mathematics employed.

3. Nor is it necessarily the transit agency's fault. As we shall see, measures needed to make substantial improvements in transit's characteristics sets relative to the private car often lie outside the authority of the transit agency.

4. Examples include Freeman (1977), Hanke and Walker (1977), Himanen (1985), Manheim (1979), Price (1974: 24), and Wildavsky (1977: 470–71).

5. Although Mishan presents a similar point of view in the concluding chapters of his book, this particular quote is from two other ardent defenders of cost–benefit analysis, H. Leonard and R. Zeckhauser (1986: 41–43). The quote continues: "That process frequently leads to stalemate and reliance on the status quo; at other times it careens in response to popular perceptions and whims of the moment." In other words, the cost–benefit paradigm promotes the analyst to the status of decisionmaker, and the role of political representatives is that of endorsing the analyst's recommendation for rejecting or accepting a project.

6. See Anderson (1988), Bromley (1982), and note 4 above.

7. Sharon Caudle and Kathryn Newcomer (1989), for example, criticize the genre of narrow, "accept–reject" methodologies and recommend use of qualitative data, examination of problems of implementation, and evaluation of possibilities for changes and improvements.

8. The information in the table can be used in several ways, as illustrated in Chapters 9–11. One use that should be avoided, however, is to assign weights (such as unity) to the qualitative grades. If one insists on mathematical parallels, some of the characteristics should have a minimum level of performance, making them more like restrictions in linear programming than values to be weighted as occurs, say, in cost–benefit analysis.

9. The mixed performance across characteristics (such as superior energy efficiency and poor flexibility) should not be confused with a variable performance on a given characteristic (such as superior-to-poor on punctuality).

Chapter 5. Public Expense, Health, and Accidents

1. See, for example, Kuntzleman and Editors of *Consumer Guide* (1978: 134–44).

2. New York Yankee pitchers avoided water for entire games; some of them went into mysterious midsummer slumps. See Halberstam (1990), especially p. 214.

3. Calculations are based on energy expenditure cited in Morehouse and Miller (1976: 136–37), considering only energy expended above that consumed while sitting by going up and down stairs at 3.2 km/h and by horizontal walking at 5.6 km/h.

4. Figures derived from Plowden and Hillman (1984: 78), using a car-occupancy factor of 1.5.

5. By taking the official Brazilian traffic death statistics at face value, there are about 2,500 traffic deaths per year in the municipality of São Paulo,

of which 70 percent are pedestrians (Gold, Grostein, and Pereira 1992). A pilot study cited in GEIPOT (1987: 61), however, shows that this is basically a count of those pronounced dead at the scene of the accident, and the correct total is 74 percent higher. Considering a population of 10 million (a guess, since this is a fast-growing region and the last census data is from 1980), the conservative figure yields 175 pedestrian deaths per million population, and the corrected total, 304 pedestrian deaths per million.

Chapter 6. Transport Characteristics and Individual Preferences

1. This obviously depends on the exchange rate. Here I consider the average of official and black-market rates.

Chapter 7. Modes of Urban Transportation

1. Several other cities are studying the O-Bahn and may implant it in the near future (Araújo 1989: 44).
2. The following classification is simplified to the minimum needed to discuss and to compare public transit modes. More detailed classifications may be found in several sources, such as Lea and Elliott Company (1989) and Vuchic (1981: 59–117).
3. Hitachi (n.d); Kikuchi and Onaka (1988: 30) Straddle-Type Monorail Group (1985).

Chapter 8. Characteristics of Cities and Their Transport Users

1. For a more technical treatment of non-Euclidean distance, see Khisty (1990a).
2. Figures cited by Pikarsky and Johnson (1983: 592), with updates for inflation.
3. Examples include Ben-Akiva and Morikawa (1990); Manheim (1979).

Chapter 10. Project Formulation and Evaluation

1. Some of the Brazilian studies include Companhia Construtora Nacional (1968); EBTU (1983); GEIPOT (1978; 1980); São Paulo Metrô (1975).
2. See detailed description in Wright (1987b).

3. These are educated guesses, as no hard data are available regarding the percentage of diesel fuel used in urban areas. We know that about 75 percent of Brazil's diesel fuel is used in road transportation (Ministério da Infraestrutura 1990: 30). The distribution of the transportation bill by mode is as follows (Castro 1990: 3–4): (1) 53 percent of bus company earnings are from urban transportation and another 34 percent are from intermunicipal routes that have a significant proportion of their mileage in urban areas, while only 13 percent are interstate and international; and (2) 39 percent of the cargo bill is urban, and another 32 percent is intermunicipal, against 29 percent interstate and international. Virtually all buses and trucks have diesel engines, although some urban vans may operate on gasoline or ethanol. If we assume diesel consumption is proportional to the transportation bill for buses and trucks, about half of diesel fuel is used in urban areas. Data on total petroleum imports are from Franco (1989).

Chapter 11. Viable and Sustainable Transport Strategies

1. For details on the single-teller system and its problems, see Damé (1990: 13); Lima and Sant'Anna (1990); Sant'Anna (1988); Wright and Lima (1987).
2. Ibid.

References

Abrúcio, Milton, Jr. 1990. "Principais Semáfaros Fazem Pedestre Correr." *Folha de São Paulo*, 24 October, C-4.

Acevedo, Jorge E. 1989. "El Servicio Ejecutivo de Buses de Transporte Público en Bogotá." Paper presented at the Fourth Latin American Technical Meeting on Urban Transport, Havana, 18–22 September.

Ackoff, Russell L. 1974. *Redesigning the Future: A Systems Approach to Societal Problems.* New York: John Wiley.

———. 1978. *The Art of Problem Solving.* New York: John Wiley.

Adas, Melhem. 1985. *Panorama Geográfico do Brasil: Aspectos Físicos, Humanos e Econômicos.* São Paulo: Editora Moderna.

Adler, Hans. 1971. *Economic Appraisal of Transport Projects: A Manual with Case Studies.* Bloomington: Indiana University Press.

Alexandre, A., and J. Barde. 1987. "The Valuation of Noise." In P. M. Nelson, ed., *Transportation Noise Reference Book*, pp. 23.1–23.10. London: Butterworths.

Alonso, George. 1990. "Passeio da Primavera Bate Recorde de Ciclistas." *Folha de São Paulo*, 24 September, p. D-3.

American Public Transit Association (APTA). 1989. *Transit Fact Book, 1989.* New York: APTA.

Anderson, Elizabeth. 1988. "Values, Risks and Market Norms." *Philosophy and Public Affairs* 17 (1): 54–65.

Anderson, J. Edward. 1988. "The TAXI 2000 Personal Rapid Transit System." *Journal of Advanced Transportation* 22 (Spring): 1–15.

Ann Arbor News, "The Best for Biking," 10 June 1990, p. D-12.

Araújo, Carlos Augusto Monteverde. 1989. "Sistema 'O-Bahn' de Transporte Público." *Revista dos Transportes Públicos* 11 (45): 37–44.

Armstrong-Wright, Anthony. 1986. "Sistemas de Transporte Público Urbano." Washington, D.C.: World Bank Working Document 525.

Assmann, Plínio. 1976. "O Lugar dos Diferentes Modos de Transporte Coletivo." Paper presented at the First International Symposium on Public Transportation, São Paulo, 27–29 October.

Atkins, S. T. 1987. "The Crisis of Transportation Planning Modelling." *Transport Reviews* 7 (4): 303–25.

Baerwald, J. E., M. J. Huber, and L. E. Keefer, eds. 1976. *1976 Transportation and Traffic Engineering Handbook*. Englewood Cliffs, N.J.: Prentice-Hall.

Balen, Peter van. 1987. "The Bicycle in Nicaragua: A Field Experience." Delft: Centre for International Cooperation and Appropriate Technology, Delft University of Technology. Photocopy.

Barker, Theo. 1987. "A German Centenary in 1986, a French in 1995 or the Real Beginnings about 1905?" In T. Barker, ed., *The Economic and Social Effects of the Spread of Motor Vehicles*. London: Macmillan Press.

Barth, Ursula. 1988. "A Methodology for Rural Transport Studies in Developing Countries: Rapid Rural Transport Demand Appraisal." Paper presented at the annual meeting of the Transportation Research Board, Washington, D.C., January.

Barwell, I. J., et al. 1985. *Rural Transport in Developing Countries*. London: Intermediate Technology Applications.

Ben-Akiva, M., and S. Lerman. 1986. *Discrete Choice Analysis: Theory and Application to Travel Demand*. Cambridge, Mass.: MIT Press.

Ben-Akiva, Moshe E., and T. Morikawa. 1990. "Comparing Ridership Attraction of Rail and Bus by Estimating Mode Choice Models." Paper presented at the annual meeting of the Transportation Research Board, Washington, D.C., 7–11 January.

Benigno, Nena. 1991. "Metro Manila's Transport Problem Deteriorates." *Manila Bulletin*, 1 March, p. HC-7.

Berman, Marshall. 1982. *All That Is Solid Melts into Air: The Experience of Modernity*. New York: Simon & Schuster.

Blair, Stephen N., et al. 1989. "Physical Fitness and All-Cause Mortality: A Prospective Study of Healthy Men and Women." *Journal of the American Medical Association* 262 (17): 2395–2401.

Bor, W. 1974. "The Impact of Urban Motorways." In P. M. Townroe, ed., *Social and Political Consequences of the Motor Car*. North Pomfret, Vt.: David and Charles.

Borrins, Sandford F. 1988. "Electronic Road Pricing: An Idea Whose Time May Never Come." *Transportation Research A* 22A (1): 37–44.

Bottles, Scott. 1987. *Los Angeles and the Automobile*. Berkeley: University of California Press.

Brazil, Secretaria do Planejamento. 1987. *Plano de Ação Governamental, 1987–1991*. Brasília: IBGE/IPLAN/IPEA.

Briggs, John P., and David F. Peat. 1984. *Looking Glass Universe: The Emerging Science of Wholeness*. New York: Simon & Schuster.

Bromley, D. 1982. "Land and Water Problems: An Institutional Perspective." *American Journal of Agricultural Economics* 64 (5): 834–44.

Broste, Steven K., et al. 1989. "Hearing Loss among High School Farm Students." *American Journal of Public Health* 79 (5): 619–22.

Brown, Warren. 1991. "Super-Efficient Engines Are Only Part of the Story." *International Herald-Tribune,* 12 September, pp. 13, 16.

Browning, Edgar K., and Jacqueline Browning. 1983. *Microeconomic Theory and Applications.* Boston: Little, Brown.

Buna, B. 1987. "Some Characteristics of Noise from Single Vehicles." In P. M. Nelson, ed., *Transportation Noise Reference Book,* pp. 4.1–4.12. London: Butterworths.

Castro, Newton. 1990. "The Road Transportation Industry in Brazil: Market Structure, Performance and Government Regulation." Discussion Text 195. Brasília: IPEA.

Caudle, Sharon, and Kathryn Newcomer. 1989. "Political Ends and Practical Needs." *Evaluation and Program Planning* 12: 279–86.

Cervero, Robert. 1986. *Suburban Gridlock.* New Brunswick, N.J.: Center for Urban Policy Research.

———. 1990. "Profiling Profitable Bus Routes." *Transportation Quarterly* 44 (2): 183–201.

CESTA (Centro Salvadoreño de Tecnologia Apropiada). 1986. "Promotion of Bicycle and Tricycle Use in El Salvador." San Salvador: CESTA paper, October.

Champion, Anthony, ed. 1989. *Counterurbanization.* London: Edward Arnold.

Chile, Ministério de Transportes y Telecomunicaciones. 1985. "La Liberalización del Transporte Urbano en Santiago de Chile." Paper presented at the First Latin American Technical Meeting on Urban Transport, Brasília, 30 September–3 October.

Coester, Oskar H. 1990. "Aerómovel: Porto Alegre's Aerómovel Development." Paper accompanying exhibit at TRANS-EXPO 1990, U.S. Department of Transportation, Washington, D.C., January.

Collin, H. J. 1990. "West Germany's Experience with 'Tempo 30': Evaluating the Five-Year Experiment." Paper presented at the annual meeting of the Transportation Research Board, Washington, D.C., 7–11 January.

Companhia Construtora Nacional, S.A. 1968. "Estudo de Viabilidade Técnica e Econômica do Metropolitano do Rio de Janeiro." Rio de Janeiro. Monograph.

Conceição, Walter Francisco. 1985. *Uso de Bicicleta em Campo Bom.* Brasília: EBTU.

Consumer Guide. 1988. *Walking for Health and Fitness.* Lincolnwood, Ill.: International Publications.

Coordinación General de Transporte, Departamiento del Distrito Federal de México. 1985. "Tránsito y Transporte en la Ciudad de México: El Sistema de Ejes Viales." Paper presented at the First Latin American Technical Meeting on Urban Transport, Brasília, 30 September–3 October.

C.R.O.W.—Centre for Research and Contract Standardization in Civil and Traffic Engineering. 1989. *Van Woonerf tot Erf*. Ede, The Netherlands: C.R.O.W.

Dall'Orto, Augusto. 1989. "Evaluación de Pistas Exclusivas Para Buses en Lima." Paper presented at the Fourth Latin American Technical Meeting on Urban Transport, Havana, 18–22 September.

Damé, Luíza. 1990. "Técnicos Apontam Falhas do Caixa Único." *Jornal de Brasília* 7 (March):13.

Demetrius, F. Joseph. 1990. *Brazil's National Alcohol Program: Technology and Development in an Authoritarian Regime*. New York: Praeger.

Departamento Nacional de Estradas de Rodagem (DNER). 1986. *Anuário Estatístico do Transporte Interestadual e Internacional de Passageiros*. Rio de Janeiro: DNER.

———. 1989. "Boletins do VIII Distrito Rodoviário." São Paulo: DNER.

De Silva, Clarence W., and David N. Wormley. 1983. *Automated-Transit Guideways: Analysis and Design*. Lexington, Mass.: Lexington Books.

De Wit, Tunis. 1990. "From 'Woonerf' to 'Erf': Learning from the Dutch Experience." Paper presented at the Transportation Research Board annual meeting, Washington, D.C., January.

Distrito Federal. 1985. *Lei Orçamentária Anual, no. 7.426, 17 Dec. 1985*. Brasília: Departamento de Imprensa Nacional.

Domenchic, T. A., and D. McFadden. 1975. *Urban Travel Demand*. Amsterdam: North Holland.

Downing, C. S. 1980. "Cycle Safety." In *Cycling as a Mode of Transport*, pp. 19–41. Crowthorne, England: Transportation and Road Research Laboratory, Supplementary Report 540.

Dunkerley, Jay, and Irving Hoch. 1987. "Energy for Transport in Developing Countries." *Energy Journal* 8 (3): 57–72.

Economic Commission for Latin America (ECLA). 1985. "Los Vehículos por Puesto en el Transporte Urbano de Caracas." Paper presented at the First Latin American Technical Meeting on Urban Transport, Brasília, 30 September–3 October.

Empresa Brasileira de Transportes Urbanos (EBTU). 1983. *Trem Urbano do Recife*. Brasília: EBTU.

———. 1988. *Plano Nacional de Transporte de Massa*. Brasília.: EBTU.

Faruqui, Akhtar Mahmud. 1985. "Noise Pollution: A Neglected Threat." *Impact of Science on Society* 138/139: 187–96.

Feenstra, Robert, and James Levinsohn. 1989a. "Identifying the Competition." Stockholm: Institute for International Economic Studies, Seminar Paper 441.

———. 1989b. "Distance, Demand and Oligopoly Pricing." Ann Arbor: Department of Economics, University of Michigan, CREST Working Paper 89-19.

Flavin, Christopher, and Nicholas Lenssen. 1990. "Beyond the Petroleum Age: Designing a Solar Economy." Washington, D.C.: Worldwatch Institute Paper 100.

Folha de São Paulo: "Passeio da Primavera Bate Recorde de Ciclistas," 24 September 1990, p. D-3; "Erundina sobe IPTU para Dar Ônibus Sem Cobrar," 29 September 1990, p. C-9; "Pai da Tarifa Zero Diz que Subsídio ao Transporte Hoje è Dinheiro Jogado Fora," 5 October 1990, p. D-1; "Principais Semáforos Fazem Pedestre Correr," 24 October 1990, p. C-4; "Reservas de Petróleo São de 97 Dias," 5 November 1990, p. B-2; "Prefeitura Vai Afastar Diretores da CMTC e Demitir 4 Mil Funcionários," 21 November 1990, p. D-1; "Transporte Coletivo Piora Ainda Mais no Segundo Ano da Gestão Erundina," 2 January 1991; p. C-1; "Ineficiência da CMTC Provoca os Aumentos de Tarifa Acima da Inflação," 10 January 1991, p. C-1; "Polícia Indicia ex-Presidente por Corrupção," 24 January 1991, p. C-5.

Francis, Gerald A., and Rolland D. King. 1988. "Proving Ground Comparison of M.A.N. Methanol and Diesel Buses." Columbus, Ohio: Battelle Columbus Division.

Franco, Otávio de Carvalho. 1989. "A Crise Atual e Perspectivas do Setor Alcooleiro e do Petróleo Para os Anos 90." In IPEA/IPLAN, *Prioridades e Perspectivas de Políticas Públicas Para a Década de 90,* pp. 185–204.

Freeman, A. Myrick, III. 1977. "Project Design and Evaluation with Multiple Objectives." In R. Haveman and J. Margolis, eds., *Public Expenditure and Policy Analysis,* pp. 239–56. Chicago: Rand McNally College Publishing.

French, Hilary F. 1990. "Clearing the Air: A Global Agenda." Washington, D.C.: Worldwatch Institute Paper 94.

GEIPOT (Empresa Brasileira de Planejamento de Transportes). 1978. *Estudo do Trem Suburbano da Região Metropolitana de Porto Alegre.* Brasília: GEIPOT.

———. 1979. *Estudo Preliminar do Transporte de Passageiros no Eixo Rio de Janeiro-Campinas.* Brasília: GEIPOT.

———. 1980. *Estudo do Trem de Subúrbio de Belo Horizonte.* Brasília: GEIPOT.

———. 1981. *Plano de Ação Imediata de Transporte—Maceió.* Brasília: GEIPOT.

———. 1987. O Acidente de Tráfego: Flagelo Nacional Evitável. Brasília: GEIPOT.

Germani, Elmir, and Pedro A. Szasz. 1985. "Controle Semafórico Centralizado SP." Paper presented at the First Latin American Technical Conference on Urban Transport, Brasília, 30 September–3 October.

Gibbons, Scott. 1990. "Mixed Land Use and Multi-Modal Transport: The Kanpur Planning Environment." Unpublished paper.

Gold, Philip A., Victor Grostein, and Roberto A. Pereira. 1992. *Vias Urbanas Mais Seguras.* Brasília: IPEA (forthcoming).

Goldsack, Paul. 1982. "It's Back to the Streets for London Commuters." *Mass Transit* 9 (9): 6–22.

———. 1983. "Bangkok." *Mass Transit* 10 (5): 36.

Goldstein, Jeffrey. 1978. "Fundamental Concepts in Sound Measurement." In David M. Lipscomb, ed., *Noise and Audiology*, pp. 3–58. Baltimore: University Park Press.

Gordon, Peter, Ajay Kumar, and Harry Richardson. 1989. "The Influence of Metropolitan Spatial Structure on Commuting Time." *Journal of Urban Economics* 26: 138–51.

Grava, Sigurd. 1976. "The Metro in Moscow." *Traffic Quarterly* 30 (2): 241–67.

Grefe, Richard, and Richard Smart. 1975. "A History of the Key Decisions in the Development of the Bay Area Rapid Transit (BART)." Washington, D.C.: U.S. Department of Transportation, Contract DOT-OS-30176, Final Report.

Gutman, J. S., and R. G. Scurfield. 1990. "Towards a More Realistic Assessment of Urban Mass Transit Systems." In *Rail Mass Transit for Developing Countries* (Institution of Civil Engineers, Conference Proceedings). London: Thomas Telford, pp. 283–94.

Halberstam, David. 1990. *Summer of '49*. New York: Avon Books.

Hanke, S., and R. Walker. 1977. "Benefit–Cost Analysis Reconsidered: An Evaluation of the Mid-State Project." In R. Haveman and J. Margolis, eds., *Public Expenditure and Policy Analysis*, pp. 329–54. Chicago: Rand McNally College Publishing.

Hanson, Mark E. 1989. "The Motor Vehicle Dominated City as a Non-Sustainable Urban Form: Mexico City and Jakarta." *Computers, Environment and Urban Systems* 13: 95–108.

Harberger, Arnold C. 1971. "Three Basic Postulates for Applied Welfare Economics: An Interpretive Essay." *Journal of Economic Literature* 9 (September): 785–97.

Harlow, Kirk C., and Duane Windsor. 1988. "Integration of Cost–Benefit and Financial Analysis in Project Evaluation." *Public Administration Review* 48 (5): 918–28.

Harris, R. A., L. F. Cohn, and W. Bowlby. 1987. "Designing Noise Barriers Using Expert System CHINA." *Journal of Transportation Engineering* 113 (2): 127–38.

Heggie, Ian G. 1989. "Reforming Transport Policy." *Finance and Development* (March): 42–44.

"Henfil." 1980. *Henfil na China*. Rio de Janeiro: Codecri.

Himanen, Veli. 1985. *Evaluation Methods for Urban Transportation Plans*. Espoo, Finland: Technical Research Centre.

Hitachi, n.d. (c. 1985), *Monorial* (n.l., n.p.).

Hodge, David C., and Richard G. Price. 1978. "Hearing Damage Risk Criteria." In David M. Lipscomb (ed.), *Noise and Audiology*, pp. 167–91. Baltimore: University Park Press.

Hoekwater, J. 1980. "Cycle Routes in the Hague and Tilbury." In *Cycling as a Means of Transport*, pp. 62–74. Crowthorne, England: Transportation and Road Research Laboratory, Supplementary Report 540.

Hoque, Md. Mazrarul. 1990. "An Analysis of Fatal Bicycle Accidents in Victoria (Australia) with a Special Reference to Nighttime Accidents." *Accident Analysis and Prevention* 22 (1): 1–11.

Horizontes Urbanos. 1990. "La Administración Urbana: Problemas y Soluciones." 14 (7): 3.

Huff, Darrell. 1954. *How to Lie with Statistics.* New York: W.W. Norton.

Hyman, David N. 1986. *Modern Microeconomics: Analysis and Applications.* St. Louis: Times Mirror/C. V. Mosby College Publishing.

Illich, Ivan. 1974. *Energy and Equity.* New York: Harper and Row.

International Road Transport Union. 1974. *The Energy Crisis and the Rate of Fuel Consumption.* Geneva: IRU.

Jansen, Gijsbertus R. M., and Tom Van Vuren. 1989. "Travel Patterns in Dutch Metropolitan Cities: The Importance of External Trips." *Transportation* 15: 317–36.

Johnson, Larry R., et al. 1989. "Maglev Vehicles and Superconductor Technology: Integration of High-Speed Ground Transportation into the Air Travel System." Argonne: Center for Transportation Research, Argonne National Laboratory, Report ANL/CNSV-67.

Jones, Emrys. 1988. "London." *World Book* 12: 432–47.

Kalette, Denise, and Lori Sharn. 1989. "Gridlock Is Creating 'Wall-to-Wall' Cars." *USA Today,* 18 September, pp. 1, 10A.

Keynes, John Maynard. 1936. *The General Theory of Employment Interest and Money.* New York: Harcourt, Brace.

Khisty, C. J. 1990a. "Use of Non-Euclidean Metrics in Non-Motorized Transport." Paper presented at the annual meeting of the Transportation Research Board, Washington, D.C., January.

———. 1990b. *Transportation Engineering: An Introduction.* Englewood Cliffs, N.J.: Prentice Hall.

Kikuchi, Shinya, and Akira Onaka. 1988. "Monorail Development and Application in Japan." *Journal of Advanced Transportation* 22 (Spring): 19–38.

Kipke, Barbara Gruehl. 1988. "Bicycle Usage in Two Cities of Africa." Paper presented at the annual meeting of the Transportation Research Board, Washington, D.C., 13 January.

Kobran, Michael F. 1990. "An Unorthodox View of Urban Transportation in the 1990s." *ITE Journal* (May): 37–40.

Kryter, Karl D. 1985. "Noise and Hearing Damage: How Much Is Too Much?" *Impact of Science on Society* 138/139: 197–205.

Kuhn, Thomas. 1962. *The Structure of Scientific Revolutions.* Chicago: University of Chicago Press.

Kuntzleman, Charles T., and the editors of *Consumer Guide.* 1978. *Rating the Exercises.* New York: William Morrow.

Lancaster, Kelvin. 1966a. "A New Approach to Consumer Theory." *Journal of Political Economy* 74: 132–57.

———. 1966b. "Change and Innovation in the Technology of Consumption." *American Economic Review* 61 (2): 14–23.

———. 1979. *Variety, Equity and Efficiency.* New York: Columbia University Press.

Lave, Charles. 1990. "Federal Subsidies and the Ruinous Decline in Transit Productivity: It Wasn't Supposed to Turn Out Like This." Paper presented at the annual meeting of the Transportation Research Board, Washington, D.C., January.

Lea and Elliott Company. 1989. *Houston System Connector Technology Assessment. Appendix E: Transit Technology Classifications.* Houston: Lea and Elliott.

Lee, Robert. 1989. "Freitragende Omnibuszelle in Faserverbundwerkstoffbauweise, Carbon-Liner." In *Nahverkehrsforschung '89.* October: 294–306.

Lee, T., et al. 1990. *Energy Aftermath.* Boston: Harvard Business School Press.

Leon, Arthur S., et al. 1987. "Leisure-time Physical Activity Levels and Risk of Coronary Heart Disease and Death: The Multiple Risk Factor Intervention Trail." *Journal of the American Medical Association* 258: 2388–95.

Leonard, Herman B., and Richard J. Zeckhauser. 1986. "Cost–Benefit Analysis Applied to Risks: Its Philosophy and Legitimacy." In D. MacLean, ed. *Values at Risk.* Totowa, N.J.: Rowman and Allanheld.

Levinson, Herbert S., et al. 1984. "Indirect Transportation Energy." *Journal of Transportation Engineering* 110 (2): 159–74.

Lewis, Simon, Peter Cook, and Marcelo Minc. 1990. "Comprehensive Transportation Models: Past, Present and Future." *Transportation Quarterly* 44 (2): 249–65.

Lima, Ieda M.O. 1989. "Retrospectivas e Perspectivas do Financiamento do Transporte Coletivo Urbano no Brasil." Brasília: CTC/IPLAN/IPEA, Technical Note.

———. 1990. "O Estado e o Transporte Rodoviário de Carga." Brasília: IPLAN/IPEA, Discussion Text 27.

Lima, Ieda Maria de Oliveira, and José Alex Sant'Anna. 1990. "Ônibus em Brasília: Tarifas e Caixa Único." Brasília: IPLAN/IPEA, Technical Note.

Lindner, Peter. Personal communication, 23 July 1990.

Lopez, Cecilia. 1989. "La Calidad de Servicio de los Modos de Transporte Público en Santiago de Chile." Paper presented at the Fourth Latin American Technical Meeting on Urban Transport, Havana, 18–22 September.

Love, John. 1986. *McDonald's behind the Arches.* New York: Bantam Books.

Lowe, Marcia D. 1989. "The Bicycle: Vehicle for a Small Planet." Washington, D.C.: Worldwatch Institute Paper 90.

Lynch, Kevin. 1960. *The Image of the City.* Cambridge, Mass.: MIT Press.

McClintock, Hugh. 1987. "On the Right Track?" *Town Planning Review* 58 (3): 267–92.

McDonald, Oliver F. 1987. "Noise: How Much Is Too Much?" *Safety and Health* 136 (November): 36–39.

McKay, John P. 1976. *Tramways and Trolleys: The Rise of Urban Mass Transport in Europe*. Princeton, N.J.: Princeton University Press.

McKnight, Claire E., et al. 1989. "Moving People." Washington, D.C.: U.S. Department of Transportation, Urban Mass Transportation Administration, Final Report.

Mackett, R. L. 1990. "The Deregulation of Bus Services in Britain." Paper presented at the Nucleus of Transport Studies, University of Brasília, 23 November.

Mackinder, I. H. 1979. "The Predictive Accuracy of British Transportation Studies: A Feasibility Study." Crowthorne, England: Transportation and Road Research Laboratory, Supplementary Report 483.

MacLean, Douglas. 1986. "Introduction." In D. MacLean, ed., *Values at Risk*. Totowa, N.J.: Rowman and Allanheld.

Mahler, Reinhard. 1990. "Turning Large Downtown Areas into Pedestrian Zones: Munich and Bologna." Paper presented at the Transportation Research Board annual meeting, Washington, D.C., January.

Manheim, Marvin. 1979. *Fundamentals of Transport Systems Analysis*. Cambridge, Mass.: MIT Press.

Martins, Nilson. 1984. "Metodologia Para Análise de Custo-Eficiência Para Seleção de Alternativas." *Proceedings of the X World Meeting of the International Road Federation*, vol. 5, pp. 207–14. Rio de Janeiro.

Mass Transit. 1985. "Trindad Chooses Busways Over Railways." 12 (8): 9, 50.

Melnick, William. 1978. "Temporary and Permanent Shift." In David M. Lipscomb, ed., *Noise and Audiology*, pp. 83–107. Baltimore: University Park Press.

Milberg, William. 1988. "The Language of Economics: Deconstructing the Neoclassical Text." *Social Concept*, pp. 33–57.

Mills, Edwin S., and Bruce W. Hamilton. 1989. *Urban Economics*. Glenview, Ill: Scott, Foresman.

Mills, John H. 1978. "Effects of Noise on Young and Old People." In David M. Lipscomb, ed., *Noise and Audiology*, pp. 229–41. Baltimore: University Park Press.

Ministério da Infraestrutura. 1990. *Balanço Energético Nacional*. Brasília: Ministério da Infraestrutura.

Mishan, E. J. 1988. *Cost–Benefit Analysis*. London: Unwin Hyman.

Mitchell, C.G.B. 1974. "Transport as an Inducer of Urban Change." In P. M. Townroe, ed., *Social and Political Consequences of the Motor Car*. North Pomfret, Vt.: David and Charles.

———. 1980. "Cycle Use in Britain." In *Cycling as a Mode of Transport*, pp. 5–18. Crowthorne, England: Transportation and Road Research Laboratory, Supplementary Report 540.

Moisés, José Álvaro and Verena Martinez-Alier. 1977. "A Revolta dos Suburbanos, ou 'Patrão, o Trem Atrasou.'" In J. A. Moisés et al., *Contradiçoes Urbanas e Movimentos Sociais*. Rio de Janeiro: Paz e Terra.

Morehouse, Lawrence E., and Leonard Gross. 1975. *Total Fitness*. New York: Simon & Schuster.

———. 1977. *Maximum Performance*. New York: Simon & Schuster.

Morehouse, Lawrence E., and Augustus T. Miller. 1976. *Physiology of Exercise*, 7th ed. St. Louis: C. V. Mosby.

Morita, Akio. 1986. *Made in Japan*. New York: Dutton.

Motor Vehicles Manufacturing Association of the United States, Inc. 1989. *MVMA Motor Vehicle Facts and Figures '89*. Detroit: MVMA.

Motta, Ronaldo Seroa. 1985. "Uma Análise de Custo–Benefício do Proálcool." Paper presented at the Seventh Meeting of the Brazilian Econometrics Society, Vitoria, December.

M'Pherson, P. K. 1986. "Systems Engineering: A Proposed Definition." *IEE Proceedings*, Part A 133 (6) (September): 330–31.

Myrdal, Gunnar. 1969. *Objectivity in Social Research*. New York: Pantheon.

National Safety Council. 1989. *Accident Facts*. Washington, D.C.: National Safety Council.

Nelson, Deborah. 1990. Personal communications, 25 June and 24 July.

Nelson, J. D., and P. J. Hills. 1990. "Innovative Bus Control for Congested Urban Corridors: The Application of Convoying Systems." *Traffic Engineering and Control* 31 (5): 299–304.

Newman, P.W.G., and J. R. Kenworthy. 1984. "The Use and Abuse of Driving Cycle Research: Clarifying the Relationship between Traffic Congestion, Energy and Emissions." *Transportation Quarterly* 38 (4): 615–35.

———. 1988. "The Transport Energy Trade-Off: Fuel Efficient Traffic versus Fuel Efficient Cities." *Transportation Research A* 22A (3): 163–74.

Nice, David C. 1989. "Consideration of High-Speed Rail Service in the United States." *Transportation Research A,* 22A (5): 359–65.

Noise Cancellation Technologies, Inc. 1987. "Noise Buster." *Safety and Health* 136: 41–43.

Odutola, A. A., and A. C. Taylor. 1990. "Services and Longevity of Paratransit Operation." *Transportation Quarterly* 44 (1): 151–62.

Paffenbarger, Ralph S., Jr. 1989. "Personal and Life-Style Characteristics as Predictors of Mortality and Longevity in Elderly Men." Paper presented at the Department of Epidemiology, University of Michigan–Ann Arbor, Thomas Francis, Jr., Memorial Lecture. 20 November.

Paffenbarger, Ralph S., Jr., et al. 1986. "Physical Activity, All-Cause Mortality, and Longevity of College Alumni." *New England Journal of Medicine* 31 (10): 605–13. And Commentary, 7 August 1986: 399–401; and 28 August 1986: 595.

Parkinson, Tom. 1987. "Skytrain in Vancouver, Canada." *International Union of Public Transport Revue* 36 (3): 213–19.

Pendakur, V. Setty. 1988. "Non-Motorized Urban Transport in India." Paper presented at the annual meeting of the Transportation Research Board, Washington, D.C., January.

————. 1990. "Conflicts between Motorized and Non-Motorized Transport in Nepal." Paper presented at the annual meeting of the Transportation Research Board, Washington, D.C., January.

Pendakur, V. Setty, and Bonita Pyplacz. 1984. "Urban Traffic Noise Abatement." *Transportation Quarterly* 38 (3): 471–86.

Pereira, L. S., and C. R. Ribeiro. 1988. "Acidentes no Trafégo Urbano." *Espaço Urbano: Pesquisa e Planejamento* (1): 58–67.

Pickrell, Don H. 1990. "Urban Rail Transit Projects: Forecast Versus Actual Ridership." Paper presented at the annual meeting of the Transportation Research Board, Washington, D.C., January.

Pikarsky, Milton, and Christine M. Johnson. 1983. "Transportation in Transition." *Energy* 8 (8–9): 589–99.

Pisarski, Alan E. 1987. *Commuting in America*. Westport, Conn.: The Eno Foundation for Transportation.

Plowden, Stephen, and Mayer Hillman. 1984. *Danger on the Road: The Needless Scourge—A Study of Obstacles in Road Safety*. London: Policy Studies Institute.

Pope, C. Arden. 1989. "Respiratory Disease Associated with Community Air Pollution and a Steel Mill, Utah Valley." *American Journal of Public Health* 79 (5): 623–28.

Prefeitura do Município de São Paulo. 1988. "Programa Monotrilho Sobreposto." São Paulo: Prefeitura Municipal. Photocopy.

Price, T. 1974. "An Introduction." In P. Townroe, ed., *Social and Political Consequences of the Motor Car*. North Pomfret, Vt.: David and Charles.

Quadri, Gabriel de la Torre. 1989. "Transporte y Contaminación Atmosférica en la Zona Metropolitana de la Ciudad de México." Paper presented at the Fourth Latin American Technical Meeting on Urban Transport, Havana, 18–22 September.

Replogle, Michael. 1988a. *Bicycles and Public Transportation: New Links to Suburban Transportation Markets*. 2d ed. Washington, D.C.: The Bicycle Federation.

————. 1988b. "Sustainable Transportation Strategies for Third World Development." Paper presented at the annual meeting of the Transportation Research Board, Washington, D.C., January.

————. 1989a. "Let Them Drive Cars." *New Internationalist,* May, pp. 18–19.

————. 1989b. "Transportation Strategies for Sustainable Development." Paper presented at the Fifth World Conference on Transport Research, Yokohama, 10–14 July.

Republic of the Philippines, National Statistical Coordination Board. 1990. *1990 Philippine Statistical Yearbook*. Manila: National Statistical Coordination Board.

Robbins, Richard M. 1976. "O Transporte Público e a Qualidade de Vida na Cidade." Paper presented at the First International Seminar on Public Transport, São Paulo, 27–29 October.

Rogers, Lee H. 1989. "Aeromóvel: Urban Transport within Jakarta and

Potential for New Technologies." Paper presented at Indonesian–U.K. Business Association meeting, Jakarta, 14 September.

———. 1990. "Aeromóvel Technology Súr Coester S.A.: Project Issues within USA Urban Transit." Washington, D.C.: Paper accompanying exhibit at TRANS-EXPO 1990, U.S. Department of Transportation, Washington, D.C., January.

Ross, Myron H. 1981. "Kalamazoo Taxis: The Case of Regulatory Overkill." *Traffic Quarterly* 35 (4): 609–22.

Royal Canadian Air Force. 1975. *Exercise Plans for Physical Fitness.* New York: Pocket Books.

Sá, J. N., and W. F. Padovani. 1987. "Os Ônibus Vencem a Guerra no Corredor." *Veja,* 17 June, pp. 8–14.

Salihi, Jalal T. 1973. "Energy Requirements for Electric Cars and Their Impact on Electric Power Generation and Distribution Systems." *IEEE Transactions on Industry Applications* 1A–9 (5): 516–33.

Sant'Anna, José Alex. 1988. "A Gerência do Transporte Coletivo do Distrito Federal." Brasília: IPLAN/IPEA, Technical Note CTC 6, 8 April.

São Paulo Metrô. 1975. Rede Básica do Metrô—SP: Estudo Preliminar. São Paulo: SP Metrô.

———. 1987. "Pesquisa Origin/Destino: Informaçoes Básicas." São Paulo: SP Metrô.

Schneider, W., and S. Meibner. 1989. "Alternativen im Stadtbusbetrieb Erprobung Hydro-Bus, Phase I." In *Nahverkehrsforschung '89,* October, 44–48.

Sen, Amartya. 1987. *On Ethics and Economics.* New York: Basil Blackwell.

Silveira, Antônio Maria. 1984. "A Indeterminação de Morgenstern." *Revista Brasileira de Economia* 38 (4): 357–83.

Simon, Herbert. 1978. "Rationality as Process and Product of Thought." *American Economic Review* 68 (2): 1–16.

———. 1979. "Rational Decision Making in Business Organizations." *American Economic Review* 69 (4): 493–513.

SIRTO. 1987. "Relatório da Câmara Técnica do Sistema de Reabilitação, Traumatologia e Ortopedia." Cited in Portaria 3946 of Ministério da Previdência e Assistência Social, 23 February.

SNCF. 1981. *Estudo Preliminar do Transporte de Passageiros no Eixo Rio de Janeiro–São Paulo–Campinas.* Brasília: GEIPOT.

Sobania, Luiz Carlos, and Charles L. Wright. 1989. "O Projeto Piloto de Curitiba do Programa Nacional de Atenção ao Acidentado de Tráfego" (quarterly and annual reports to SIRTO). Brasília: IPLAN/IPEA.

Sperling, Daniel. 1988. *New Transportation Fuels: A Strategic Approach to Technological Change.* Berkeley: University of California Press.

Stallings, Robin. 1981. "The Present Role of the Bicycle in Iran, Afghanistan, Pakistan, and India." Washington, D.C.: Institute for Transportation and Development Policy. Photocopy.

Stone, Tabor. 1971. *Beyond the Automobile: Reshaping the Transportation Environment.* Englewood Cliffs, N.J.: Prentice-Hall.

Straddle-Type Monorail Group. 1985. *Urban Transit Monorail System.* Tokyo: STMG Publication in commemoration of the inauguration of the Kokura Line of the Kitakyushu Monorail System.

Stutts, Jane C., et al. 1990. "Bicycle Accidents and Injuries: A Pilot Study Comparing Hospital- and Police-Reported Data." *Accident Analysis and Prevention* 22 (1): 67–78.

Sür Coester S/A. 1988. *Aerómovel.* Washington, D.C.: The Match Institution.

Szasz, Pedro, and Elmir Germani. 1985. "Comboio de Ônibus Ordenado Comonor-SP." Paper presented at the First Latin American Technical Conference on Urban Transport, Brasília, 30 September–3 October.

Takyi, Isaac K. 1990. "An Evaluation of Jitney Systems in Developing Countries." *Transportation Quarterly* 44 (1): 163–77.

Talley, W. K. 1990. "Paratransit Services, Contracting-Out and Cost Saving for Public Transit Firms: A Firm Specific Analysis." *Transportation Planning and Technology* 15: 13–25.

Tapin, Michael R. 1989. "Light Rail Renaissance in North America." *UITP Review* 4/88 January–February: 311–22.

Taylor S. Martin, and Peter A. Wilkens. 1987. "Health Effects." In P. M. Nelson, ed., *Transportation Noise Reference Book,* pp. 4.1–4.12. London: Butterworths.

Thomson, Ian. 1983. "Alguns Aspectos de la Justificación Socio-Económica de los Ferrocarriles Metropolitanos en América del Sur." *Temas de Transporte* 8 (May): 4–26.

———. 1984. "Some High-Capacity Bus Lanes in Latin American Cities." Santiago: CEPAL.

Thünen, Johann Heinrich von. 1966. *Von Thünen's "Isolated State" (1826).* Edited by Peter Hall. Glasgow: Pergamon Press.

Transportation Research Board. 1985. *Highway Capacity Manual.* Washington, D.C.: TRB/NRC, Special Report 209.

Trevelyan, P. 1980. "Design Criteria." In *Cycling as a Mode of Transport,* pp. 47–60. Crowthorne, England: Transportation and Road Research Laboratory, Supplementary Report 540.

Urbema—Empresa Municipal de Urbanização. 1985. "Informe Estatístico." Campina Grande: Prefeitura Municipal. Bulletin.

U.S. Department of Commerce, Bureau of the Census. 1988. *County and City Data Book, 1988.* Washington, D.C.: U.S. Government Printing Cffice.

U.S. Department of Transportation. 1974. *Energy Primer.* Washington, D.C.: U.S. DOT.

———. 1980. *Downtown People Mover: Detroit, Michigan. Final Environmental Impact Statement.* Washington, D.C.: U.S. DOT/UMTA.

———. 1990. *National Transportation Strategic Planning Study.* Washington, D.C.: U.S. DOT.

Vallet, Michel. 1987. "Sleep Disturbance." In P. M. Nelson, ed., *Transportation Noise Reference Book,* pp. 5.1–5.18. London: Butterworths.

Vander Tuin, J. 1986. "Human-Powered Utility Vehicles: Trucks and Trailers of the Cycling World." *Bike Tech* 5 (3): 1–5.

Venezuela, Ministerio de Transportes. 1986. *El Metro de Caracas*. Film presented by the Venezuelan Delegation at the Meeting of the Latin American Public Transport Association, Rio de Janeiro, July.

Vicente, Olga, and Patricia Brennan. 1989. "Los Servicios Diferenciales en la Región Metropolitana de Buenos Aires." Paper presented at the Fourth Latin American Technical Meeting on Urban Transport, Havana, 18–22 September.

Von Thurn, Dawn R., and Peter Van Eck. 1987. "1986 Bicycle Use Survey." Ann Arbor, Mich.: City of Ann Arbor. Photocopy.

Vuchic, Vukan. 1981. *Urban Public Transportation: Systems and Technology*. Englewood Cliffs, N.J.: Prentice-Hall.

Walter, J. D., and F. S. Conant. 1974. "Energy Loss in Tires." *Tire Science and Technology* 2 (4): 235–60.

Watson, Peter L., and P. Holland. 1978. "Relieving Traffic Congestion: The Singapore Area License Scheme." Washington, D.C.: World Bank Staff Working Paper 238.

Wayte, F. A. 1989. "The Adelaide O-Bahn Application: The Northeast Busway." In *Nahverkehrsforschung '89*, October, pp. 315–22.

Webster, John C. 1978. "Speech Interference Aspects of Noise." In David M. Lipscomb, ed., *Noise and Audiology*, pp. 193–223. Baltimore: University Park Press.

White, Michelle. 1989. "Commuting, Congestion and Zoning." Ann Arbor: Department of Economics, University of Michigan. Unpublished paper.

White, Robert M. 1988. "Beyond the Millennium: Transportation and the Economy." *TR News*, September–October, pp. 3–6.

Whitelegg, John. 1983. "Road Safety: Defeat, Complicity and the Bankruptcy of Science." *Accident Analysis and Prevention* 15 (2): 153–60.

Wilcockson, John. 1980. *Bicycle*. London: Marshall Cavendish Books.

Wildavsky, Aaron. 1977. "Rescuing Policy Analysis from PPBS." In R. Haveman and J. Margolis, eds., *Public Expenditure and Policy Analysis*. Chicago: Markham Publishing.

Wilson, James A. 1990. "Fishing for Knowledge." *Land Economics* 66 (1): 12–29.

World Bank. 1975. *Urban Transport: Sector Policy Paper*. Washington, D.C.: World Bank.

Wright, Charles L. 1978. "Income Distribution and Economic Growth: Examining the Evidence." *Journal of Developing Areas* 13 (1): 49–66.

———. 1982. "A Regulamentação Econômica dos Transportes." *Revista Brasileira de Economia* 36 (2): 129–60.

———. 1986. "A Economia Política dos Acidentes de Tráfego." *Revista dos Transportes Públicos* 8 (31): 7–37.

———. 1987a. "Transport in Brasília: The Limits of Aesthetics." *Transport Reviews* 7 (4): 281–305.

————. 1987b. "Capacidade de Rodovias: O PAG e a Experiência da Via Dutra." Brasília: IPLAN/IPEA, Technical Note CTC 50, 22 October.

————. 1988. *O Que É Transporte Urbano*. São Paulo: Brasiliense.

————. 1989a. "Transporte Rodoviário por Ônibus." Brasília: IPLAN/IPEA.

————. 1989b. "Aspectos Complementares da Circulação Urbana." *Revista dos Transportes Públicos* 11 (44): 45–64.

————. 1990. "A Characteristics Analysis of Non-Motorized Transportation." *UMTRI Research Review* 20 (5): 1–11.

Wright, Charles L., et al. 1989. "Trem de Alta Velocidade entre Rio de Janeiro and São Paulo." Brasília: IPLAN/IPEA/SEPES/MF, Technical Note, June.

Wright, Charles L., and Ieda M. O. Lima. 1987. "Estudo de Viabilidade Técnica do Caixa Único do Sistema de Transporte do Distrito Federal." Brasília: IPLAN/IPEA, Technical Note CTC 7, 3 February.

Wright, Charles L., and Antônio Maurício Ferreira Netto. 1985. "Estudo sobre as Alternativas de Transporte de Pessoas no Distrito Federal." Brasília: Department of Economics, University of Brasília, Discussion Text 167.

Wright, Charles L., and José Alex Sant'Anna. 1989. "Os Transportes Urbanos na Década de 1990: Problemas e Perspectivas." Brasília: IPEA, Série Acompanhamento de Políticas Públicas 8.

Wright, Charles L., and Benamy Turkienicz. 1988. "Brasília and the Ageing of Modernism." *Cities* 5 (4): 347–64.

Zimmerman, Samuel L. 1990. "The Urban Transportation Administration and Major Investments: Evaluation Process and Results." Paper presented at the annual meeting of the Transportation Research Board, Washington, D.C., January.

Zinsser, William. 1988. *Writing to Learn*. New York: Harper & Row, pp. 184–87.

Index